Cantate Domino

WORLD'S STUDENT CHRISTIAN FEDERATION HYMNAL
Copyright
13, Rue Calvin
Geneva Switzerland

IMPRIMERIE LA CONCORDE, LAUSANNE (SUISSE)

1951

PREFACE

Cantate Domino, the hymnbook of the World's Student Christian Federation, has been by far the most widely used of its publications. Originally created to meet a student need, it has found its way into many ecumenical organisations and assemblies. Consequently, a new edition, revised so drastically as to become almost a new book, must be introduced to its public with an adequate explanation of its nature and purpose.

The first *Cantate Domino*, edited with such loving care by M\ufffflle Suzanne Bidgrain more than twenty-five years ago, and revised by her on several occasions, was basically a collection of some of the favourite hymns of national student Christian movements. It therefore combined a notable breadth of ecumenical origin with a definite limitation of spiritual range. The result was that, as time went on, many hymns proved so generally unfamiliar that they were seldom sung, and the list of subjects became increasingly inadequate with each succeeding student generation. When, in 1946, it was found that the plates, from which successive prints had been made, were becoming unusable, it was decided that a new edition should be prepared.

Many discussions were held in W.S.C.F. committees from 1946 to 1950. But the key decision was that the national movements should not be asked to send selected hymns for the new edition. The reason for this change in policy was simply the outstanding success of *Cantate Domino*, in spite of its limitations. No one any longer thought of it as an ecumenical anthology, but as a necessary aid to worship in ecumenical gatherings.

The editorial task, therefore, became one of omitting hymns which were seldom sung, or had not stood the test of usage because of content or music, and of adding hymns which were better known, and would fill gaps in the requirements of worship when Christians of many countries are met together. Advice, therefore, has been sought not so much from national movements as from representative leaders in the Federation and in the other world Christian organisations.

There are a number of points about the present edition which should be clearly stated so as to avoid misunderstanding. In the first place no one should expect *Cantate Domino* to contain an adequate selection of hymns from any national tradition. It is obviously limited in its range, and must be regarded as supplementary to the hymnbooks which students and young people use in different countries; it is certainly not meant to take their place. Then, because of the prevailing experience and custom of ecumenical meetings, all the hymns appear in English, French and German versions. This means that they can be very widely used, but it has had a marked effect upon their selection. For example, original hymns in other European languages are not proportionately well represented. Further, the selected hymns belong predominantly to churches of the West. Much time was given to the possibility of more hymns of Asian origin, but in the end only a few have been introduced. The musical idioms, in which many otherwise suitable hymns have been written, are not widely familiar in either East or West, and the editors were reluctant to use music in the "international" style for translations of Asian hymns. This remains an unsolved problem of ecumenical hymnology.

In setting up this new edition care has been taken to relate it to the previous one. While more than half of the hymns are new to *Cantate Domino*, the old numbers of hymns which are in the previous edition have been added in brackets, thus readily enabling the most familiar hymns to be sung by a group which has both editions available. Greater attention has been paid in this edition to choosing hymns suitable for the seasons of the Christian year. Subject headings have also been provided, which it is hoped will help those who lead worship to select hymns suitable for different themes and occasions.

The preparation of an ecumenical hymnbook in several languages is a tremendous task. The editor in chief has been Miss Helen Morton of the U.S.A., a former Vice-Chairman of the Federation, and one of its most devoted friends. Without her genial and self-effacing leadership since the Spring of 1948 nothing would have been accomplished. M. Frédéric Mathil of Geneva has proved to be a musical editor of great skill, and equal generosity of spirit. All his work was studied and heartily approved by Mr. G. Wallace Woodsworth of Harvard University. It should be realised that changes in melody or harmonisation, which involve new settings for familiar hymns, are the result of careful research into purer, or more authentic, sources of old music. Mrs. Margaret House and Pastor Wolfgang Schweitzer have given untiring advice and scholarly assistance from the beginning of the venture, and Mrs. Hilary Nicholls and Mrs. Elizabeth Bridston have carried out the irksome final tasks of editing. A veritable army of translators has been required for more than a hundred translations. It is their imaginative contribution which has really made the hymn book serviceable for its purpose. One further name must receive a special mention. Mlle Adeline Du Pasquier has prepared every previous edition of *Cantate Domino* for the printer, and so it was a godsend when she agreed to prepare yet another. Hours and hours of skilled copying of words and music, not to speak of correspondence all over the world, have been given lovingly by one whose service of the Federation began almost thirty years ago.

Our thanks are also due to the Proprietors of "Psautier Romand", of the "Gesangbuch der Evangelischen Reformierten Kirche der deutschen Schweiz", of the "Psautier Laufer" and of "Louange et Prière".

Permission for the use of hymns and tunes has been sought, wherever it was required. Thanks are due to all who have given it, and our apology is recorded here, if any unintentional oversight has taken place. Gifts in paper from the Student Christian Movement of Finland, and in money from the Hazen Foundation in the U.S.A., have made the practical side of this venture possible. And so *Cantate Domino* summons a new generation in the life of the Federation, and in the life of the whole Church of Jesus Christ throughout the world, to sing to he Lord. May He receive this gift of praise and consecrate it to His glory.

R. C. MACKIE.

PRÉFACE

Cantate Domino, le psautier de la Fédération Universelle des Associations Chrétiennes d'Etudiants a été de loin sa publication la plus répandue. A l'origine, il avait été créé pour répondre à un besoin réel des étudiants, mais bientôt il fut aussi employé par de nombreuses organisations et assemblées œcuméniques. C'est pourquoi nous devons expliquer dans notre introduction la nature et le but de cette nouvelle édition, car la révision a été si complète que nous nous trouvons presque en présence d'un nouveau livre.

Le premier *Cantate Domino*, que Mlle Suzanne Bidgrain édita avec tant d'amour il y a plus de vingt-cinq ans, et qu'elle révisa plusieurs fois depuis, était à l'origine une sélection des hymnes favoris des mouvements nationaux d'étudiants chrétiens. C'est pourquoi il alliait une grande richesse d'inspiration œcuménique à une limitation inévitable dans le domaine spirituel. Avec le temps, beaucoup de cantiques devinrent si peu familiers qu'ils ne furent presque plus chantés, et certains des sujets ne s'adaptèrent plus aux besoins des nouvelles générations d'étudiants. En 1946, lorsqu'on découvrit que les empreintes qui avaient servi à plusieurs réimpressions étaient devenues inutilisables, on décida de préparer une nouvelle édition.

Cela suscita de nombreuses discussions aux comités de la F. U. A. C. E. de 1946 à 1950. La décision primordiale fut de ne pas demander aux mouvements nationaux d'envoyer un choix de cantiques pour la nouvelle édition. Ce changement de politique fut motivé par le succès grandissant du *Cantate Domino*, malgré ses imperfections. Plus personne ne le considérait comme une anthologie œcuménique, mais on trouvait en lui un auxiliaire indispensable du culte des réunions œcuméniques.

La tâche de l'éditeur fut donc tout d'abord d'omettre les cantiques rarement chantés ou ceux qui n'avaient pas résisté à l'épreuve du temps, soit à cause du texte, soit à cause de la musique, et d'ajouter des cantiques plus connus afin de compléter certaines sections liturgiques particulièrement importantes quand des chrétiens de plusieurs pays s'unissent dans l'adoration. C'est pourquoi ce n'est pas tant aux mouvements nationaux que nous avons demandé conseil qu'aux dirigeants de la Fédération et d'autres organisations chrétiennes internationales.

Nous devons préciser certains points afin d'éviter des malentendus. Tout d'abord, il ne faut pas s'attendre à trouver dans le *Cantate Domino* un grand nombre de cantiques de chaque tradition nationale. Il est évident que nous avons dû limiter notre choix, et qu'il faut considérer ce recueil comme un complément aux psautiers employés par les étudiants et les mouvements de jeunesse des divers pays, car il n'a pas la prétention de les remplacer. Puis, l'expérience des rencontres œcuméniques a prouvé la nécessité d'avoir une version anglaise, française et allemande pour chaque cantique. De ce fait, de nombreux chrétiens pourront les chanter, mais cela nous a malheureusement limités dans notre choix. Par exemple, les hymnes dont les originaux sont dans d'autres langues européennes ne sont pas représentés en nombre suffisant. En outre, les cantiques choisis appartiennent en majeure partie aux églises occidentales. Nous avons pourtant consacré beaucoup de temps à la recherche d'hymnes asiatiques, mais nous n'avons finalement pu en introduire que quelques-uns. Le langage musical dans lequel nombre des cantiques proposés ont été écrits n'appartient en propre ni aux pays de l'Est ni à ceux de l'Ouest, et les éditeurs étaient peu disposés à introduire une musique de style « international » pour des hymnes asiatiques. Ceci demeurera un des problèmes de l'hymnologie œcuménique.

En publiant cette nouvelle édition, nous avons pris soin de la rattacher à l'édition précédente. Bien que plus de la moitié des cantiques soient nouveaux, les anciens numéros de ceux qui figuraient dans l'édition précédente ont été indiqués entre parenthèses, afin de permettre à des groupes qui posséderaient les deux éditions de chanter les cantiques les plus connus. Dans la présente édition, nous nous sommes efforcés, encore plus que dans les précédentes, de faire un choix judicieux de cantiques pour chaque saison de l'année ecclésiastique. Nous avons ajouté des sous-titres par sujets, afin d'aider ceux qui dirigent des cultes à choisir des cantiques s'adaptant aux thèmes qu'ils désirent traiter.

La préparation d'un psautier en plusieurs langues est une tâche écrasante. L'éditeur en chef a été Miss Helen Morton, des Etats-Unis, ancienne Vice-Présidente de la Fédération, et l'une de ses amies les plus fidèles. Elle n'a jamais voulu se mettre au premier plan, mais sans sa bonne humeur et sa direction éclairée depuis le printemps 1948, rien n'aurait pu se faire. Notre éditeur musical, M. Frédéric Mathil, de Genève, s'est montré d'une compétence qui n'a d'égale que sa générosité d'esprit. Tout son travail fut étudié et entièrement approuvé par Mr. G. Wallace Woodsworth, de l'Université de Harvard. On devra comprendre que les changements que nous avons effectués dans les mélodies ou les harmonisations de cantiques déjà connus sont le résultat de recherches minutieuses ayant pour but de retourner à la source même de la musique ancienne dans sa forme la plus pure ou la plus authentique. Mrs. Margaret House et le pasteur Wolfgang Schweitzer nous ont prodigué leur temps et leurs conseils avisés depuis le début de cette entreprise, et Mmes Hilary Nicholls et Elizabeth Bridston ont assumé la tâche périlleuse de l'édition définitive. Une véritable armée de traducteurs a effectué plus d'une centaine de traductions. C'est leur apport littéraire qui a réellement permis à ce livre de remplir son but. Un dernier nom mérite une mention toute spéciale : Mlle Adeline Du Pasquier a préparé toutes les précédentes éditions du *Cantate Domino* pour l'imprimeur, et c'est pourquoi ce fut une bénédiction qu'elle accepte d'en préparer encore une. Elle consacra des centaines d'heures à la copie impeccable de la musique et des paroles, ainsi qu'à une correspondance mondiale, elle qui entra au service de la Fédération il y a près de trente ans.

Nous devons encore remercier les éditeurs du « Psautier romand », du « Psautier de l'Eglise réformée évangélique de Suisse alémanique », du « Psautier Laufer », et de « Louange et Prière ».

L'autorisation de publier des cantiques et des textes musicaux a été demandée lorsqu'elle était nécessaire. Nous remercions tous ceux qui nous l'ont donnée et, si jamais un oubli avait eu lieu par inadvertance, nous nous en excusons ici. Des dons de papier de l'Association Chrétienne d'Etudiants de Finlande et l'aide financière de la Fondation Hazen aux Etats-Unis nous ont permis la réalisation matérielle de cette entreprise. Ainsi le *Cantate Domino* appelle une nouvelle génération de la Fédération et de l'Eglise de Jésus-Christ à chanter au Seigneur. Puisse notre Dieu recevoir ce don de notre adoration et le consacrer à sa gloire.

R. C. MACKIE.

VORWORT

Cantate Domino, das Gesangbuch des Christlichen Studentenweltbundes, ist unter allen Büchern, die der Weltbund herausgebracht hat, das weitverbreitetste. Obwohl es ursprünglich nur geschaffen wurde, um einem Mangel unter Studenten abzuhelfen, hat es seinen Weg in viele ökumenische Organisationen und Versammlungen gefunden. Infolgedessen muss seine Neuausgabe, die so drastisch revidiert wurde, dass fast ein neues Buch daraus entstanden ist, seinen Benutzern schon mit einer genaueren Erklärung seiner Eigenart und seines Zweckes vorgelegt werden.

Das erste *Cantate Domino* wurde vor mehr als fünfundzwanzig Jahren von Suzanne Bidgrain mit liebevoller Sorgfalt herausgegeben und bei verschiedenen Gelegenheiten revidiert. Es war im Grunde eine Sammlung von Lieblingsliedern der nationalen Christlichen Studentenbewegungen. Es vereinigte deshalb in sich eine wirklich bemerkenswerte Weite ökumenischen Ursprungs mit einer ganz bestimmten Begrenzung seiner geistlichen Reichweite. Das hatte zum Ergebnis, dass im Laufe der Zeit viele Lieder sich als weithin unbekannt erwiesen und selten gesungen wurden; mit jeder nachfolgenden Studentengeneration wurde die Liste der brauchbaren Möglichkeiten immer kürzer. Als sich im Jahre 1946 ausserdem ergab, dass die Platten durch die aufeinanderfolgenden Drucke unbrauchbar wurden, entschied man sich für die Herstellung einer neuen Ausgabe.

In den Weltbund Kommittees fanden in den Jahren von 1946-1950 darüber noch viele Besprechungen statt. Die Hauptentscheidung aber war, dass die einzelnen nationalen Studentenbewegungen diesmal nicht um eine Auswahl von Liedern gebeten werden sollten. Der Grund für diese Verfahrensänderung war einfach der ausserordentliche Erfolg, den *Cantate Domino* trotz seiner sachlichen Begrenzungen hatte. Niemand betrachtete es mehr als eine ökumenische Anthologie, sondern als eine tatsächlich notwendige Hilfe für den Gottesdienst in ökumenischen Versammlungen.

Damit verwandelte sich die Aufgabe der Herausgeber mehr in die, selten gesungene Lieder herauszunehmen — mit ihnen auch diejenigen, welche im Gebrauch auf Grund ihres Inhaltes oder ihrer Melodie nicht standhielten — und dafür neue einzusetzen, die besser bekannt waren und die Lücken füllen konnten, die in den Notwendigkeiten eines gemeinsamen Gottesdienstes für Christen aus aller Welt immer wieder entstehen. Notwendige Ratschläge wurden darum nicht so sehr von den nationalen Gruppen als vielmehr von verantwortlichen Führern des Weltbundes und anderer christlicher Weltorganisationen in Anspruch genommen.

Im Hinblick auf die vorliegende Ausgabe müssen ein paar Punkte sehr klar verdeutlicht werden, wenn ernsthafte Missverständnisse vermieden werden sollen. Zunächst einmal sollte niemand erwarten, dass *Cantate Domino* aus jeder nationalen Tradition eine angemessene Auswahl von Liedern enthalten könne. Sein Fassungsvermögen ist begrenzt, und man kann es daher nur als einen Anhang zu den eigenen Liederbüchern betrachten, die Studenten und andere junge Leute in den verschiedenen Ländern benutzen; auf keinen Fall soll es diese ersetzen.

Zum anderen erscheinen auf Grund der vorherrschenden Erfahrung und Gewohnheit bei ökumenischen Treffen alle Lieder in englischer, französischer und deutscher Fassung. Das bedeutet zwar, dass man sie in umfangreichem Masse gebrauchen kann, aber es hat auch schon bei ihrer Auswahl einen starken Einfluss ausgeübt. So sind zum Beispiel Lieder in anderen europäischen Sprachen nicht im gleichen abgewogenen Masse vertreten. Dazu kommt, dass die ausgesuchten Lieder vornehmlich aus den Kirchen des Westens stammen. Viel Zeit wurde darauf verwendet, möglichst eine grössere Zahl von Liedern aus Asien zu erhalten, aber schliesslich wurden doch nur einige wenige aufgenommen. Die musikalischen Ausdrucksformen, derer sich manche sonst sehr geeignete Lieder bedienen, sind weder im Westen noch im Osten sehr bekannt, und die Herausgeber konnten sich nicht entschliessen, die asiatischen Lieder in den Stil « internationaler » Musik zu übersetzen. So bleibt dies ein ungelöstes Problem ökumenischer Hymnologie.

Beim Aufbau dieser neuen Ausgabe ist sorgfältig darauf geachtet worden, sie auf die alte abzustimmen. Zwar sind mehr als die Hälfte der Lieder im *Cantate Domino* neu, aber die alten Nummern der Lieder, die auch in der alten Ausgabe stehen, sind in Klammern beigefügt, sodass die bekanntesten unter ihnen auch in einer Gruppe gesungen werden können, die beide Ausgaben in der Hand hat. Grössere Aufmerksamkeit ist in dieser Ausgabe auch auf eine Auswahl der Lieder mit Rücksicht auf das Kirchenjahr verwendet worden. Sachüberschriften sollen den Leitern ökumenischer Gottesdienste helfen, passende Lieder für verschiedene Themen und Gelegenheiten schneller zu finden. Die Vorbereitungsarbeit für ein ökumenisches Liederbuch in mehreren Sprachen ist eine ungeheure Aufgabe. Hauptherausgeber ist Miss Helen Morton aus U. S. A., ehemalige Vizepräsidentin des Weltbundes und eine seiner treuesten Freundinnen. Ohne ihre fähige und selbstlose Leitung seit dem Frühjahr 1948 wäre nichts zustande gekommen. M. Frederic Mathil aus Genf erwies sich als ein äusserst geschickter und geistreicher Redakteur auf musikalischem Gebiet. Seine gesamte Arbeit wurde von Mr. Wallace G. Woodsworth von der Harvard Universität durchgesehen und fand freudige Zustimmung. Hierbei sei noch darauf hingewiesen, dass alle Änderungen in Melodie oder Harmonisierung, auch in den Sätzen altbekannter Lieder, das Ergebnis einer sorgfältigen Untersuchung besserer und mehr authentischer Quellen alter Musik darstellen. Mrs. Margaret House und Pastor Wolfgang Schweitzer haben von Anfang an unermüdlich mit Rat und wissenschaftlicher Unterstützung dem Unternehmen beigestanden, und Mrs. Hilary Nicholls sowie Mrs. Elizabeth Bridston haben die mühevolle Aufgabe der abschliessenden Redaktion auf sich genommen. Eine regelrechte Armee von Übersetzern war für die mehr als hundert Übertragungen notwendig. Ihre einfallsreich e und geschickte Mitarbeit ist es, die das Buch für seinen Zweck wirklich brauchbar machte. Ein weiterer Name muss noch besonders erwähnt werden. Mlle Adeline Du Pasquier hat schon alle vorherigen Ausgaben von *Cantate Domino* für den Druck vorbereitet, und so war es ein Segen für die Sache, dass sie sich auch dieser Ausgabe annahm. Viele Stunden sorgfältigen Kopierens von Text und Noten — gar nicht zu reden von einer Korrespondenz nach allen Weltteilen — hat sie, deren Dienst im Weltbund vor fast dreissig Jahren begann, liebevoll daran gewendet.

Unser Dank gilt ferner den Herausgebern des « Psautier Romand », des « Gesangbuches der Evangelischen Reformierten Kirche der deutschen Schweiz », des « Psautier Laufer » und der « Louange et Prière ».

Um Erlaubnis für die Verwendung der Lieder und Melodien ist überall nachgesucht worden, wo das notwendig war. Ein Dank gebührt allen denen, die diese

Erlaubnis erteilt haben und wir bitten hier zugleich, ein etwaiges Versäumnis zu entschuldigen, das unbeabsichtigt stattgefunden haben mag. Gaben von der Christlichen Studentenbewegung Finnlands in Form von Papier und von der Hazen Foundation in U.S.A. in Form von Geld haben auf materiellem Gebiet dieses Unternehmen ermöglicht. Und so ruft *Cantate Domino* eine neue Generation im Leben des Weltbundes und im Leben der ganzen Kirche Christi in aller Welt dazu auf, dem Herrn zu singen. Möge er diese Gabe des Lobpreises gnädig empfangen und zu seinem Ruhm segnen.

R. C. MACKIE.

— 1 (1) —

Katholisches Gesangbuch (1774).

Gros - ser Gott, wir lo - ben dich, Herr, wir prei - sen
Grand Dieu, nous te bé - nis - sons, Nous cé - lé - brons
Ho - ly God, Thy Name we bless, All Thy prais - es

dei - ne Stär - ke. Vor dir neigt die Er - de sich Und be-
tes lou - an - ges. E - ter - nel, nous t'ex - al - tons, De con-
cel - e - brat - ing, And for our un-worth - i - ness Thy for-

wun - dert dei - ne Wer - ke. Wie du warst vor al - ler
cert a - vec les an - ges, Et, pros - ter - nés de - vant
give - ness sup - pli - cat - ing. With the an - gels thus we

Zeit, So bleibst du in E - wig - keit. Wie du warst vor
toi, Nous t'a - do - rons, ô grand Roi ! Et, pros - ter - nés
bring A - dor - a - tion to our King. With the an - gels

al - ler Zeit, So bleibst du in E - wig - keit.
de - vant toi, Nous t'a - do - rons, ô grand Roi !
thus we bring A - dor - a - tion to our King.

2.

Alles, was dich preisen kann,
   Cherubim und Seraphinen
Stimmen dir ein Loblied an ;
   Alle Engel, die dir dienen,
Rufen dir stets ohne Ruh : ⎫ *bis*
« Heilig, heilig, heilig » zu. ⎭

3.

Heilig, Herr Gott Zebaoth !
   Heilig, Herr der Kriegesheere !
Starker Helfer in der Not !
   Himmel, Erde, Luft und Meere
Sind erfüllt von deinem Ruhm ⎫ *bis*
Alles ist dein Eigentum. ⎭

4.

Auf dem ganzen Erdenkreis
   Loben Grosse und auch Kleine
Dich, Gott Vater, dir zum Preis
   Singt die heilige Gemeine ;
Sie ehrt auch auf seinem Thron ⎫ *bis*
Deinen eingebornen Sohn. ⎭

5.

Sie verehrt den heil'gen Geist,
   Welcher uns mit seinen Lehren
Und mit Troste kräftig speist,
   Der, O König, voller Ehren,
Der mit dir, Herr Jesu Christ, ⎫ *bis*
Und dem Vater ewig ist. ⎭

Nach AMBROSIUS († 397).

* * *

2.

Les saints et les bienheureux,
   Les trônes et les puissances,
Toutes les vertus des cieux
   Disent tes magnificences,
Proclamant dans leurs concerts ⎫ *bis*
Le grand Dieu de l'univers. ⎭

3.

Saint, saint, saint est l'Eternel,
   Le Seigneur, Dieu des armées !
Son pouvoir est immortel ;
   Ses œuvres partout semées
Font éclater sa grandeur, ⎫ *bis*
Sa majesté, sa splendeur. ⎭

4.

Ton Eglise dans les cieux
   A la gloire parvenue,
Et ton Eglise en tous lieux
   Sur la terre répandue
Entonnent d'un même cœur ⎫ *bis*
Un saint hymne au Rédempteur. ⎭

5.

Gloire soit au Saint-Esprit !
   Gloire soit à Dieu, le Père !
Gloire soit à Jésus-Christ,
   Notre Sauveur, notre Frère !
Son immense charité, ⎫ *bis*
Dure à perpétuité. ⎭

Trad. H. L. EMPAYTAZ (1790-1853).

* * *

2.

All the hosts of heav'nly light
  Saints in bliss before Thee bending,
Thrones and pow'rs in glory bright
  Hymn Thy praise in concert blending
They Thy Majesty proclaim   ⎱ *bis*
Praising Thy thrice-holy name. ⎰

3.

Holy, holy, holy Lord
  Whom the hosts on high are praising;
Saviour worshipped and adored,
  All the world its hymn is raising.
Singing grateful praise to Thee ⎱ *bis*
For Thy love and mercy free. ⎰

4.

From the earth's remotest bounds
  Great and small unite to hymn Thee :
Father God, Thy praise resounds
  Where Thy Church delights to sing Thee :
With Thy sole-begotten Son   ⎱ *bis*
Reigning with Thee on Thy Throne. ⎰

5.

Glory through eternity,
  Spirit, Son and blessed Father !
God of gracious tenderness,
  At Thy feet we sinners gather.
All Thy great and wondrous love ⎱ *bis*
We shall through the ages prove. ⎰

Trans. R. Birch-Hoyle (1923).

— 2 (75) —

Cologne, (1623).
Harm. FRÉDÉRIC MATHIL (1950)

All crea-tures of our God and King, Al - le - lu - ia !
Vous cré - a - tu - res du Sei - gneur, Al - lé - lu - ia !
Got - tes Ge-schöp - fe kommt zu Hauf! Hal - le - lu - ja !

Lift   up your voice and with us sing Al - le -   lu - ia ! Thou
Chan - tez tou - jours en son hon-neur, Al - lé -   lu - ia ! Car
Lasst brau-sen   hoch zum Him-mel auf, Eu - er   Lo - ben, Du

burn-ing sun with gol - den beam, Al - le - lu - ia! Thou
c'est lui seul qu'il faut lou - er, Al - lé - lu - ia! Il
Son-ne hell mit Gold-nem Strahl, Hal-le - lu - ja! Mond

sil - ver moon with soft-er gleam, Al - le - lu - ia! O
donne au so - leil sa clar - té, Al - lé - lu - ia! Ren-dez
leuch-tend hoch vom Himmels - saal Hal-le - lu - ja! Singt ihm

praise Him, O praise Him, Al - le - lu - ia!
gloi - re! Ren - dez gloi - re! Al - lé - lu - ia!
Eh - re! Singt ihm Eh - re! Hal-le - lu - ja!

2. Thou rushing wind that art so strong, Alleluia!
Ye clouds that sail in heav'n along, Alleluia!
Thou rising morn, in praise rejoice, Alleluia!
Ye lights of evening, find a voice, Alleluia!
   O praise Him, O praise Him, Alleluia!

3. Thou flowing water, pure and clear, Alleluia!
Make music for thy Lord to hear, Alleluia!
Thou fire so masterful and bright, Alleluia!
That givest man both warmth and light, Alleluia!
   O praise Him, O praise Him, Alleluia!

4. Dear mother earth, who day by day, Alleluia !
   Unfoldest blessings on our way, Alleluia !
   The flowers and fruit that in Thee grow, Alleluia !
   Let them His glory also show, Alleluia !
      O praise Him, O praise Him, Alleluia !

5. And ye all men of tender heart, Alleluia !
   Forgiving others, take your part, Alleluia !
   Ye, who long pain and sorrow bear, Alleluia !
   Praise God and on Him cast your care, Alleluia !
      O praise Him, O praise Him, Alleluia !

6. And thou most kind and gentle Death, Alleluia !
   Waiting to hush our latest breath, Alleluia !
   Thou leadest home the child of God, Alleluia !
   And Christ our Lord the way hath trod, Alleluia !
      O praise Him, O praise Him, Alleluia !

7. Let all things their Creator bless, Alleluia !
   And worship Him in humbleness, Alleluia !
   Praise, praise the Father, praise the Son, Alleluia !
   And praise the Spirit, Three in One, Alleluia !
      O praise Him, O praise Him, Alleluia !

St. FRANCIS OF ASSISI (1182-1226).
Trans. W. H. DRAPER (About 1913) *.

★ ★ ★

2. Dieu, sois loué pour le soleil, Alléluia !
   Pour ce grand frère sans pareil, Alléluia !
   Et pour la lune et sa lueur, Alléluia !
   Pour chaque étoile notre sœur, Alléluia !
      Rendons gloire, rendons gloire, Alléluia !

3. Loué sois-tu pour frère vent, Alléluia !
   Pour le ciel pur, pour tous les temps, Alléluia !
   L'eau qui nous vient de toi, Seigneur, Alléluia !
   Nous est une humble et chaste sœur, Alléluia !
      Rendons goire, rendons gloire, Alléluia !

4. Loué sois-tu pour sire feu, Alléluia !
   Vivant, robuste, glorieux, Alléluia !
   La terre, en maternelle sœur, Alléluia !
   Nous comble de ses mille fleurs, Alléluia !
      Rendons gloire, rendons gloire, Alléluia !

5. Heureux les artisans de paix, Alléluia !
   Leur nom soit béni à jamais, Alléluia !
   Ceux qui ont souffert et pâti, Alléluia !
   Ils te remettent leurs soucis, Alléluia !
      A toi montent leurs louanges, Alléluia !

6. Loué sois-tu pour notre mort, Alléluia !
   Elle prendra nos pauvres corps, Alléluia !
   Tu accueilleras dans les cieux, Alléluia !
   Ceux qui t'ont obéi, ô Dieu, Alléluia !
      Rendons gloire, rendons goire, Alléluia !

7. Dieu trois fois saint, nous te louons, Alléluia !
   Nous te chantons, nous t'adorons, Alléluia !
   Gloire au Père et louange au Fils, Alléluia !
   Et loué soit le Saint-Esprit, Alléluia !
      Rendons gloire, rendons gloire, Alléluia !

Trad. revue par J.-J. Bovet (1950).

★ ★ ★

2. Du Sturm, der durch die Welten zieht, Halleluja !
   Du Wolke, die am Himmel flieht, Halleluja !
   Du Sommers junges Morgenrot, Halleluja !
   Du Abendschein, der prächtig loht, Halleluja !
      Singt ihm Ehre ! Singt ihm Ehre ! Halleluja !

3. Ihr Quellen all, lachende Flut, Halleluja !
   Lasst euren Lauf dem Schöpfer gut, Halleluja !
   Du Feuers Flamme auf dem Herd, Halleluja !
   Daran der Mensch sich wärmt und nährt, Halleluja !
      Singt ihm Ehre ! Singt ihm Ehre ! Halleluja !

4. Du, Mutter Erde gut und mild, Halleluja !
   Daraus uns lauter Segen quillt, Halleluja !
   Ihr Blumen bunt, ihr Früchte treu, Halleluja !
   Die Jahr um Jahr uns reifen neu, Halleluja !
      Singt ihm Ehre ! Singt ihm Ehre ! Halleluja !

5. Ihr Herzen, drin die Liebe wohnt, Halleluja !
   Die ihr den Feind verzeihend schont, Halleluja !
   Ihr, die ihr traget schweres Leid, Halleluja !
   Es Gott zu opfern still bereit, Halleluja !
      Singt ihm Ehre ! Singt ihm Ehre ! Halleluja !

6. Du, der empfängt in letzter Not, Halleluja !
   Den Odem mein, O Bruder Tod, Halleluja !
   Führ Gottes Kinder himmelan, Halleluja !
   Den Weg, den Jesus ging voran ! Halleluja !
      Ihm zu Ehre ! Ihm zu Ehre ! Halleluja !

7. Ihr Kreaturen, eint zum Chor, Halleluja !
   Niedrig wie hoch, zu Gott empor, Euer Loben !
   Vater und Sohn und Heil'gem Geist, Halleluja !
   Dreieinig, heilig, hochgepreist, Halleluja !
      Sei die Ehre ! Sei die Ehre ! Halleluja !

Übers. Karl Budde (1929).

Moderato

JOHANN CRÜGER (1598-1662).

Ne te dé - so - le point, Si - on, sè - che tes
Volk Got - tes, lass den Harm und trock - ne dei - ne
O Zi - on, do not grieve, but cease thy bit - ter

lar - mes, L'E - ter - nel est ton Dieu, ne sois plus en a-
Zäh - ren. Es wird mit ew'-gem Arm dein Gott der Drang - sal
weep - ing; Th'E-ter - nal is thy God, His pro - mise to thee

lar - mes; Il te reste un re - pos dans la ter - re de
weh - ren. Wo Heil und Frie - de wohnt, bleibt dir die Stadt be-
keep - ing; A rest - ing place a - waits thee on that peace - ful

paix; Le Sei-gneur te ra - mène et te garde à ja - mais.
reit. Dein Herr, der dro-ben thront, be-schirmt dich al - le - zeit.
shore; The Lord will lead thee home and keep thee e - ver-more.

2.

Il te relèvera du sein de tes ruines ;
La vigne et l'olivier couvriront tes collines ;
Tout sera rétabli comme en tes plus beaux jours,
Les murs de tes cités, tes remparts et tes tours.

3.

Relève ton courage, ô Sion désolée !
Par le Dieu tout-puissant tu seras consolée ;
Il vient pour rassembler tes enfants bienheureux ;
Bientôt tu les verras réunis sous tes yeux.

Félix Neff (1797-1829).

★ ★ ★

2.

Er hebt dich stark empor aus Trauer und aus Trümmern.
Wo sich dein Glanz verlor, wird neuer Schatz erschimmern.
Und strahlend wird ersteh'n, was unterging im Sturm,
Wie ehe stark und schön, dein Mauer, Wall und Turm.

3.

Drum auf, mit frohem Mut, Volk Gottes, ohn' Betrüben !
Dein Herr macht alles gut, des Trost dir nachgeblieben.
Er wird mit Lied und Lust versammeln deine Schar,
Dass du erfahren musst : Er bleibet, der Er war !

Übers. Erwin Kleine (1950).

★ ★ ★

2.

The Lord will raise thee up from all thy devastation,
Vineyards and olive-groves return to cultivation.
All things shall be restored as in thy happiest hours,
Thy walls and citadels, thy ramparts and thy towers.

3.

Renew thy courage, then, City of desolation !
In the Almighty God thou shalt find consolation ;
He comes to gather up thy scattered family,
And this reunion blest thy faithful eyes shall see.

Trans. Margaret House (1950).

Ps. 33.
Mél. LOYS BOURGEOIS (1544).
Harmonisation d'après CL. GOUDIMEL.
(ED. JAQUI, 1565.)

Moderato animato

Ré - veil - le toi, peu - ple fi - dè - le, Pour lou - er
Jauchzt al - le ! Gott sei hoch er - ho - ben ! Ge - rech - te,
Rise, faith - ful ser - vants of the Lord, See how His

Dieu tout d'u - ne voix ! La lou - ange est sé - ante et
freu - et euch des Herrn ! Den From-men ziemt es, ihn zu
works show forth His might : See, and give thanks with one ac-

bel - le En la bou - che des hom - mes droits.
lo - ben ; Schön ist es, und er hört es gern !
cord : To wor - ship Him is our de - light.

Qu'a - vec har - mo - ni - e On chante, on pu - bli - e
Gebt dem Herrn die Eh - re, Dass es je - der hö - re,
Trum-pet, harp and lute, Psalt - e - ry and flute

L'œu-vre du Sei-gneur; Que de nos can-ti-ques
Mit der Har-fen Klang. Eu-res Psal-ters Sai-ten
Spread a-broad His praise. Heart and tongue with joy

Les sons ma-gni-fi-ques Di-sent sa gran-deur!
Müs-sen froh be-glei-ten Eu-ren Lob-ge-sang.
Lust-i-ly em-ploy Psalms and hymns to raise.

2.

L'Eternel ici-bas regarde
Nuit et jour du plus haut des cieux;
A tous les mortels il prend garde,
Rien ne se dérobe à ses yeux.
  Redoutable et juste,
  De son trône auguste,
  Il voit constamment
  Tout ce qui se passe
  Dans le vaste espace,
  Sous le firmament.

3.

Dieu, par sa suprême puissance,
Fit le cœur de tous les humains;
Il a parfaite connaissance
De toute l'œuvre de leurs mains.
  L'ombre de ses ailes
  Couvre les fidèles;
  Il veille toujours
  Sur qui le révère,
  Et qui rien n'espère
  Que de son secours.

CLÉMENT MAROT (1543). Révisé par CONRART (1677).

* * *

2.

Er schützet seiner Diener Leben,
Er rettet von dem nahen Tod,
Und er wird Brot in Fülle geben
In Teurung und in Hungersnot.
  Drum wird's unsern Seelen
  Nie am Guten fehlen,
  Denn sie harren sein.
  Er ist Schild und Stärke,
  Und zu jedem Werke
  Gibt er uns Gedeih'n.

3.

Kommt, lasst uns immer auf ihn schauen,
Da unser Herz sich seiner freut,
Auf seinen heil'gen Namen trauen
Und ihn erhöh'n in Freud und Leid.
  Gib, dass uns behüte,
  Vater, deine Güte!
  Halt dein Vaterherz
  Immer für uns offen,
  Wie wir auf dich hoffen,
  Heil'ge Freud und Schmerz.

Übers. MATTHIAS JORISSEN (1739-1823).

* * *

2.

God in His mighty pow'r and love
Hath framed the hearts of all mankind;
He watches o'er them from above,
And knows the working of their mind.
 To His own He brings
 Healing in His wings
From His heav'nly throne;
 Men need never fear
 Danger threat'ning near,
 Who trust Him alone.

3.

Our soul hath waited for the Lord;
He is our helper and our shield;
Our heart rejoiceth in His word;
His mercy hath our hope revealed.
 Inspire with Thy grace
 Those seeking Thy face,
Mighty King and Lord!
 We trust in Thy will
 Our hope to fulfil,
 God, ever adored.

Trans. MARGARET HOUSE (1938).

— 5 (7) —

Religioso

JOACHIM NEANDER (1650-1680).

Gott ist ge - gen - wär - tig! Las - set uns an - be - ten
God re - veals His pre - sence: Let us now a - dore Him,
Dieu vient dans sa gloi - re! Que cha - cun l'a - do - re,

Und in Ehr - furcht vor ihn tre - ten. Gott ist in der
And with awe ap - pear be - fore Him. God is in His
D'un pro - fond res - pect l'ho - no - re. Dieu de la vic -

Mit - ten! Al - les in uns schwei - ge Und sich in - nigst
tem - ple: All with - in keep si - lence, Pros - trate lie with
toi - re! Qu'en nous tout se tai - se, Se pros - ter - ne en -

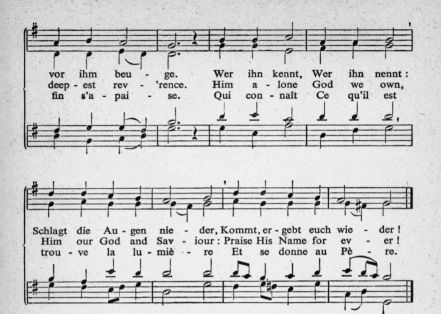

vor ihm beu - ge. Wer ihn kennt, Wer ihn nennt :
deep - est rev - 'rence. Him a - lone God we own,
fin s'a - pai - se. Qui con - naît Ce qu'il est

Schlagt die Au - gen nie - der, Kommt, er - gebt euch wie - der !
Him our God and Sav - iour : Praise His Name for ev - er !
trou - ve la lu - miè - re Et se donne au Pè - re.

2. Wir entsagen willig allen Eitelkeiten,
   Aller Erdenlust und Freuden ;
   Da liegt unser Wille, Seele, Leib und Leben
   Dir zum Eigentum ergeben :
   Du allein — Sollst es sein,
   Unser Gott und Herre, — Dir gebührt die Ehre.

3. Majestätisch Wesen, möcht ich recht dich preisen
   Und im Geist dir Dienst erweisen !
   Möcht ich, wie die Engel, immer vor dir stehen
   Und dich gegenwärtig sehen !
   Lass mich dir — Für und für
   Trachten zu gefallen, — Liebster Gott, in allem !

4. Mache mich einfältig, innig, abgeschieden,
   Sanft und still in deinem Frieden ;
   Mach mich reines Herzens, dass ich deine Klarheit.
   Schauen mag im Geist und Wahrheit !
   Lass mein Herz — Überwärts
   Wie ein Adler schweben — Und in dir nur leben.

GERHARD TERSTEEGEN (1697-1769).

* * *

2. God reveals His presence : — Hear the harps resounding,
   See the crowds the throne surrounding :
   Holy, holy, holy ! — Hear the hymn ascending,
   Angels, saints, their voices blending.
   Bow Thine ear — To us here ;
   Harken, O Lord Jesus, — To our meaner praises.

3. Jesus dwell within me : — Whilst on earth I tarry,
   Make me Thy blest sanctuary ;
   Then, on angel pinions, — Waft me to those regions
   Filled with bright seraphic legions.
   May this hope — Bear me up,
   Till these eyes for ever — Gaze on Thee, my Saviour.

4. O Thou Fount of blessing, — Purify my spirit,
   Trusting only in Thy merit :
   Like the holy angels — Who behold Thy glory,
   May I ceaselessly adore Thee.
   Let Thy will — Ever still
   Rule Thy Church terrestrial, — As the hosts celestial.

Trans. F. W. FORSTER (1760-1835), J. MILLER (1756-1790)
and W. MERCER (1811-1873).

★ ★ ★

2. Dieu, je t'abandonne — Plaisirs et chimères,
   Vanités, jeux de la terre.
   De plein gré je donne — En tes mains ma vie,
   Volonté, corps, âme, envie.
   Que l'honneur — Au Seigneur
   Toujours appartienne — Car aux cieux il règne.

3. Dieu, que mes louanges — Chantent ta puissance,
   Témoignent de ta présence.
   Comme les archanges — Puissé-je, en ta grâce
   Me tenir devant ta face.
   Laisse-moi, — Devant toi
   A ton sacrifice, — Offrir mon service.

4. Rends-moi pur et simple, — Cœur humble et docile,
   En ta paix doux et tranquille.
   Et que je contemple — Ta clarté sereine,
   Ta vérité souveraine.
   Que mon cœur, — O Seigneur,
   Plane comme l'aigle — Et suive ta règle.

Trad. PAULINE MARTIN (1951).

GIOVANNI PALESTRINA (1524-1594).

Glo - ri - a Pa - tri et Fi - li - o, Glo - ri - a
Glo - ry to God, the Fa-ther and Son, Glo - ry to
Gloire à Dieu no - tre cré - a - teur, Gloire à Jé-
Ehr' sei dem Va - ter und dem Sohn! Ehr' sei dem

Pa - tri et Fi - li - o, Et Spi - ri - tu - i Sanc - to, Et Spi-
God, the Fa-ther and Son, And the Ho - ly Spi - rit, And the
sus, le Ré - demp-teur, A l'Es-prit lou-an - ge et gloi - re
Va - ter und dem Sohn! Und dem Hei - li - gen Gei - ste Und dem

ri - tu - i Sanc - to, Al - le - lu - ia! Al - le - lu - ia!
Ho - ly Spi - rit, Al - le - lu - ia! Al - le - lu - ia!
Dans l'é - ter - ni - té. Al - lé - lu - ia! Al - lé - lu - ia!
Hei - li - gen Gei - ste, Hal - le - lu - jah! Hal - le - lu - jah!

— 7 (3) —

Ps. 100.
LOYS BOURGEOIS (1551).
Harm. d'après CL. GOUDIMEL (1565).

Vous qui sur la terre ha - bi - tez, Chan - tez à
All peo - ple that on earth do dwell, Sing to the
Nun jauchzt dem Her - ren al - le Welt ! Kommt her, zu

hau - te voix, chan - tez ! Ré - jou - is - sez - vous
Lord with cheer - ful voice ; Him serve with mirth, His
sei - nem Dienst euch stellt, Kommt mit Froh - lok - ken,

au Sei - gneur, E - gay - ez - vous à son hon - neur.
praise forth tell ; Come ye be - fore Him and re - joice.
säu - met nicht, Kommt vor sein hei - lig An - ge - sicht !

2. Car il est le Dieu souverain,
Celui qui nous fit de sa main,
Nous tous, le peuple qu'il chérit,
Et l'heureux troupeau qu'il nourrit.

3. Entrez dans son temple aujourd'hui
Et présentez-vous devant lui ;
Célébrez son nom glorieux,
Qui remplit la terre et les cieux.

4. C'est un Dieu rempli de bonté,
   D'une éternelle vérité ;
   Il nous comble de ses bienfaits
   Et sa grâce dure à jamais.

THÉODORE DE BÈZE (1562).
Arrangé par CONRART (1679).

★ ★ ★

2. The Lord ye know is God indeed ;
   Without our aid He did us make ;
   We are His folk, He doth us feed,
   And for His sheep He doth us take.

3. O enter then His gates with praise ;
   Approach with joy His courts unto ;
   Praise, laud, and bless His name always,
   For it is seemly so to do.

4. For why, the Lord our God is good ;
   His mercy is for ever sure ;
   His truth at all times firmly stood,
   And shall from age to age endure.

Trans. WILLIAM KETHE (1560).

★ ★ ★

2. Erkennt, dass Gott ist unser Herr,
   Der uns erschaffen ihm zur Ehr,
   Und nicht wir selbst ; durch Gottes Gnad
   Ein jeder Mensch sein Leben hat.

3. Die ihr nun wollet bei ihm sein,
   Kommt, geht zu seinen Toren ein
   Mit Loben durch der Psalmen Klang,
   Zu seinem Vorhof mit Gesang.

4. Er ist voll Güt und Freundlichkeit,
   Voll Lieb und Treu zu jeder Zeit ;
   Sein Gnade währet dort und hier
   Und seine Wahrheit für und für.

Nach CORNELIUS BECKER (1561-1604)
und DAVID DENICKE (1603-1680).

« Hanover »
Ascribed to WILLIAM CROFT
(1678-1727).

O wor-ship the King, all glor-ious a-bove, O grate-full-y
Lou-ons du Sei-gneur le nom glo-ri-eux Et pour son a-
Er-he-bet den Herrn, sein Lob stim-met an ! O dan-ket ihm

sing His pow'r and His love; Our Shield and De-fend-er, the
mour Ren-dons grâce à Dieu; Il est mon re-fu-ge, mon
gern, Was er uns ge-tan! Schutz schafft er und Weh-re, er

An-cient of days, Pa-vil-ioned in splen-dour, and gird-ed with praise.
seul dé-fen-seur, Et dans les cieux rè-gne, nim-bé de splen-deur.
hilft al-ler-weis. Er zel-tet in Eh-re, ge-gür-tet mit Preis.

2. O tell of His might, O sing of His grace,
Whose robe is the light, whose canopy space.
His chariots of wrath the deep thunder clouds form,
And dark is His path on the wings of the storm.

3. This earth with its store of wonders untold,
Almighty, Thy power hath founded of old,
Hath 'stablished it fast by a changeless decree,
And round it hath cast, like a mantle, the sea.

4. Thy bountiful care what tongue can recite?
It breathes in the air, it shines in the light;
It streams from the hills, it descends to the plain,
And sweetly distils in the dew and the rain.

Sir ROBERT GRANT (1779-1838).

* * *

2. Vantons son pouvoir, chantons sa bonté;
Il vit dans les cieux, vêtu de beauté;
L'ouragan fait rage, tout est déchaîné,
Et l'orage gronde, s'il est irrité.

3. Le Dieu tout-puissant créa l'univers
Puis il l'entoura du manteau des mers.
Il régit le monde, tout lui obéit,
Ses lois immuables règlent l'infini.

4. Qui chantera donc sa grande bonté?
Elle imprègne l'air, luit dans la clarté,
Et dans les montagnes, dans tous les vallons,
S'exhale en rosée, nous comble de dons.

Trad. FLOSSETTE DU PASQUIER (1951).

* * *

2. Erzählet doch weit sein Allmacht und Gnad',
Der Sonnen zum Kleid, zum Stuhl Zeiten hat.
Sein Zornwagen funkelt, von Donnern bewacht,
Sein Weg ist umdunkelt von stürmischer Nacht.

3. Du, Gott, schufst die Welt mit mächtiger Hand.
Mit Wundern bestellt ist ihr ganzes Land.
Und der du sie gründest, willst dass sie besteh'.
Und um sie hin windest als Tuch du die See.

4. Wo fänd' sich ein Mund zu solchem Bericht?
Es duftet das Rund, es leuchtet das Licht,
Es strömt von den Höhen hernieder zur Au,
Es gleicht mildem Regen und schimmerndem Tau.

Übers. ERWIN KLEINE (1950).

— 9 —

Herrnhut Melodie
Gezangenbundel der Nederlandse Hervormde Kerk *.
Harm. Leonard Johannes Mens (1879- ?).

Wij knie - len voor uw ze - tel neer, Wij, Heer en al uw
le - den, En ee - ren U als on - zen Heer met
lied' - ren en - ge - be - den. Dat al - le macht, hoe
hoog, hoe groot, voor U, O Gods - ge - tui - ge, O

Be - fore Thy throne, O Lord, we kneel In hum - ble a - do -
ra - tion, With all Thy Church u - ni - ted there In
song and sup - pli - ca - tion. Thou art the King of
Kings on earth, Thy faith - ful wit - ness bear - ing, The

Vor dei - nem Thro - ne knie - en wir Ge - bückt, all dei - ne
Glie - der Und brin - gen, Herr, zur Eh - re dir Ge -
be - te dar und Lie - der. Dass al - le Macht, wie
hoch und gross, Vor dir, du Got - tes zeu - ge, Du

De - vant ton trô - ne pros - ter - nés, Nous t'a - do - rons en -
sem - ble. Pour lou - er ta fi - dé - li - té, ton
peu - ple se ras - sem - ble Et veut, ô mes - sa -
ger de Dieu, dis - pen - sa - teur de vi - e, Que

eerst - ge - bo - ren' uit den dood, zich diep eer - bie - dig bui - ge!
first be - got - ten of the dead, The Fa - ther's glo - ry shar - - ing.
Ers- tling aus des To - des Schoss, Sich tief in Ehr-furcht beu - - ge!
les plus grands pou-voirs hu - mains De - vant toi s'hu - mi - li - ent.

2.

Die ons, gereinigd door uw bloed,
  Tot priesters hebt verheven,
En ons den hoogen rang, den moed
  Van koningen gegeven,
U zij de roem, U zij de lof,
  U d'eerkroon opgedragen !
Geheel deez' aard'en 't hemelhof
  Moet van Uw eer gewagen.

3.

U, die als Heer der heerlijkheid
  Verreest tot heil der volken,
Verwachten wij in majesteit
  Eens weder op de wolken.
Hij komt, elks ooge zal Hem zien,
  Ook die hem heeft doorsteken !
Elk zal Hem juichend hulde biên,
  Of om ontferming smeeken.

4.

Hoe ras of traag de tijd verdwijnt,
  Die dag zal zeker komen.
Het licht, dat aan de kim verschijnt,
  Wordt reeds van ver vernomen.
Ja, halleluja, ja Hij komt !
  Juicht, menschen, eng'len samen,
Juicht met een vreugd, die 't al verstomt,
  Juicht allen ! Amen, Amen !

CLARA FEYOENA VAN RAESFELT-VAN SYTZAMA
(1729-1807).

* * *

2.

Washed by Thy blood Thou didst us raise
  To serve as priests before Thee,
And we whom Thou hast ranked with kings,
  Assemble to adore Thee.
To Thee all glory and all praise
  And honour now be given !
The story of Thy love and power
  Must sound through earth and heaven.

3.

Thee, Who didst come as Lord of lords
  To bring the nations healing,
We see return upon the clouds,
  Thy majesty revealing.
Behold, He comes ! And every eye
  With joy or grief shall see Him,
The saints and those who pierced His
  Together rise to meet Him.   [side

4.

How fast or slow our time may pass,
  That day draws surely nearer :
The light that in the distance shines
  Is ever glowing clearer.

* By kind permission of the Secretary of the General Synod of the Dutch Reformed Church.

Yea, Alleluia ! Lo, He comes !
Angels in heaven and all men
Rejoice with joy surpassing all.
Hosanna ! Amen, Amen !

Trans. MARGARET and FRANCIS HOUSE (1951)
(Based on Revelation I : 5-7.)

* * *

2.

Du hast, o Wunder, durch dein Blut
  Zu Priestern uns erhoben,
Füllst uns mit königlichem Mut
  Und lenkst das Herz nach oben !
Drum schall dein Lob und aller Ruhm,
  Ja aller Ehren Krone
Schwing von der Erde um und um
  Sich auf zum Himmelsthrone !

3.

Du, der als Herr der Herrlichkeit
  Erstanden jedem Volke,
Du kommst ja einst zu deiner Zeit
  Hernieder in der Wolke
Und jedes Auge muss dich sehn,
  Auch wer dich einst durchstochen.
Wir wollen dir entgegen geh'n
  Und auf Erbarmung pochen.

4.

Geht rasch, geht träg' der Zeiten Lauf —
  Dein Tag wird sicher nahen !
Dein Licht, es dämmert schon herauf,
  Wie's die Propheten sahen.
Halleluja ! Der Herr kommt bald.
  Jauchz' Himm'l und Erd zusammen !
Durch's stumme All der Jubel schallt,
  Jauchzt alle ! Amen, Amen.

Übers. WILHELM HORKEL (1950).

* * *

2.

Tu donnas ton sang sur la croix
  Et fis de nous tes prêtres
Et d'esclaves que nous étions,
  Rois nous as fait renaître ;
A toi seul soit l'honneur, ô Christ,
  A toi soit toute gloire.
La terre et les cieux s'uniront
  Pour chanter ta victoire.

3.

Toi qui vins au milieu de nous
  Pour racheter le monde,
Nous contemplons ta majesté
  A nulle autre seconde.
Il vient : tout œil le percevra ;
  Voyez ses bourreaux mêmes
Lui rendre gloire et implorer
  Sa charité suprême.

4.

Bientôt sur les ailes du temps
  Viendra le jour de gloire ;
Alors partout retentira
  Son hymne de victoire.
Il vient ! Il vient ! Alléluia !
  Adorez-le, saints anges
Chantez l'universel « Amen »
  De joie et de louanges.

Trad. EVA DUBSKA-KUSCHNER (1949).

PHILIPPUS NICOLAI (1556-1608).
Originalsatz (1598)

Wie schön leuch - tet der Mor - gen - stern, Voll Gnad und
Bril - lante é - toi - le du ma - tin, A - mour vi -
How bright - ly beams the Morn - ing - star With grace and

Wahr - heit von dem Herrn, Die süs - se Wur - zel
vant, En - fant di - vin, Jé - sus, mon cœur, ma
truth from heav'n a - far! Our Jess - e tree now

Jes - se! Du Sohn Da - vids aus Ja - kobs Stamm,
vi - e! Ra - meau bé - ni, fils de Da - vid,
blow - eth: Of Jac - ob's stem, and Dav - id's line,

Mein Kö - nig und mein Bräu - ti - gam, Hast mir mein Herz be -
Jail - li du vieux tronc d'I - sa - I Que nous don - na Ma -
For Thee my Bride-groom, King div - ine, My soul with love o'er -

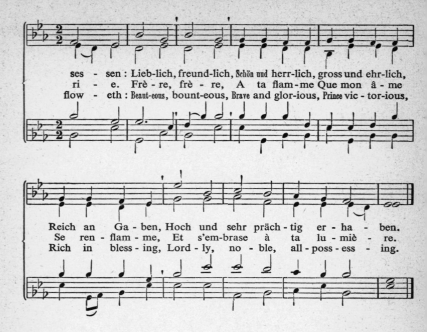

ses - sen : Lieb-lich, freund-lich, Schön und herr-lich, gross und ehr-lich,
ri - e. Frè - re, frè - re, A ta flam-me Que mon â - me
flow - eth : Beaut-eous, bount-eous, Brave and glor-ious, Prince vic - tor-ious,

Reich an Ga - ben, Hoch und sehr präch - tig er - ha - ben.
Se ren - flam-me, Et s'em-brase à ta lu - miè - re.
Rich in bless - ing, Lord - ly, no - ble, all - poss - ess - ing.

2.

Ei, meine Perl, du werte Kron,
Wahr' Gottes und Mariensohn,
  Ein hochgeborner König !
Mein Herz heisst dich ein Himmelsblum ;
Dein süsses Evangelium
  Ist lauter Milch und Honig.
Jesu ! Jesu ! Hosianna !
Himmlisch' Manna, das wir essen,
Deiner kann ich nicht vergessen.

3.

Von Gott kommt mir ein Freudenlicht,
Wenn du mit deinem Angesicht,
  Mich freundlich tust anblicken.
O Herr Jesu, mein trautes Gut,
Dein Wort, dein Geist, dein Leib und
  Mich innerlich erquicken.   [Blut
Nimm mich freundlich in die Arme,
Herr, erbarme dich in Gnaden,
Auf dein Wort komm ich geladen.

4.

Herr Gott Vater, mein starker Held,
Du hast mich ewig vor der Welt
  In deinem Sohn geliebet.
Dein Sohn hat mich ihm selbst vertraut,
Er ist mein Freund, ich seine Braut,
  Drum mich auch nichts betrübet.
Eia, eia, himmlisch Leben
Wird er geben mir dort oben :
Ewig soll mein Herz ihn loben.

PHILIPPUS NICOLAI (1556-1608).

* * *

2.

Seigneur Jésus, trésor des cieux,
Enfant de Dieu, fils précieux,
 O Roi de grand' naissance !
Ton Evangile est sans pareil
Il en découle lait et miel
 Pour nous en abondance.
Joie ! Joie ! O pâture,
Nourriture sainte et pure,
Manne que Dieu nous envoie !

3.

Mon cœur tremblant vibre d'émoi
Quand ton regard, Jésus, sur moi
 Avec amour se pose.
Ton corps, ton sang, ton Saint-Esprit
Ont pour mon âme plus de prix
 Seigneur, que toute chose.
Donne ! donne ! ta parole
Qui console et pardonne !
Qu'à toi seul je m'abandonne.

4.

En Christ, ton Fils, ton premier-né,
Dieu trois fois saint, tu m'as aimé
 Devant la terre entière.
Oui, tu me donnes par Jésus
La vie heureuse des élus
 Dans ton royaume, ô Père !
Gloire ! gloire ! que mon âme
Te proclame, qu'elle clame
Qu'elle chante ta victoire !

Trad. PAULINE MARTIN (1950).

★ ★ ★

2.

Hail, Son of Mary, Pearl and Crown,
True Son of God, of high renown,
 Of kingly race descended :
My heart doth hail Thee Lily-flower ;
Thy doctrine droppeth sweet as shower ;
 'Tis milk and honey blended ;
Jesu ! Jesu ! Hail ! Hosanna !
Heavenly Manna ! Food supernal,
Leading up to life eternal.

3.

Shed deep within my heart Thy light,
Thou Ruby red and Jasper bright ;
 Thy charity will cheer me :
Head of the Body, in Thy side
Thy living member let me bide
 With Thee, my Saviour, near me :
Wo's me for thee ! Graciosa
Celi rosa, here in anguish
For Thy scent I pine and languish.

4.

Awake the sound of harp and string,
And tuneful hymns of gladness sing,
 Pure hearts with voices blending :
But let me sit at Jesu's feet,
My heav'nly Bridegroom, passing sweet,
 In joyance never-ending :
Meetly, featly, sing Cantate,
Jubilate : spread the story ;
Great is Christ, the King of glory.

Trans. G. R. WOODWARD * (1910).

Moderato

Stralsund (? 1665).

Lo - be den Her - ren, den mäch - ti - gen Kö - nig der
Praise to the Lord! the Al - migh - ty, the King of cre -
Cé - lé - brons l'E - ter - nel, no - tre Dieu, no - tre seul

Eh - ren! Mei - ne ge - lie - be - te See - le, das
a - tion! O my soul, praise Him, for He is thy
Pè - re, Tout puis - sant cré - a - teur et des cieux

ist mein Be - geh - ren. Kom - met zu Hauf! Psal - ter und
health and sal - va - tion! All ye who hear, Now to His
et de la ter - re! Ce Dieu d'a - mour, De ses en -

Har - fe, wacht auf! Las - set den Lob - ge - sang hö - ren!
tem - ple draw near, Serve Him in glad a - dor - a - tion!
fants, cha - que jour Veut ex - au - cer la pri - è - re.

2. Lobe den Herren, der alles so herrlich regieret,
Der dich auf Adelers Fittichen sicher geführet,
Der dich erhält, — Wie es dir selber gefällt.
    Hast du nicht dieses verspüret?

3. Lobe den Herren, der deinen Stand sichtbar gesegnet,
Der aus dem Himmel mit Strömen der Liebe geregnet!
Denke daran, — Was der Allmächtige kann,
    Der dir mit Liebe begegnet!

4. Alles was Odem hat, lobe mit Abrahams Samen,
Lob ihn mit allen, die seine Verheissung bekamen!
Er ist dein Licht, — Seele, vergiss es ja nicht!
    Lob ihn in Ewigkeit! Amen!

JOACHIM NEANDER (1650-1680).

★ ★ ★

2. Praise to the Lord! Who o'er all things so wondrously reigneth,
Shielding thee gently from harm and from fainting sustaineth;
Hast thou not seen — How thy desires have been
    Granted in what He ordaineth?

3. Praise to the Lord! Who doth prosper thy work and defend thee,
Surely His goodness and mercy here daily attend thee;
Ponder anew — What the Almighty can do,
    If with His love He befriend thee!

4. Praise to the Lord! Oh let all that is in me adore Him!
All that hath life and breath come now with praises before Him!
Let the Amen — Sound from His people again,
    Gladly for aye we adore Him.

Trans. C. WINKWORTH (1858).

★ ★ ★

2. Célébrons Jésus-Christ, le chef béni de l'Eglise!
Qu'à sa divine loi toute âme enfin soit soumise.
Ce bon Sauveur sur la croix, pour le pécheur,
    Acquit la grâce promise.

3. Célébrons l'Esprit saint, lui qui, sur toute la terre,
Assemble les pécheurs et de ses dons les éclaire,
Et les unit en un seul corps, qu'il bénit
    Par sa force et sa lumière.

4. Seigneur, Dieu trois fois saint, que chacun de nous fléchisse
Devant toi les genoux, et t'adore et te bénisse!
D'un même cœur, célébrons tous le Seigneur.
    O grand Dieu, sois-nous propice!

CH. PFENDER (1908).

With force and dignity

Adapted from
a Hebrew melody by M. LEONI (1770).

The God of A-braham praise, Who reigns enthroned a-
Gott A-brams, der du thronst, Im ho-hen Him-mel
Lou-é soit à ja-mais Le Dieu de nos aï-

bove, An-cient of ev-er-last-ing days, And God of love. Je-
wohnst, Lob sei dir, der noch im-mer-dar Die Lie-be war! Je-
eux, Il rè-gne pour l'é-ter-ni-té Dans les hauts lieux. Je

ho-vah, great I am! By earth and heav'n con-fessed, I
ho-va ist dein Nam', der Erd' und Him-mel treibt, Von
suis grand, dit Yah-vé, L'u-ni-vers est à moi A-

bow and bless the sa-cred Name For ev-er blest.
dem uns al-ler Se-gen kam, Der e-wig bleibt.
do-rons le nom vé-né-ré De no-tre Roi.

2. The God of Abraham praise,
   At whose supreme command
   From earth I rise and seek the joys
       At His right hand.
   I all on earth forsake,
   Its wisdom, fame and power,
   And Him my only portion make,
       My shield and tower.

3. He by Himself hath sworn,
   I on His oath depend ;
   I shall, on eagle's wings upborne
       To heaven ascend ;
   I shall behold His face,
   I shall His power adore,
   And sing the wonders of His grace
       For evermore.

4. There dwells the Lord our King,
   The Lord our righteousness,
   Triumphant, o'er the world and sin,
       The Prince of Peace ;
   On Zion's sacred height
   His Kingdom He maintains,
   And glorious with His saints in light
       For ever reigns.

5. The whole triumphant host
   Give thanks to God on high ;
   " Hail, Father, Son and Holy Ghost !"
       They ever cry,
   Hail, Abraham's God and mine !
   I join the heavenly lays,
   All might and majesty are Thine,
       And endless praise.

THOMAS OLIVER (1725-1799).

* * *

2. Gott Abrams, dir die Ehr' !
   Dein Wink führt mich davon.
   Du holst mich zu der Freuden Meer
       An deinen Thron.
   Der Welt vergess' ich gern,
   Auch Weisheit, Ruhm und Macht,
   Hab ich nur Teil an meinem Herrn,
       Mein Schild und Wacht !

3. Er schwor es einst bei sich,
   Sein Eid steht für mich ein :
   Auf Adlerschwingen führt er mich
       Zum Himmel ein !
   Ich darf sein Antlitz schau'n,
   Schau'n seiner Allmacht Kleid,
   Darf seiner Gnade Wunder trau'n
       In Ewigkeit.

4. Dort wohnt, der uns versöhnt,
   Gerechtigkeit ihn krönt,
   Herr über Sünde, Tod und Welt,
       Der Friedensheld !
   In Zion's Heiligtum
   Glänzt seiner Herrschaft Ruhm
   Mit allen Heiligen im Licht
       Und stirbet nicht.

5. Das ganze Himmelsheer
   Dankt Gott und ruft empor :
   «Dem Vater, Sohn und Geist sei Ehr !»
       Im Ew'gen Chor.
   Preis' dir, Gott ! Ich stimm' ein
   Ins Lied der obern Schar !
   All' Majestät und Macht sind dein,
       Dein immerdar !

Übers. WILHELM HORKEL (1950).

* * *

2. Loué soit le Seigneur
   Mon Roi, mon seul Sauveur ;
   Je chercherai le vrai bonheur
       En l'adorant.
   Je renonce à mes biens
   Pour servir Jésus-Christ
   Et je ne manquerai de rien
       Dans ses parvis.

3. Mon Sauveur et mon Dieu
   M'a juré son amour ;
   Je monterai jusques aux cieux
       Plus haut toujours.
   Là je verrai mon Roi
   Et, louant ses bienfaits,
   Chanterai sa gloire avec foi
       A tout jamais.

4. Sur les monts de Sion
   Il demeure à jamais,
   Victorieux des passions,
       En toute paix :
   Il vit avec les Saints ;
   Il a la royauté ;
   Il accomplit tous ses desseins
       Dans la clarté.

5. Au seuil de ses parvis
   Chantent les bienheureux :
   «Louange au Fils, au Saint-Esprit,
       A notre Dieu. »
   Je joins ma voix aux leurs
   Chantant la majesté
   Et le pouvoir de mon Seigneur
       Et sa bonté.

Trad. FLOSSETTE DU PASQUIER (1951)

JOHANN CRÜGER (1598-1662).

Nun dan - ket al - le Gott Mit Her - zen, Mund und
Now thank we all our God, With heart and hands and
Lou - ons le Cré - a - teur, Chan - tons à Dieu lou-

Hän - den. Der gros - se Din - ge tut An uns und al - len
voic - es, Who won-drous things hath done, In whom His world re-
an - ges ! Et joi - gnons no - tre voix Au con - cert des saints

En - den, Der uns von Mut - ter - leib Und Kin - des - bei - nen
joic - es ; Who from our moth - er's arms Hath blessed us on our
an - ges ! Dès les bras ma - ter - nels Il nous a pro - té-

an, Un - zäh - lig viel zu gut, Und noch jetzt und ge - tan.
way With count-less gifts of love, And still is ours to - day.
gés Et, jus - qu'au der - nier jour, Il est no - tre ber - ger.

2.

Der ewig reiche Gott,
Woll' uns in unserm Leben
Ein immer fröhlich Herz
Und edlen Frieden geben
Und uns in seiner Gnad
Erhalten fort und fort
Und uns aus aller Not
Erlösen hier und dort.

3.

Lob, Ehr' und Preis sei Gott,
Dem Vater und dem Sohne,
Und dem, der beiden gleich
Im höchsten Himmelsthrone,
Ihm, dem dreiein'gen Gott,
Wie er im Anfang war
Und ist und bleiben wird,
Jetzo und immerdar.

MARTIN RINCKART (1586-1649).

* * *

2.

O may this bounteous God
Through all our life be near us,
With ever joyful hearts
And blessed peace to cheer us,
And keep us in His grace,
And guide us when perplexed,
And free us from all ills
In this world and the next.

3.

All praise and thanks to God
The Father now be given,
The Son, and Him who reigns
With them in highest heaven,
The one eternal God,
Whom earth and heaven adore;
For thus it was, is now,
And shall be evermore.

Trans. CATHERINE WINKWORTH (1829-1878).

* * *

2.

Loué soit notre Dieu !
Que notre vie entière
Tous nous vivions joyeux
Sous le regard du Père,
Qu'il nous tienne en sa grâce
Et nous guide toujours,
Nous garde du malheur
Par son unique amour.

3.

De ce Dieu trois fois saint
Qui règne dans la gloire,
Chrétiens, empressons-nous
De chanter la victoire ;
Son Royaume est aux cieux
Où, plein de majesté,
Il règne, seul vrai Dieu,
De toute éternité.

Trad. FLOSSETTE DU PASQUIER (1950).

— 14 (15) —

Ancient Chinese tune.
Adaptation du Ps. 136.

全 當 歡 樂 讚 美 主 因 主
Let us with a glad - some mind, Praise the
A mon Dieu, je me con - fi - e, Sa clé -
Brü - der, macht die Her - zen weit, Eu - ern

恩 典 多 難 數 上 帝 恒 懷 慈 悲
(副歌)
Lord for He is kind; For His mer - cies shall en -
mence est in - fi - ni - e. Ta pen - sée, ô Dieu d'a -
Mund zum Lob be - reit ! Got - tes Gü - te, Got - tes

念 慈 悲 長 久 不 改 變
dure, Ev - er faith - ful, ev - er sure.
mour, Est fi - dè - le, é - ter - nel - le.
Treu Sind an je - dem Mor - gen neu.

五

所以我當樂讚主
因主恩典多難數
副歌

四

今我既然在苦處
我主慈目仍看顧
副歌

三

選民在野遭危險
普蒙主佑恩非淺
副歌

二

主之權能甚奇異
造光照滿新天地
副歌

* * *

2.

He with all-commanding might,
Filled the new-made world with light;
    For His mercies...

3.

He His chosen race did bless
In the wasteful wilderness;
    For His mercies...

4.

He hath, with a piteous eye,
Looked upon our misery;
    For His mercies...

5.

Let us then with gladsome mind
Praise the Lord for He is kind:
    For His mercies...

        JOHN MILTON (1608-1674).

* * *

2.

La lumière radieuse
Est ton œuvre merveilleuse.
    Ta pensée, ô Dieu...

3.

Tu consoles, tu pardonnes,
Ta bonté, sur tous, rayonne.
    Ta pensée, ô Dieu...

4.

Par ta grâce prévenante
L'âme s'ouvre à l'espérance.
    Ta pensée, ô Dieu...

5.

Tout à toi je me confie,
Ta clémence est infinie.
    Ta pensée, ô Dieu...

        Trad. S. BIDGRAIN (1924).

* * *

2.

Gottes Hand erschafft die Welt,
Finsternis sein Wort erhellt.
    Gottes Güte...

3.

Je und je sein Segen war
Über der erwählten Schar.
    Gottes Güte...

4.

Und sein Blick aus Himmelshöh'n
Hat das Elend angeseh'n.
    Gottes Güte...

5.

Macht darum die Herzen weit,
Euern Mund zum Lob bereit!
    Gottes Güte...

        Übers. JOHANN CHRISTOPH HAMPE (1950).

Mélodie grégorienne.
Harmonisée par F. Mathil (1950).

Ve - ni, ve - ni Em - ma - nu - el, Cap - ti - vum sol-
Oh ! viens bien - tôt, Em - ma - nu - el ! Nous dé - li - vrer
O komm, o komm, Em - ma - nu - el ! Nach dir sehnt sich
O come, O come, Em - ma - nu - el ! And ran - som cap-

ve Is - ra - el Qui ge - mit in ex - si - li - o
du joug cru - el, Et du pé - ché bri - ser la loi,
dein Is - ra - el, In Sün - den - jam - mer wei - nen wir
tive Is - ra - el, That mourns in lone - ly ex - ile here,

Pri - va - tus De - i Fi - li - o. Gau - de, gau - de,
Ton peu - ple en - tier s'at - tend à toi. Chan - tez, chan - tez,
Und flehn und flehn hin - auf zu dir. Freu dich, freu dich,
Un - til the Son of God ap - pear. Re - joice ! Re - joice !

Em - ma - nu-el Nas - ce - tur pro te, Is - ra-el.
Il vient du ciel, Il vient à nous, Em - ma - nu-el!
O Is - ra-el, Bald kommt, bald kommt Em - ma - nu-el!
Em - ma - nu-el Shall come to thee, O Is - ra-el.

2. Veni, O Jesse virgula,
   Ex hostis tuos ungula,
   De specu tuos tartari
   Educ, et antro barathri
   Gaude, gaude, Emmanuel...

3. Veni, veni O Oriens,
   Solare nos adveniens,
   Noctis depelle nebulas
   Dirasque noctis tenebras.
   Gaude, gaude, Emmanuel...

4. Veni Clavis davidica,
   Regna reclude caelica,
   Fac iter tutum superum
   Et claude vias inferum.
   Gaude, gaude, Emmanuel...

13th Cent. Hymn in
Psalteriolum Cantionum Catholicorum (1710)

* * *

2. Oh ! viens bientôt, descends vers nous
   Saint Fils du ciel, aimant et doux.
   Aux cœurs troublés apporte donc
   La paix divine du pardon.
   Chantez, chantez, il vient...

3. Oh ! viens bientôt, que ta clarté,
   Dissipe nos obscurités.
   Errants et tristes dans la nuit,
   Nous appelons le jour qui luit.
   Chantez, chantez, il vient...

4. Oh ! viens bientôt, puissant Seigneur,
   Nous réveiller de nos langueurs !
   Il n'est que toi, céleste pain,
   Qui peux apaiser notre faim.
   Chantez, chantez, il vient...

Trad. H. ECUYER (1924).

* * *

2. O komm, du holdes Himmelskind,
   So hehr und gross, so mildgesinnt !
   Wir seufzen tief in Sündenschuld ;
   O bring uns deines Vaters Huld.
   Freu dich, freu dich, O Israel...

3. O komm, du wahres Licht der Welt,
   Das unsre Finsternis erhellt !
   Wir irren hier in Trug und Wahn ;
   O führ uns auf des Lichtes Bahn !
   Freu dich, freu dich, O Israel...

4. O komm, Erlöser, Gottes Sohn,
   Und bring uns Gnad von Gottes Thron !
   Die Seele fühlt hier Hungersnot ;
   O gib uns dich, lebendig Brot !
   Freu dich, freu dich, O Israel...

Aus dem Lateinischen.

* * *

2.

O come, Thou Rod of Jesse, free
Thine own from Satan's tyranny ;
From depths of hell Thy people save,
And give them vict'ry o'er the grave.
Rejoice ! Rejoice ! Emmanuel...

3.

O come, Thou Dayspring, come and cheer
Our spirits by Thine advent here ;
Disperse the gloomy clouds of night,
And death's dark shadows put to flight.
Rejoice ! Rejoice ! Emmanuel...

4.

O come, Thou Key of David, come,
And open wide our heavenly home ;
Make safe the way that leads on high,
And close the path to misery.
Rejoice ! Rejoice ! Emmanuel...

Trans. from the Latin, J. M. NEALE (1818-1866)

— 16 —

« St. Thomas ».
Melody from S. WEBBE'S
Motetts or Antiphons (1792).

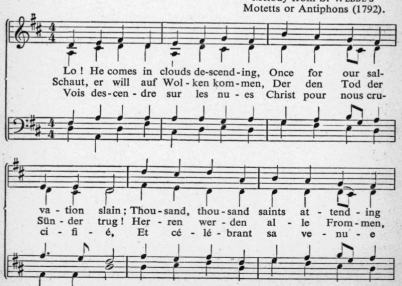

Lo ! He comes in clouds de-scend-ing, Once for our sal-
Schaut, er will auf Wol-ken kom-men, Der den Tod der
Vois des-cen-dre sur les nu-es Christ pour nous cru-

va - tion slain ; Thou-sand, thou-sand saints at - tend - ing
Sün - der trug ! Her - ren wer - den al - le From - men,
ci - fi - é, Et cé - lé - brant sa ve - nu - e

Swell the tri - umph of His train : Al - le - lu - ia !
Ju - belnd fol - gen sei - nem Zug : Hal - le - lu - ja !
Tous les saints l'ont en - tou - ré ; Al - lé - lu - ia !

Al - le - lu - ia ! Christ the Lord re - turns to reign.
Hal - le - lu - ja ! Got - tes Arm den Sa - tan schlug.
Al - lé - lu - ia ! Jé - sus Christ vient pour ré - gner.

2.

Every eye shall now behold Him
   Robed in dreadful majesty ;
Those who set at nought and sold Him,
   Pierced and nailed Him to the tree,
     Deeply wailing, *(bis)*
Shall their true Messiah see.

3.

Now redemption long expected
   See in solemn pomp appear :
All His saints, by men rejected,
   Now shall meet Him in the air :
     Alleluia ! *(bis)*
See the day of God appear.

4.

Yea, Amen ; let all adore Thee,
   High on Thine eternal throne ;
Saviour, take the power and glory ;
   Claim the kingdoms for Thine own :
     Alleluia ! *(bis)*
Thou shalt reign, and Thou alone. Amen.

JOHN CONNINCK (1750).
CHARLES WESLEY (1759).

★ ★ ★

2.

Dann wird er vor alle treten,
   Majestätisch, herrlich, schön,
Und die ihn auf Erden schmähten,
   Kreuzigten, sie werden steh'n,
     Werden weinen, *(bis)*
Wenn sie ihren Heiland seh'n.

3.

Nun erlöst er, die in Banden,
   Lang nach dem Erlöser schrien,
Macht den Spott der Welt zuschanden.
   Alle Heil'gen schauen ihn :
     Halleluja ! *(bis)*
Seht, der Tag des Heils erschien !

4.

Laut erschallen lasst die Chöre,
Lasst die Freude völlig sein !
Nimm, o Heiland, Thron und Ehre,
Tritt in deine Herrschaft ein,
Halleluja ! (*bis*)
Du sollst herrschen, du allein.

Übers. JOHANN CHRISTOPH HAMPE (1950).

★ ★ ★

2.

Tous les yeux verront la gloire
De notre Seigneur Jésus,
Car au jour de sa victoire
Ceux qui l'ont trahi, vendu,
Pleins d'angoisse (*bis*)
Verront triompher ce roi.

3.

Tremblez, c'est la fin du monde,
Le Messie est revenu,
Des saints la joie est profonde,
Ils sont autour de l'élu.
Alléluia (*bis*)
Le jour du Christ est venu.

4.

Christ, tu règnes dans la gloire,
Tous nous chanterons ton nom ;
A toi seul est la victoire,
Nos êtres t'appartiendront.
Alléluia (*bis*)
Jésus-Christ est notre roi.

Trad. FLOSSETTE DU PASQUIER (1951).

— 17 (16) —

Composer unknown.
Probably XVIIIth Century.

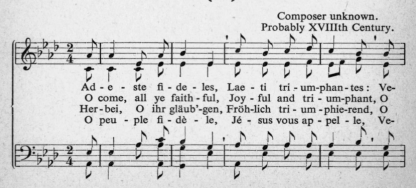

Ad - e - ste fi - de - les, Lae - ti tri - um-phan-tes : Ve-
O come, all ye faith - ful, Joy - ful and tri - um-phant, O
Her - bei, O ihr gläub'-gen, Fröh-lich tri - um -phie-rend, O
O peu - ple fi - dè - le, Jé - sus vous ap - pel - le, Ve-

ni - te, ve - ni - te in Beth - le - hem. Na-tum vi - de - te,
come ye, O come ye, to Beth - le - hem; Come and be-hold Him
kom - met, O kom - met nach Beth - le - hem ! Se - het das Kind-lein,
nez, tri-om-phants, joy-eux En ces lieux. Peu - ple fi - dè - le,

Re-gem An - ge - lo - rum: Ve - ni - te, ad - o - re - mus, Ve-
born the King of An - gels; O come, let us a - dore Him, O
uns zum Heil ge - bo - ren ! O las - set uns an - be - ten, O
Ve-nez voir le roi des cieux. Que votre a - mour l'im-plo - re, Que

ni - te ad - o - re-mus, Ve - ni - te ad - o - re-mus Do - mi - num.
come let us a - dore Him, O come let us a-dore Him, Christ, the Lord.
las-set uns an - be - ten, O las - set uns an-be - ten den Kön - ig.
vo-tre foi l'a - do - re, Et qu'el-le chante en-co - re Ce don de Dieu.

2. En grege relicto, — Humiles ad cunas
   Vocati pastores approperant :
   Et nos ovanti gradu festinemus :
   Venite, adoremus (*ter*) Dominum.

3. Aeterni Parentis — Splendorem aeternum
   Velatum sub carne videbimus :
   Deum infantem, pannis involutum :
   Venite, adoremus (*ter*) Dominum.

4. Pro nobis egenum — et foeno cubantem
   Piis foveamus amplexibus :
   Sic nos amantem quis non redamaret :
   Venite, adoremus (*ter*) Dominum.

★ ★ ★

2. Sing, choirs of angels, — Sing in exultation,
   Sing, all ye citizens of Heav'n above :
   "Glory to God in the highest,"
   O come, let us adore Him (*ter*), Christ the Lord.

3. God of God, — Light of light,
   Lo ! He abhors not the Virgin's womb,
   Very God, begotten, not created ;
   O come, let us adore Him (*ter*), Christ the Lord.

4. Yea, Lord, we greet Thee, — Born this happy morning ;
   Jesus, to Thee be glory given ;
   Word of the Father, now in flesh appearing ;
   O come, let us adore Him (*ter*), Christ the Lord.

Trans. F. OAKELEY (1841).

* * *

2. Kommt, singet dem Herren, — Singt ihm Engelchöre.
   Frohlocket, frohlocket, ihr Seligen :
   Ehre sei Gott im Himmel und auf Erden !
   O lasset uns anbeten (*ter*) den König !

3. Du König der Ehren — Herrscher der Heerscharen,
   Verschmähst nicht zu ruh'n in Mariens Schoss,
   Du wahrer Gott von Ewigkeit geboren !
   O lasset uns anbeten (*ter*) den König.

4. Ja, dir, der du heute — Mensch für uns geboren,
   Herr Jesu, sei Ehre und Preis und Ruhm,
   Dir, Fleisch geword'nes Wort des ew'gen Vaters !
   O lasset uns anbeten (*ter*) den König !

Aus dem Lateinischen.

* * *

2. Quoi, dans l'humble étable — Froide et misérable,
   Des bergers le grand amour — Forme une cour.
   Dans l'humble étable — Accourez à votre tour.
   Que votre amour l'implore, — Que votre foi l'adore,
   Et qu'elle chante encore — Son grand amour.

3. C'est le roi des anges — Captif dans les langes,
   Splendeur pure et sans déclin — De son destin.
   Le roi des anges — Paraît sous un corps humain.
   Que votre amour l'implore, — Que votre foi l'adore,
   Et qu'elle chante encore, — L'enfant divin.

4. Il vient sur la terre — Fléchir la colère
   De Dieu, notre Créateur, — Ce roi sauveur.
   C'est notre frère, — Notre puissant Rédempteur
   Que notre amour l'adore, — Que notre foi l'implore,
   Et qu'elle chante encore — Notre Seigneur.

D'après *Louange et Prière*.

— 18 —

Nederlandse voorreformatorische Melodie*.
Getoonzert door JOH. WAGENAAR.
Gezangenbundel der Nederlandse Hervormde Kerk.

Komt, ver - won - dert u hier, men - sen, Ziet, hoe
Kommt, und stau -net, all ihr Leu - te, Seht, wie
E - mer - veil - lons - nous en - sem - ble D'être ain-
Come ye here in ad - or - a - tion, See God's

dat u God be - mint, Ziet ver - vuld der zie - len
Gott euch lieb ge - winnt! Eu - rer See - len höchs - te
si ai - més de Dieu! Dans ce nou - veau - né qui
love re - vealed this morn, See ful - filled the soul's deep

wen - sen, Ziet dit nieuw - ge - bo - ren Kind! Ziet, die
Freu - de Ist dies neu - ge - bor - ne Kind! Er, das
trem - ble S'ac - com - plit tout no - tre vœu. Il est
long - ing In this lit - tle Child new born! See the

* By kind permission of the Secretary of the General Synod of the Dutch Reformed Church.

2.

Ziet, hoe dat men met Hem handelt
Hoe men Hem in doeken bindt,
Die met zijne godheid wandelt
Op de vleugels van de wind.
Ziet, hoe ligt Hij hier in lijden
Zonder teken van verstand,
Die de hemel moet verblijden,
Die de kroon der wijsheid spant.
Ziet, hoe tere is de Here,
Die 't al draagt in zijne hand.

3.

O Heer Jesu, God en mense,
Die aanvaard hebt deze staat,
Geef mij, dat ik door U wense,
Geef mij door uw kindsheid raad.
Sterk mij door uw tere handen
Maak mij door uw kleinheid groot,
Maak mij vrij door uwe banden,
Maak mij rijk door uwe nood,
Maak mij blijde door uw lijden,
Maak mij levend door uw dood !

Oud-Nederlands Lied.

* * *

2.

Welt, wie hast du Ihn behandelt !
Arme Windeln trägt der Herr,
Der mit Gott dem Vater wandelt
Mächtig über Wind und Meer !
Muss die Krippe hier erleiden,
Wo er schlummernd hingelegt,
Der, erwählt zu Himmelsfreuden,
Dort die Kron der Weisheit trägt.
Armer Herr — die ganze Erde
Ist von seiner Hand geprägt !

3.

O Herr Jesu, offenbarer
Mensch und Gott, du Gast der Welt,
Mache meine Sehnsucht klarer,
Kindlein, Rat und Kraft und Held !
Stärk mich, der du schwach gewesen,
Der du klein, erhöhe mich,
Der in Angst und Haft gesessen,
Meine Not und Bande brich !
Mach mich fröhlich, weil du littest,
Weil du starbst, lass leben mich !

Übers. WILHELM HORKEL (1950).

* * *

2.

Lui qui vient d'auprès des anges,
Voyez comme il est traité !
On l'enveloppe de langes
Malgré sa divinité.
Il gît en cette indigence
Et n'en sait pas la raison,
Quand, au paradis immense
Il avait tout à foison,
Et que planait sa puissance
Jusqu'au dernier horizon.

3.

O Jésus qui voulus naître
Plus bas que je ne suis né
Permets que mon cœur puisse être
Par ton berceau dominé,
Grandi par ta déchéance,
Par tes mains frêles plus fort,
J'ai ton joug pour délivrance,
Ta pauvreté pour trésor,
Pour bonheur j'ai ta souffrance,
Et j'ai ma vie en ta mort.

Trad. CHARLES DOMBRE (1936).

* * *

2.

Come and see how they receive Him,
How they try to keep Him warm,
He who in His Godhead travels
With the lightning and the storm.
See Him lying in discomfort
Seeming not to understand,
He who gives delight in Heaven,
Who the world in wisdom planned.
See how fragile is this infant
Who holds all things in His hand.

3.

Dear Lord Jesus, God and mortal
Who adopts our earthly state,
May I grow through your example,
May your smallness make me great !
Make me strong with gentle fingers,
Wise through your simplicity,
Make me rich through your privation,
May your bondage set me free,
May your sorrow make me joyful,
May your death give life to me.

Trans. MARGARET HOUSE (1950).

19

Deutsches Weihnachtslied aus dem XVI. Jahrhundert.
Harm. von MICHAEL PRAETORIUS (1571-1621).

Es ist ein Ros' ent-sprun-gen, Aus ei-ner
Lo, how a rose e'er bloom-ing From ten-der
U - ne fleur vient d'é - clo - re, Sur le tronc

Wur - zel zart, Wie uns die Al-ten sun-gen: von Jes - se
stem hath sprung, Of Jes - se's line-age com-ing, As men of
d'I - sa - ï. Sur son é-corce en - co - re U - ne pousse

kam die Art Und hat ein Blüm-lein bracht, Mit-
old have sung. It came, a flow'-ret bright, A-
a jail - li. Et sur le tronc dur - ci, Dans

ten im kal-ten Win - ter, Wohl zu der hal - ben Nacht.
mid the cold of win - ter, When half spent was the night.
l'om-bre a-vant l'au-ro - re, U - ne rose a fleu - ri.

2. Das Röslein, das ich meine,
   Davon Jesaias sagt,
   Hat uns gebracht alleine,
   Marie, die reine Magd ;
   Aus Gottes ew'gem Rat
   Hat sie ein Kind geboren
   Wohl zu der halben Nacht.

3. Das Blümelein so kleine,
   Das duftet uns so süss,
   Mit seinem hellen Scheine
   Vertreibt's die Finsternis.
   Wahr'r Mensch und wahrer Gott,
   Hilft uns aus allem Leide,
   Rettet von Sünd und Tod.

4. O Jesu, bis zum Scheiden
   Aus diesem Jammertal
   Lass dein Hilf uns geleiten
   Hin bis zum Freudensaal
   In deines Vaters Reich,
   Da wir dich ewig loben ;
   O Gott, uns das verleih'.

Vorreformatorisch Köln (1599).

* * *

2. Isaiah 'twas foretold it,
   The Rose I have in mind,
   With Mary we behold it,
   The Virgin Mother kind.
   To show God's love aright
   She bore to them a Saviour,
   When half spent was the night.

3. This little flow'ret fragrant
   Is full of sweet delight,
   And with its dewy brilliance
   Illuminates the night.
   True man yet truly God,
   Be with us in our trouble
   While half spent is the night.

Dr. THEODORE BAKER (1931)*.

4. Lord Jesus, till Thou call us
   To leave our earthly plight,
   We pray Thee lead us onward
   Towards those mansions bright
   In God the Father's home,
   And we shall sing Thy praises,
   When full spent is the night.

Trans. MARGARET HOUSE (1950).

* * *

2. Rameau que le prophète
   Autrefois a prédit,
   Une vierge parfaite
   Nous l'apporte aujourd'hui.
   Dieu l'ayant ordonné
   Elle a transmis la vie
   A son Fils bien-aimé.

3. Fleur fraîchement éclose,
   Bourgeon prédestiné,
   Cette éclatante rose
   Perce l'obscurité.
   C'est Dieu qui l'a formé
   Maître de toute chose :
   Mort, détresse et péché.

4. Christ, lorsqu'à cette terre
   Nous devrons dire adieu,
   Vers la maison du Père
   Guide-nous dans les cieux.
   Les anges du saint-lieu
   Chantent dans la lumière :
   Gloire au Fils ! Gloire à Dieu !

Trad. PAULINE MARTIN (1950).

* From the Home and Community Song Book. Copyright 1931 by E. C. Schirmer Music Co. Used by kind permission.

20

"Mendelssohn"
Adapted by W. H. CUMMINGS *
F. MENDELSSOHN-BARTHOLDY
(1809-1847).

In moderate time

Hark ! the her - ald an - gels sing Glo - ry to the new - born
E - cou - tez le chant des an-ges: Gloire au di - vin en - fant
Hört die En - gel-chö - re sin-gen: Un - ser Kö - nig ward ge-

King ; Peace on earth and mer - cy mild, God and sin - ners re - con -
roi, Ap - por - tez - lui vos lou-an-ges, Vos hom-ma - ges, vo - tre
bor'n! Frie-den, Gna - de wird er brin-gen Und ver - söh - nen Got - tes

ciled : Joy - ful all ye na - tions rise, Join the tri-umph of the
foi. Le - vez - vous gaî-ment, ô frè - res, Au-jour-d'hui naît la lu-
Zorn. Völ - ker lasst das Lied er - schal-len Mit des Him-mels Hee-ren

skies, With th'an-gel-ic host pro-claim, Christ is born in Be-thle-
miè - re, A - vec les cieux pro - cla - mez, A Bé - thlé - hem Christ est
al - len, Rühmt, was sich be - ge - ben hat : Chri-stus kam in Da-vids

* By Permission of Novello and Co, Ltd.

hem. Hark! the her-ald an-gels sing Glo-ry to the new-born King.
né, E - cou-tez le chant du ciel, Jé-sus naît en Is - ra - ël.
Stadt. Hört die En-gel-chö-re singen: Un-ser Kö-nig ward ge-born!

2. Christ, by highest heaven adored,
    Christ, the everlasting Lord,
Late in time behold Him come
    Offspring of a Virgin's womb!
Veiled in flesh the Godhead see,
Hail the incarnate Deity!
Pleased as man with man to dwell,
Jesus, our Emmanuel.
Hark! the herald Angels sing
Glory to the new-born King.

3. Hail the heaven-born Prince of peace!
    Hail the Sun of Righteousness!
Light and life to all He brings,
    Risen with healing in His wings;
Mild He lays His glory by,
Born that man no more may die,
Born to raise the sons of earth,
Born to give them second birth.
Hark! the herald Angels sing
Glory to the new-born King.

C. WESLEY (1743) and others.

* * *

2. O Christ que le ciel révère,
    Eternellement béni,
Te voici qui viens sur terre,
    D'une vierge tu naquis.
Toi qui nais parmi les hommes,
Pour tes frères tu te donnes,
Et vers nous descends du ciel,
Jésus, notre Emmanuel.
Ecoutez le chant du ciel,
Jésus naît en Israël.

3. Salut, prince de justice!
    Salut, prince de la paix!
Te servir est mon délice
    Tu me bénis à jamais.
Tu renonças à la gloire,
Mais nous chantons ta victoire,
Car tu as vaincu la mort
Et tu changes notre sort.
Ecoutez le chant du ciel,
Jésus naît en Israël.

Trad. VIOLETTE DU PASQUIER (1951).

* * *

2. Den verehrt die Majestäten,
    Der ein Herr seit Anfang war,
Ist heut unter uns getreten,
    Eine Jungfrau ihn gebar.
Gott, des Ruhm die Himmel füllen,
Kommt zu uns in Fleischeshüllen,
Hier zu wohnen ihm gefällt,
Jesus, Heiland aller Welt.
Hört, die Engelchöre singen:
Unser König ward geborn!

3. Heil dem hohen Friedensfürsten,
    Sonne, die das Licht gebracht,
Leben allen, welche dürsten,
    Heil, in unsres Unheils Nacht.
Er, der Herr sucht die Geringen,
Dass dem Tode sie entgingen,
Ward geboren auf die Erd',
Dass ich neugeboren werd'.
Hört, die Engelchöre singen!
Unser König ward geborn!

Übers. JOHANN CHRISTOPH HAMPE (1951).

21

Geistliche Lieder, Leipzig (1539).
Satz: H. L. HASSLER (1608)

Vom Him - mel hoch, da komm ich her, Ich bring euch
Good news from heav'n the an - gels bring, Glad ti - dings
Je viens à vous des plus hauts cieux, Je viens en

gu - te neu - e Mär; Der gu - ten Mär bring ich so
to the earth they sing: To us this day a Child is
mes - sa - ger de Dieu: Ce jour, l'en - fant pro - mis est

viel, Da - von ich sing'n und sa - gen will.
giv'n, To crown us with the joy of heav'n.
né, Ma - rie en - fin vous l'a don - né.

2.

Euch ist ein Kindlein heut geborn
Von einer Jungfrau auserkorn ;
Ein Kindelein so zart und fein
Dass soll eur Freud und Wonne sein.

3.

Es ist Herr Christ, unser Gott.
Der will euch führ'n aus aller Not,
Et will eur Heiland selber sein,
Von allen Sünden machen rein.

4.

Bis willekommen, edler Gast !
Den Sünder nicht verschmähet hast
Und kommst ins Elend her zu mir ?
Wie soll ich immer danken dir ?

5.

Ach mein herzliebes Jesulein,
Mach dir ein rein sanft Bettelein,
Zu ruhn in meines Herzens Schrein,
Dass ich nimmer vergesse dein.

6.

Lob, Ehr sei Gott im höchsten Thron,
Der uns schenkt seinen ein'gen Sohn,
Des freuet sich der Engel Schar
Und singet uns solch neues Jahr.

MARTIN LUTHER (1483-1546).

★ ★ ★

2.

This is the Christ, our God and Lord,
Who in all need shall aid afford ;
He will Himself our Saviour be,
From all our sins to set us free.

3.

All Hail, Thou noble Guest, this morn,
Whose love did not the sinner scorn ;
In my distress Thou com'st to me ;
What thanks shall I return to Thee ?

4.

Were earth a thousand times as fair,
Beset with gold and jewels rare,
She yet were far too poor to be
A narrow cradle, Lord, for Thee.

5.

Ah ! dearest Jesu, Holy Child,
Make Thee a bed, soft, undefiled,
Within my heart, that it may be
A quiet chamber kept for Thee.

6.

Praise God upon His heavenly throne,
Who gave to us His only Son ;
For this His hosts, on joyful wing,
A blest New Year of mercy sing.

Trans. ARTHUR TOZER RUSSELL (1806-1874)
and CATHERINE WINKWORTH (1829-1878).

★ ★ ★

2.

C'est lui le Christ, le Rédempteur,
Jésus, ton frère, ton Sauveur.
Il veut au mal vous arracher,
Vous rendre purs de tout péché.

3.

O sois le bienvenu, Seigneur !
Tu prends pitié de tout pécheur ;
Oui dans l'abîme tu me vois
Mon cœur s'abandonne à ta loi.

4.

Le monde serait bien plus grand,
Etincelant d'or et d'argent,
Encor serait-il trop étroit
Pour toi mon Seigneur et mon Roi.

5.

Enfant Jésus, Sauveur béni
En moi je t'offre un doux abri ;
Mon cœur ouvert pour t'accueillir
Voudrait toujours te retenir.

6.

Louange au Père, au Dieu vivant
Qui donne au monde son enfant !
Joyeux, les anges dans le ciel
Entonnent l'hymne de Noël !

Trad. PAULINE MARTIN (1950).

— 22 —

Later form of melody from Himmelslust (1679).
Harm. by J.-S. BACH (1685-1750).

Bright-est and best of the sons of the morn - ing, Dawn on our
As - tre bril - lant qui ré-pands sur la ter - re Un vif é-
Himm - li - scher Mor-gen stern, du Licht der Hei - den, Zeig uns das

dark - ness, and lend us Thine aid; Star of the east, the hor-
clat qui di - ri - ge nos pas, A l'o - ri - ent nos sen-
Ziel und den Weg durch die Nacht! Gott will be - en - den die

i - zon a - dorn-ing, Guide where our in - fant Re-deem - er is laid.
tiers tu é - clai - res : Car un Sau-veur nous est né i - ci - bas.
Angst und das Lei - den, Hat sich uns sel - ber als Kind dar - ge - bracht.

2. Cold on His cradle the dewdrops are shining ;
   Low lies His head with the beasts of the stall ;
   Angels adore Him in slumber reclining,
   Maker and Monarch and Saviour of all.

3. Say, shall we yield Him, in costly devotion,
   Odours of Edom, and offering divine,
   Gems of the mountains and pearls of the ocean,
   Myrrh from the forest or gold from the mine ?

4. Vainly we offer each ample oblation,
    Vainly with gifts would His favour secure ;
Richer by far is the heart's adoration ;
    Dearer to God are the prayers of the poor.

5. Brightest and best of the sons of the morning,
    Dawn on our darkness, and lend us Thine aid ;
Star of the east, the horizon adorning,
    Guide where our infant Redeemer is laid.

REGINALD HEBER (1783-1826).

* * *

2. Dans son berceau la rosée étincelle,
    Jésus repose auprès des animaux,
Les anges louent l'enfant qui sommeille
    Et qui déjà sur lui prend tous nos maux.

3. Donnerons-nous en offrande sacrée
    Parfums d'Edom ou perles de la mer,
Joyaux sans prix ou la myrrhe embaumée,
    Or précieux, trésors de l'univers ?

4. Les dons les plus précieux de la terre
    N'obtiendront pas sa grâce et ses faveurs :
Des pauvres gens Dieu bénit la misère
    Et ce qu'il veut, c'est le don de nos cœurs.

5. Astre brillant qui répands sur la terre
    Un vif éclat qui dirige nos pas,
A l'orient nos sentiers tu éclaires :
    L'enfant Jésus vient de naître ici-bas.

Trad. FLOSSETTE DU PASQUIER (1951).

* * *

2. Kind in der Krippe, Erlöser der Welten,
    Liegst bei den Tieren im finsteren Stall !
Solcherlei Liebe kann keiner vergelten !
    König, dir dienen die Engel mit Schall !

3. Sag, sollen wir, da die Himmlischen singen,
    Weihrauch dir opfern aus Edom und Gold
Aus dem Gebirge — und Myrrhen dir bringen ?
    Wir sind Beschenkte denn du bist uns hold.

4. Ach, wir erkennen, wie arm unsre Gaben,
    Wissen auf einmal wie leer unser Sinn.
Du aber nimmst was an Armut wir haben,
    Gibst uns dafür deine Seligkeit hin.

5. Himmlischer Morgenstern, du Licht der Heiden,
    Zeig uns das Ziel und den Weg durch die Nacht !
Gott will beenden die Angst und das Leiden,
    Hat sich uns selber als Kind dargebracht.

Übers. HELGA RUSCHE (1950).

— 23 (18) —

Leo Hassler (1564-1612).

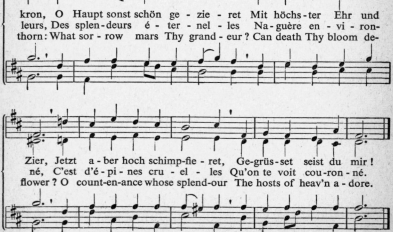

O Haupt voll Blut und Wun - den, Voll Schmerz und vol - ler
Chef cou - vert de bles - su - res, Meur - tri pour nous pé -
O sac - red head, sore wound - ed, De - filed and put to

Hohn, O Haupt zu Spott ge - bun - den Mit ei - ner Dor - nen-
cheurs, Chef ac - ca - blé d'in - ju - res, D'op - pro - bre, de dou -
scorn; O king - ly head, sur - round - ed With mock - ing crown of

kron, O Haupt sonst schön ge - zie - ret Mit höchs - ter Ehr und
leurs, Des splen - deurs é - ter - nel - les Na - guère en - vi - ron-
thorn: What sor - row mars Thy grand - eur? Can death Thy bloom de-

Zier, Jetzt a - ber hoch schimp-fie - ret, Ge-grüs - set seist du mir!
né, C'est d'é - pi - nes cru - el - les Qu'on te voit cou - ron - né.
flower? O count-en-ance whose splend-our The hosts of heav'n a - dore.

2.

Nun, was du Herr, erduldet,
Ist alles meine Last,
Ich, ich hab es verschuldet,
Was du getragen hast.
Schau her ! hier steh ich Armer,
Der Zorn verdienet hat.
Gib mir, o mein Erbarmer,
Den Anblick deiner Gnad !

3.

Ich danke dir von Herzen,
O Jesu, liebster Freund,
Für deine Todesschmerzen,
Da du's so gut gemeint.
Ach gib, dass ich mich halte
Zu dir und deiner Treu,
Und, wenn ich einst erkalte,
In dir mein Ende sei.

4.

Erscheine mir zum Schilde, — Zum Trost in meinen Tod,
Und lass mich seh'n dein Bilde — In deiner Kreuzesnot.
Da will ich nach dir blicken, — Da will ich glaubensvoll
Fest an mein Herz dich drücken : — Wer so stirbt, der stirbt wohl.

PAULUS GERHARDT (1607-1676).

* * *

2.

C'est ainsi que tu paies
Le prix de ma rançon.
Tes langueurs et tes plaies,
Voilà ma guérison.
Mon âme criminelle
Est à tes pieds, Seigneur ;
Daigne jeter sur elle
Un regard de faveur.

3.

Au sein de ma misère,
Sauvé par ton amour,
Pour toi que puis-je faire ?
Que t'offrir en retour ?
Ah ! du moins, Dieu suprême,
Prends à jamais mon cœur :
Qu'il te serve et qu'il t'aime,
Plein d'une sainte ardeur.

4.

A mon heure suprême — Ne m'abandonne pas.
Viens alors, viens toi-même — Me prendre dans tes bras.
Au fort de l'agonie, — Me serrant sur ton cœur,
Ouvre-moi la Patrie — Et l'éternel bonheur.

Trad. Psautier morave (1757).

* * *

2.

Thy beauty, long-desirèd,
Hath vanished from our sight ;
Thy power is all expirèd,
And quenched the light of light.
Ah me ! for whom Thou diest,
Hide not so far Thy grace :
Show me, O Love most highest,
The brightness of Thy face.

3.

In Thy most bitter passion
My heart to share doth cry,
With Thee for my salvation
Upon the Cross to die.
Ah, keep my heart thus movèd
To stand Thy Cross beneath,
To mourn Thee, well-belovèd,
Yet thank Thee for Thy death.

4.

My days are few, O fail not, — With Thine immortal power,
To hold me, that I quail not — In death's most fearful hour :
That I may fight befriended, — And see in my last strife
To me Thine arms extended — Upon the Cross of life.

Trans. ROBERT BRIDGES (1844-1930) *.

* From the Yattendon Hymnal edited by Robert Bridges and H. Ellis Wooldridge, by permission of the Clarendon Press, Oxford.

Byzantine Melody.
Harm. by WLADIMIR DIAKOFF (1950).

Sostenuto (♩ = 76)

Τίς Θε - ὸς μέ - - - γας ὡς ὁ Θε - ὸς
What God is so great as our God, as
Sei - gneur, toi qui es tout-puis-sant é - ter - nel - le -
Wer ist so gross wie un - ser Gott, un - ser Gott so

ἡ - μῶν; Σύ ἐι Σύ ἐι ὁ Θε - ὸς
God, our Lord? Thou art, Thou art the God
ment, à jamais, toi seul, toi seul ac - com - plis
gross. Un - ser Gott, du bist's, du bist der Gott

ὁ ποι - ῶν θαυ - μα - σί - - α μόν - - νος.
Who a - lone do - est won - drous things, won - drous things!
des mi - ra - cles é - ton - nants, toi seul es grand.
der al - lein Wun - der tut, du al - lein, al - lein.

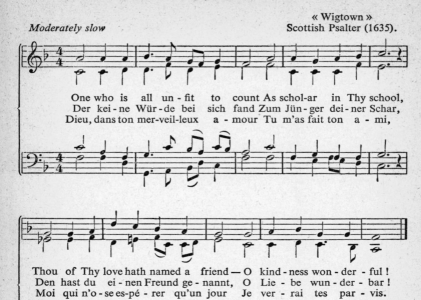

Moderately slow

« Wigtown »
Scottish Psalter (1635).

One who is all un-fit to count As schol-ar in Thy school,
Der kei-ne Wür-de bei sich fand Zum Jün-ger dei-ner Schar,
Dieu, dans ton mer-veil-leux a-mour Tu m'as fait ton a-mi,

Thou of Thy love hath named a friend — O kind-ness won-der-ful!
Den hast du ei-nen Freund ge-nannt, O Lie-be wun-der-bar!
Moi qui n'o-se es-pé-rer qu'un jour Je ver-rai tes par-vis.

2.

Thou dwellest in unshadowed light,
  All sin and shame above —
That Thou shouldst bear our sin and
  How can I tell such love ?   [shame,

3.

When in His flesh they drove the nails,
  Did He not all endure ?
What name is there to fit a life
  So patient and so pure ?

4.

So, Love itself in human form,
  For love of me He came ;
I cannot look upon His face
  For shame, for bitter shame.

5.

If there is aught of worth in me,
  It comes from Thee alone ;
Then keep me safe, for so, O Lord,
  Thou keepest but Thine own.

From the Marathi of Narayan Vaman Tilak
(1862-1919).
Trans. by Nicol MacNicol (1870).

★ ★ ★

2.

Du, Reiner, der die Sünde hasst,
  Der du gewohnt im Licht,
Wie trägst du nun mein' Sündenlast ?
  Begreif' es ewig nicht.

3.

Es hub dein Mund nicht an zu schrei'n,
  Da man die Nägel schlug.
Wer so ertrug die Todespein,
  Wie nenn ich ihn mit Fug ?

4.

Die Lieb in unser Fleisch und Blut
  Nur mir zuliebe kam,
Doch wenn ihr Auge auf mir ruht,
  Brennt mich die Scham, die Scham.

5.

Du hast gemacht, was in mir wär'
  Von irgendeinem Wert.
Halt mich bei dir, denn so, o Herr,
  Hältst du, was dir gehört.

Übers. JOHANN CHRISTOPH HAMPE (1951).

★ ★ ★

2.

Tu pris sur toi mon vil péché
  Toi qui régnais au ciel.
Qui pourra chanter ta bonté,
  Ton amour paternel !

3.

Quand on cloua sa chair au bois
  Le Christ supporta tout ;
Don ineffable de la foi :
  Jésus est mort pour nous.

4.

Dieu d'amour, du ciel descendu
  Par amour incarné,
Couvert de honte, je n'ai pu
  Ta face contempler.

5.

Y aurait-il du bien en moi,
  Tu l'y a mis, Seigneur ;
Garde-moi donc auprès de toi,
  Je suis ton serviteur.

Trad. VIOLETTE DU PASQUIER (1951).

— 26 (20) —

Andante   American Negro Folk Song *.

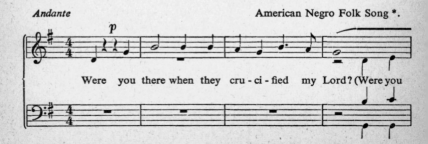

Were you there when they cru-ci-fied my Lord? (Were you

there?) Were you there when they cru-ci-fied my Lord? Oh!

Pendosi- - - - - -

Some-times it caus-es me to trem-ble, trem-ble,

- - - - - *mf*

trem-ble, Were you there when they cru-ci-fied my Lord?

* Published with the kind permission of the Hampton Institute, Hampton, Virginia.

2.

2. Were you there when they nailed Him to the tree? (*bis*)
   Oh! sometimes it causes me to tremble...
   Were you there when they nailed Him to the tree?

3. Were you there when they pierced Him in the side? (*bis*)
   Oh! sometimes it causes me to tremble...
   Were you there when they pierced Him in the side?

4. Were you there when the sun refused to shine? (*bis*)
   Oh! sometimes it causes me to tremble...
   Were you there when the sun refused to shine?

5. Were you there when they laid Him in the tomb? (*bis*)
   Oh! sometimes it causes me to tremble...
   Were you there when they laid Him in the tomb?

« Rockingham »
E. MILLER (1731-1807) — S. WEBBE.

Adagio

When I sur-vey the won-drous Cross, On which the
Schau ich dein Kreuz, o Hei-land an, An dem du
Quand je me tour-ne vers la croix Où Christ ex-

Prince of Glo-ry died, My rich-est gain I count but
star-best, Herr und Held, Zer-bricht des Reich-tums blin-der
pi-re sur le bois Mon cœur bles-sé, rem-pli de

loss, And pour con-tempt on all my pride.
Wahn Und al-ler Stolz in nichts zer-fällt.
deuil Prend en dé-goût mon fol or-gueil.

2. Forbid it, Lord, that I should boast
   Save in the death of Christ my God ;
   All the vain things that charm me most,
   I sacrifice them to His Blood.

3. See from His head, His hands, His feet,
   Sorrow and love flow mingled down ;
   Did e'er such love and sorrow meet,
   Or thorns compose so rich a crown ?

4. His dying crimson like a robe,
   Spreads o'er His body on the Tree ;
   Then I am dead to all the globe,
   And all the globe is dead to me.

5. Were the whole realm of nature mine,
   That were a present far too small ;
   Love so amazing, so divine,
   Demands my soul, my life, my all.

ISAAC WATTS (1674-1748).

* * *

2. Schütz' mich vor falscher Sicherheit !
   Mein Ruhm in deinem Tode ruht.
   Ich opf're Tand und Eitelkeit,
   Die mich umgarnen, deinem Blut.

3. Seht, wie von seinen Wunden her
   Das Blut der Liebe ihm entquillt !
   Wo find ich solcher Liebe Meer,
   Wo solcher Krone Ebenbild ?

4. Dich überströmt es scharlachrot,
   Gleich ein Gewand, am Marterstamm.
   Mir ist die ganze Welt wie tot.
   Ich sterb ihr ab, du Gotteslamm !

5. Wie dank ich's ihm ? Wär zu gering,
   Gäb' ich all irdisch Gold und Glanz.
   Du, Liebe, die am Kreuze hing,
   Willst Leib und Seele, willst mich ganz

Übers. WILHELM HORKEL (1951).

* * *

2. Qui donc pourrait calmer ce cœur
   Hormis la croix de mon Sauveur ?
   Tous mes plaisirs, mes vains désirs
   Je veux, ô Christ, te les offrir.

3. O vois, des mains, de son côté,
   Du front d'épines couronné,
   Douleur, angoisse, amour mêlés,
   Descendre pour nous racheter.

4. Grâce à ton sang, Christ, que je vois
   Couler, flot pourpre, sur le bois
   La terre entière meurt pour moi ;
   Je meurs moi-même loin de toi.

5. Si je t'offrais le monde entier
   Ce don serait pris en pitié.
   Amour si grand, si pur, si doux
   Veut âme, corps, mon cœur, mon tout !

Trad. PAULINE MARTIN (1951).

Allegro maestoso　　　　　　　　　　　　　　G. F. Haendel (1685-1759).

A toi la gloi - re, O Res - sus - ci - té!
Held, der dem Gra - be Sieg - ge - krönt ent - stieg.
Thine is the glo - ry, Ri - sen, con-qu'ring Son,

FINE

A toi la vic - toi - re Pour l'é - ter - ni - té!
Dein ist Macht und Eh - re, E - wig dein der Sieg.
End - less is the vict' - ry Thou o'er death hast won.

Bril - lant de lu - miè - re, L'ange est des - cen - du,
Wir auch sol - len le - ben Mit dem Herrn zu - gleich,
An - gels in bright rai - ment Rolled the stone a - way,

Da Capo

Il rou - le la pier - re Du tom - beau vain - cu.
Er will uns er - he - ben In sein himm-lisch Reich.
Kept the fold - ed grave-clothes Where Thy bo - dy lay.

Da Capo

2. Vois-le paraître :
C'est lui, c'est Jésus,
Ton Sauveur, ton Maître !
Oh ! ne doute plus ;
Sois dans l'allégresse,
Peuple du Seigneur,
Et redis sans cesse
Que Christ est vainqueur !
    A toi la gloire...

3. Craindrais-je encore ?
Il vit à jamais,
Celui que j'adore,
Le Prince de paix ;
Il est ma victoire,
Mon puissant soutien,
Ma vie et ma gloire :
Non, je ne crains rien !
    A toi la gloire...

EDMOND BUDRY (1884).

* * *

2. Auf unser Flehen
Gibt er und vergibt.
Jeder kann es sehen,
Dass er lebt und liebt.
Volk des Herrn, O freue
Deines Königs dich !
Seine Huld und Treue
Währet ewiglich.
    Held, der dem Grabe...

3. Was kann uns scheiden
Von der Liebe sein ?
Trübsal oder Leiden,
Irgend eine Pein ?
Wovor soll mir grauen ?
Als ein Kind des Lichts
Darf ich ihm vertrauen :
Nein, ich fürchte nichts.
    Held, der dem Grabe...

Übers. JOHANNA MEYER († 1921).

* * *

2. Lo ! Jesus meets thee,
Risen from the tomb ;
Lovingly He greets thee,
Scatters fear and gloom ;
Let His church with gladness
Hymns of triumph sing,
For her Lord now liveth ;
Death hath lost its sting.
    Thine is the glory...

3. No more we doubt Thee,
Glorious Prince of life !
Life is nought without Thee ;
Aid us in our strife ;
Make us more than conqu'rors,
Through Thy deathless love.
Bring us safe through Jordan
To Thy home above.
    Thine is the glory...

Trans. R. BIRCH HOYLE (1923).

* * *

— 29 (72) —

First three lines adapted from a "Gloria Patri"
by G. Da Palestrina (1594).
Alleluia by W. H. Monk.

Andante

Fi - ni - ta   jam sunt   prae - li - a,
The strife is   o'er, the   bat - tle done;
Es ging das   grim - me   Krie - gen lang,
Chan - te mon cœur, ré - jou - is - toi,

Est par - ta   jam vic - to - ri - a! Gau - de - a -
Now is   the   Vic -tor's   tri - umph won; O let the
Doch un - ser   Herr den   Sieg er - rang. Drum lasst er -
Christ a li - vré son   dur com - bat, Mais il re -

mus, et   ca - na - mus: Al - le - lu - ia!
song of praise   be sung: Al - le - lu - ia!
schal - len den   Ge - sang!   Hal - le - lu - ja!
vient vic - to - ri - eux,   Al - lé - lu - ia!

2. Post fata mortis barbara
   Devicit Jesus tartara.
   Applaudamus et psallamus :
   Alleluia !

3. Surrexit die tertia
   Coelesti clarus gratia.
   Ipsonemus, et cantemus :
   Alleluia !

4. Sunt clausa stygis ostia,
   Et coeli patent atria.
   Gaudeamus, et canamus :
   Alleluia !

* * *

2. Death's mightiest powers have done their
   And Jesus hath His foes dispersed ; [worst,
   Let shouts of praise and joy outburst ;
   Alleluia !

3. On the third morn He rose again
   Glorious in majesty to reign ;
   O let us swell the joyful strain ;
   Alleluia !

4. He brake the age-bound chains of hell ;
   The bars from heaven's high portals fell ;
   Let hymns of praise His triumph tell ;
   Alleluia !

Trans. FRANCIS POTT (1859) *.

* * *

2. Nachdem er litt die Todesstund,
   Gab Jesus sich der Hölle kund.
   Nun rühmt ihn dankbar jeder Mund
   Halleluja !

3. Und aus dem Grabe er ersteht
   Am dritten Tag in Majestät.
   Sein Lob von allen Lippen geht.
   Halleluja !

4. Versiegelt Hölle, Tod und Nacht,
   Et hat den Himmel aufgemacht,
   Wo ewig unsre Freude lacht.
   Halleluja !

Übers. JOHANN CHRISTOPH HAMPE (1950).

* * *

2. Pour nous il a souffert la mort
   Mais des enfers, vainqueur, il sort.
   Psalmodions, louons-le tous,
   Alléluia !

3. Après trois jours le Rédempteur
   Nous revient en triomphateur.
   Exaltons-le, chantons son nom :
   Alléluia !

4. Il clôt les portes des enfers,
   Pour nous les cieux se sont ouverts,
   Nous exultons, et nous chantons :
   Alléluia !

Trad. FLOSSETTE DU PASQUIER (1951).

30

Gregorianische Melodie
vom 12. oder 13. Jahrhundert.
Harm. bei H. L. HASSLER (1608).

Christ ist er-stan - den von der Mar-ter al - le! Des
Christ is a - ri - sen, ri - sen from His suff'-rings! Then
Christ res-sus-ci - te, Hors de tout sup - pli - ce. Ré-

soll'n wir al - le froh sein, Christ will un - ser Trost sein. Ky-
shall we all re-joice and say, Christ will com-fort us to - day. Ky-
jou - is-sons-nous en ce jour, Christ vi - vant l'est pour tou-jours. Ky-

ri - e - leis! Wär' er nicht er - stan - den, Die Welt, die wär' ver-
ri - e - leis! If He were not ri - sen, The world would be lost
ri - e - leis! Les en - fers suc- com - bent, Il a vain-cu la

gan - gen. Seit dass er er - stan-den ist, So lob'n wir den Va - ter
with Him. Since He is a - risen to - day We praise God the Fa - ther
tom - be, Il a en - ten - du nos cris. Lou-ange au Pè - re,

Je - su Christ. Ky - ri - e - leis! Hal - le - lu - ja!
and we say: Ky - ri - e - leis! Al - le - lu - ia!
gloire au Fils! Ky - ri - e - leis! Al - lé - lu - ia!

Hal - le - lu - ja! Hal - le - lu - ja! Des sol'n wir al - le
Al - le - lu - ia! Al - le - lu - ia! Then shall we all re-
Al - lé - lu - ia! Al - lé - lu - ia! Ré - jou - is - sons-nous

froh sein, Christ will un - ser Trost sein, Ky - ri - e - leis!
joice and say, Christ will com-fort us to - day. Ky - ri - e - leis!
en ce jour, Christ vi-vant l'est pour tou-jours. Ky - ri - e - leis!

13. Jahrhundert.
English version by MARGARET HOUSE (1950).
Version française
par THÉO PREISS et PIERRE CHAZEL (1950).

31

Moderately slow

St. Magnus — Nottingham.*
Probably by J. CLARK (1670-1707).

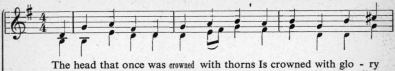

The head that once was crowned with thorns Is crowned with glo - ry
Das Haupt, dem Dor-nen ein - ge-drückt, Prangt nun in Herr-lich-
Le front d'é-pi - nes cou - ron - né Jé - sus pour nous est

now: A roy-al di - a-dem a-dorns The might-y vict-or's brow.
keit. Die ew'-ge Kö-nigs-kro-ne schmückt Den Sie - ger nach dem Streit.
mort; Mais glo - ri-eux il va ré-gner, Il chan-ge no-tre sort.

2.

The highest place that heaven affords
  Is His, is His by right,
The King of kings and Lord of lords,
  And heaven's eternal Light ;

3.

The joy of all who dwell above,
  The joy of all below,
To whom He manifests His love,
  And grants His name to know.

4.

To them the Cross, with all its shame,
  With all its grace, is given :
Their name an everlasting name,
  Their joy the joy of heaven.

5.

They suffer with their Lord below,
  They reign with Him above,
Their profit and their joy to know
  The mystery of His love.

* By permission of the Faith Press Ltd.

6.

The Cross He bore is life and health
Though shame and death to Him;
His people's hope, His people wealth,
Their everlasting theme.

T. KELLY (1769-1854).

* * *

2.

Den höchsten Rang im Himmel fern
Hat Gott ihm zugericht'.
Der Kön'ge König, Herr der Herrn,
Des Himmels ew'ges Licht!

3.

Er ist das Glück der obern Schar
Und der', die unten sind,
Macht seine Liebe offenbar
Und nimmt sie an als Kind.

4.

Für sie litt er des Kreuzes Pein,
Dass sie die Gnade schmück'.
Sein Name schliesst den ihren ein,
Ihr Glück — des Himmels Glück!

5.

Sie leiden, wie ihr Herr hier tat,
Sie herrschen, wo er siegt',
Sind fröhlich, weil sein Liebesrat
Vor ihnen offen liegt.

6.

Sein Kreuz bracht' Heil und Leben nur,
Ihm zwar des Todes Schmach.
Sein Volk ergreift der Hoffnung Spur
Und denkt ihm ewig nach.

Übers. WILHELM HORKEL (1950).

* * *

2.

Car maintenant, ô Roi des rois
Tu règnes dans les cieux;
C'est le triomphe après la croix
Du Christ victorieux.

3.

A tous les habitants des cieux,
A nous pauvres humains,
Il donne un bonheur radieux
Par son amour divin.

4.

Pour les humains tu t'abaissas
Puis tu mourus, Seigneur.
Et tu nous sauves par ta croix!
Ne versons plus de pleurs!

5.

Avec le Christ portons la croix
Car un jour, dans les cieux,
Tous ceux qui vivent dans la foi
Verront enfin leur Dieu.

6.

Ta croix, ô Christ, est le salut
Ta mort sauva les tiens;
T'aimer, Seigneur, voilà mon but,
Tu es mon seul vrai bien.

Trad. FLOSSETTE DU PASQUIER (1951).

— 32 —

MELCHIOR VULPIUS (1609).

Ge - lobt sei Gott im höchs-ten Thron Samt sei - nem
Lou - ange à Dieu! Lou - ange au Christ! Gloire à Jé-
All praise to God in high - est heav'n, And His in-

ein - ge - bor - nen Sohn, Der für uns hat ge - nug ge - tan.
sus, le Fils bé - ni! Il a pour nous tout ac - com - pli.
car - nate Son, be giv'n, Who glor-ious - ly for us hath striv'n.

Hal-le-lu - ja, Hal-le-lu - ja, Hal-le-lu - ja.
Al - lé-lu - ia! Al - lé-lu - ia! Al - lé-lu - ia!
Al - le-lu - ia! Al - le-lu - ia! Al - le-lu - ia!

2.

Des Morgens früh am dritten Tag,
Da noch der Stein am Grabe lag,
Erstand er frei ohn' alle Klag.
  Halleluja. (*ter*)

3.

Der Engel sprach: Fürchtet euch nicht;
Denn ich weiss wohl, was euch gebricht.
Ihr sucht Jesum und findt ihn nicht.
  Halleluja. (*ter*)

4.

Er ist erstanden von dem Tod,
Hat überwunden alle Not;
Kommt, seht, wo er gelegen hat.
  Halleluja. (*ter*)

5.

Nun bitten wir dich, Jesu Christ.
Weil du vom Tod erstanden bist,
Verleihe, was uns selig ist.
  Halleluja. (*ter*)

6.

Damit von Sünden wir befreit,
Dem Namen dein gebenedeit
Frei mögen singen allezeit.
    Halleluja. *(ter)*

MICHAEL WEISSE, (†1534).

* * *

2.

Quand ses amis, après trois jours,
Un matin vinrent tour à tour,
La tombe était vide à toujours.
    Alléluia ! *(ter)*

3.

L'ange leur dit : Ne craignez point !
Ne cherchez pas, ne pleurez point,
Christ est vivant, j'en suis témoin.
    Alléluia ! *(ter)*

4.

Dieu de la mort l'a délivré,
C'est là, voyez, qu'il fut couché,
Hors de la tombe il s'est dressé.
    Alléluia ! *(ter)*

5.

Nous t'en prions, Jésus Sauveur
Qui du trépas sort en vainqueur,
Viens et délivre notre cœur.
    Alléluia ! *(ter)*

6.

Alors, lavés de tout péché,
Libérés pour l'éternité,
Nous chanterons ton nom sacré !
    Alléluia ! *(ter)*

Trad. PAULINE MARTIN (1950).

* * *

2.

On the third morn at break of day,
While still the stone above Him lay,
Free He arose, to go His way.
    Alleluia ! *(ter)*

3.

Then spake the angel, "Fear ye naught !
I know why ye be thus distraught :
Ye cannot find the Lord ye sought."
    Alleluia ! *(ter)*

4.

"He is arisen from the dead,
And all travail hath conquered.
Lo, where He lay, His shroud is spread."
    Alleluia ! *(ter)*

5.

Saviour and Lord, we pray to Thee,
In Thine uprisen majesty,
Grant us to live right blessedly.
    Alleluia ! *(ter)*

6.

That we, set free from sin and shame,
Freely may sing and praise Thy Name,
In adoration of the same.
    Alleluia ! *(ter)*

Trans. MARGARET BARCLAY (1950).

— 33 —

Moderately slow

« Caersalem ».
R. EDWARDS (1797-1862).

Guide me, O Thou great Re-deem - er, Pil - grim through this
O du e - wi - ges Er - bar - men, Sieh mich an, mir
Gui - de - moi, ber - ger fi - dè - le, En ce mon - de

bar - ren land; I am weak, but Thou art might - y,
fehlt die Kraft, Hal - te mich mit dei - nen Ar - men
pè - le - rin, Prends à toi mon cœur re - bel - le,

Hold me with Thy power - ful hand: Bread of heav - en,
Auf der ban - gen Wan - der - schaft, Him - mels - spei - se,
Gui - de - moi, sois mon sou - tien, Pain de vi - e,

Bread of heav-en, Bread of heav-en, Feed me till I want no more.
Him-mels-spei-se, Him-mels-spei-se, Spei-se in der Wüs-te mich!
Pain de vi-e, Pain de vi-e, De ta grâ-ce nour-ris-moi.

2.

Open now the crystal fountain,
  Whence the healing stream doth flow;
Let the fire and cloudy pillar
  Lead me all my journey through:
    Strong deliverer, (*ter*)
Be Thou still my strength and shield.

3.

When I tread the verge of Jordan,
  Bid my anxious fears subside;
Death of death, and hell's Destruction
  Land me safe on Canaan's side:
    Songs of praises, (*ter*)
I will ever give to Thee.

W. WILLIAMS (1717-1791).
Trans. P. and W. WILLIAMS.

* * *

2.

Reiss die Felsen auseinander,
  Mach, dass mich dein Quell erquickt,
Dass die Feuersäule wander',
  Freundlich mit mir weiterrückt!
    Mein Erlöser, (*ter*)
Sei du stets mein Schutz und Schild!

3.

Wenn ich durch den Jordan schreite,
  Seine Flut mich übermannt,
Halte du die Flut zur Seite,
  Führer ins gelobte Land!
    Preis und Ehre (*ter*)
Werd dir ewig dargebracht.

Übers. JOHANN CHRISTOPH HAMPE (1950).

* * *

2.

Christ, tu es la source vive
  Des biens les plus précieux,
Fais que pour toi seul je vive,
  Guide-moi du haut des cieux.
    Viens, protège, (*ter*)
Sois mon roc, mon bouclier.

3.

Du Jourdain je suis les rives;
  Quand j'ai peur, rassure-moi.
A Sion, qu'enfin j'arrive,
  Affermis ma faible foi;
    Tes louanges (*ter*)
A jamais je chanterai.

Trad. FLOSSETTE DU PASQUIER (1951).

« Hyfrydol »
ROWLAND HUGH PRICHARD (1811-1887).

Love di - vine, all loves ex - cell - ing, Joy of
Lie - be, komm he - rab zur Er - de ! Die du
Cha - ri - té de Dieu le Pè - re, Saint a-

heav'n, to earth come down; Fix in us Thy hum - ble
nicht von die - ser Welt, Mach dass sie die dei - ne
mour de Jé - sus - Christ, Oh ! Re - viens sur cet - te

dwell - ing, All Thy faith - ful mer - cies crown. Fa - ther,
wer - de, Schla - ge bei uns auf dein Zelt ! Lie - be
ter - re, Rem - plis - nous de ton es - prit. Ta mi-

Thou art all com - pas - sion, Pure un-bound - ed love Thou
komm, du heisst Er - bar - men, Kei - ne Schran - ke schränkt dich
sé - ri - corde im - men - se Af - fer - mit nos cœurs trem-

art : Vis - it us with Thy sal - va - tion,
ein, Da - rum lass auch bei uns Ar - men
blants, Fais - nous sen - tir ta puis - san - ce,

En - ter ev - 'ry trem - bling heart.
Heu - te dein Er - bar - men sein !
Prends pi - tié de tes en - fants !

2. Breathe, O breathe Thy loving Spirit
   Into ev'ry troubled breast ;
   Let us all in Thee inherit,
   Let us find Thy promised rest.
   Come, Almighty to deliver,
   Let us all Thy life receive :
   Graciously return, and never,
   Never more Thy temples leave.

CHARLES WESLEY (1707-1788).

★ ★ ★

2. Noch ist unser Herz gefangen,
   Angst and Trauer hält uns fest,
   Aber es war dein Verlangen,
   Das uns Ruhe finden lässt.
   Liebe komm, komm und befreie
   Eilend uns aus aller Not,
   Schenk das Leben uns, das neue,
   Schenk das Leben ohne Tod !

Übers. JOHANN CHRISTOPH HAMPE (1950).

★ ★ ★

2. Saint-Esprit, esprit de vie,
   Sois vainqueur de notre effroi !
   Ton peuple en toi se confie,
   Notre repos est en toi.
   Sauve-nous, céleste Frère,
   Nous espérons ton retour ;
   Reçois-nous dès cette terre
   A l'autel de ton amour.

Trad. EVA DUBSKA-KUSHNER (1950).

— 35 (17) —

Moderato Schlesisches Volkslied (1677).

Schön-ster Herr Je - su, Herr-scher al - ler En - den,
Fair - est Lord Je - sus, Lord of all cre - a - tion,
Doux et bon Maî - tre, Sou - ve - rain des ê - tres,

Got - tes — und Ma - ri - en Sohn! Dich will ich lie - ben,
Je - sus of God, and Ma - ry's Son; Thee will I cher - ish,
O Jé - sus, Roi glo - ri - eux, Seul je t'a - do - re,

Dich will ich eh - ren, Du mei - ner See - le Freud und Kron.
Thee will I hon - our, O Thou my soul's de - light and crown.
Seul je t'ho - no - re, O toi mon Sau - veur et mon Dieu.

2.
Schön sind die Felder,
Schöner sind die Wälder
In der schönen Frühlingszeit :
　　Jesus ist schöner,
　　Jesus ist reiner,
Der unser traurig Herz erfreut.

3.
Schön leucht der Monde,
Schöner leucht die Sonne
Und die Sternlein allzumal.
　　Jesus leucht schöner,
　　Jesus leucht reiner,
Als all die Eng'l im Himmelssaal.

4.
Schön sind die Blumen,
Schöner sind die Menschen,
Die in frischer Jugend sein.
　　Sie müssen sterben,
　　Müssen verderben ;
Doch Jesus lebt in Ewigkeit.

5.
Alle die Schönheit
Himmel und der Erden
Ist gefasst in dir allein.
　　Keiner soll werden
　　Lieber auf Erden,
Als du, der schönste Jesus mein.

6.

Wenn ich dann sterbe, — Dass ich nicht verderbe,
Lass mich dir befohlen sein ! — Wann's Herz wird brechen,
Lass es dann sprechen : — Jesu, Jesu, du Liebster mein !

Dichter unbekannt (1842).

* * *

2.

Fair are the meadows,
Fairer still the woodlands,
Robed in the verdure and bloom of spring.
  Jesus is fairer,
  Jesus is purer,
He makes the saddest heart to sing.

3.

Fair is the moonlight,
Fairer still the sunshine,
Fair is the shimmering, starry sky :
  Jesus shines brighter,
  Jesus shines clearer,
Than all the heavenly host on high.

4.

Fair are the flowers,
Fairer still the sons of men,
In all the freshness of youth arrayed :
  Yet is their beauty
  Fading and fleeting ;
My Jesus, Thine will never fade.

5.

All fairest beauty
Heavenly and earthly,
Wondrously, Jesus, is found in Thee
  None can be nearer,
  Fairer or dearer,
Than Thou, my Saviour, art to me.

6.

When I lie dying — Still on Thee relying
Suffer me not from Thine arms to fall : — At my last hour
Be Thou my power — For Thou, Lord Jesus, art my All.

Trans. LILIAN STEVENSON (1924).

* * *

2.

Belles campagnes,
Plus belles montagnes
Quand verdit le doux printemps,
  Plus pur encore,
  Clair dans l'aurore,
Jésus guérit nos cœurs tremblants.

3.

La lune brille
Le soleil scintille,
Et tout l'or vibrant des cieux,
  Jésus se donne,
  Seul il rayonne
Plus que les anges du Saint Lieu.

4.

O fleurs mignonnes
Plus beaux sont les hommes
Dans leur jeune nouveauté ;
  L'homme trépasse
  Et la fleur passe :
Jésus vit dans l'éternité.

5.

Tout le mystère
Du ciel, de la terre,
O Jésus se trouve en toi,
  Rien n'est semblable,
  N'est comparable
A toi Jésus, mon Dieu, mon Roi.

6.

Que la mort vienne : — Ah ! qu'il me souvienne
De marcher à ton côté. — Et s'il se brise
Mon cœur te dise : — Seigneur Jésus, Roi bien-aimé !

Trad. PAULINE MARTIN (1951).

« Richmond C. M. »
Adapted from T. HAWEIS (1734-1820)
by S. WEBBE (the younger).

Moderately slow

Praise to the Hol - iest in the height, And
Lob sei dem Herrn in Him - mels - höhn; Es
Gloire au Très - Haut, lou - ange à Dieu Du

in the depth be praise; In all His words most
rüh - me Land und Meer Ihn, des - sen Wort und
ciel au fond des mers, Car - son pou - voir mys-

won - der - ful, Most sure in all His ways.
Weg so klar, So si - cher und so hehr.
té - ri - eux Ré - git tout l'u - ni - vers.

2.
Oh, loving wisdom of our God !
  When all was sin and shame,
A second Adam to the fight,
  And to the rescue came.

3.
Oh, wisest love ! that flesh and blood
  Which did in Adam fail,
Should strive afresh against their foe,
  Should strive and should prevail !

4.

And that a higher gift than grace
  Should flesh and blood refine,
God's presence, and His very self,
  And essence all divine !

5.

Oh ! generous love ! that He, Who
  In man for man the foe,   [smote
The double agony in man
  For man should undergo ;

6.

And in the garden secretly,
  And on the Cross on high,
Should teach His brethren and inspire
  To suffer and to die !

7.

Praise to the Holiest...

J. H. NEWMAN (1801-1890).

* * *

2.

O ew'ger Weisheit Liebesrat :
  Als Schmach und Sündenschuld
Uns ganz umfing, da sandtest du
  Den Heiland voller Huld !

3.

O weise Liebe ! Fleisch und Blut,
  Dem Tode schon geweiht
Durch Adams Fall, nun steh'n sie auf
  Zu siegreich starkem Streit !

4.

Und nicht nur Gnade war die Kraft,
  Die läuternd sie befreit :
Gott selbst kam, der Allheilige
  In seiner Wesenheit !

5.

O edle Liebe, die den Feind
  Als Mensch für Menschen schlug,
Und dafür zwiefach Todesschmerz
  Als Mensch für Menschen trug !

6.

Die dort im Garten und am Kreuz
  Von Qual und Schmach beschwert,
Wie leiden man und sterben soll,
  Die Brüder hat gelehrt !

7.

Lob sei dem Herrn...

Übers. C. LECHLER (1923).

* * *

2.

Dans son amour le Dieu vivant
  Son Fils nous a donné,
Suscitant un second Adam
  Nous sauvant du péché.

3.

La chair infirme aux jours lointains
  En Adam succombait,
L'amour de Christ, vainqueur enfin,
  Triomphe pour jamais.

4.

Dieu, nous donnant le Rédempteur,
  De la mort nous sauva ;
Sa grâce apporte le bonheur
  A tous, dès ici-bas.

5.

Christ incarna l'amour divin
  Et vint lutter pour nous
Et pour nous il se fit humain,
  Fidèle jusqu'au bout.

6.

Dans le jardin et sur la Croix
  Tu t'es donné, ô Christ,
Apprends-nous donc, ô divin Roi,
  A vivre en ton Esprit.

7.

Gloire au Très-Haut...

Trad. FLOSSETTE DU PASQUIER (1951).

37

JOHANN CRÜGER (1653) Satz : 1936.

Je - su mei - ne Freu - de, Mei - nes Her - zens Wei - de,
O Jé - sus, ma joi - e, Toi que Dieu m'en - voi - e,
Je - sus, price-less trea - sure, Source of pur - est plea - sure,

Je - su mei - ne Zier, Ach wie lang, ach lan - ge Ist dem Her - zen
Sou - tien de ma foi. Sou - vent l'â - me plei - ne De deuil et de
Tru-est Friend to me ; Long my heart hath pant - ed Till it well-nigh

ban - ge, Und ver-langt nach dir. Got-tes Lamm, mein Bräu - ti - gam,
pei - ne Sou - pire a - près toi A-gneau saint, A - mi di - vin,
faint - ed, Thirst-ing af - ter Thee. Thine I am, O spot - less Lamb,

Aus - ser dir soll mir auf Er - den, Nichts sonst lie - ber wer - den.
Il n'est rien sur cet - te ter - re Qu'à toi je pré - fè - re.
I will suf - fer nought to hide Thee, Ask for nought be-side Thee.

2.

Unter deinem Schirmen,
Bin ich vor den Stürmen
   Aller Feinde frei.
Lass von Ungewittern
Rings die Welt erzittern,
   Mir steht Jesus bei.
Ob's mit Macht gleich blitzt und kracht,
Wenn gleich Sünd und Hölle schrecken
   Jesus will mich decken.

3.

Weicht, ihr Trauergeister;
Denn mein Freudenmeister,
   Jesus tritt herein.
Denen, die Gott lieben,
Muss auch ihr Betrüben
   Lauter Freude sein.
Duld ich schon hier Spott und Hohn
Dennoch bleibst du auch im Leide,
   Jesu meine Freude.

JOHANN FRANCK (1618-1677).

* * *

2.

Seigneur, sous ton aile,
Ta sainte tutelle,
   Mon cœur ne craint rien.
Les vents et l'orage
Ont beau faire rage,
   Jésus me soutient.
Le péché, le monde entier
Satan même en vain m'assiègent ;
   Jésus me protège.

3.

Le deuil qui m'oppresse
Cède à l'allégresse
   Quand Jésus paraît.
La souffrance même
Est un bien suprême
   Pour qui le connaît.
En dépit des ennemis,
Lorsque la douleur me ploie
   Il reste ma joie.

Trad. G. PUCHER (1949).

* * *

2.

In Thine arm I rest me ;
Foes who would molest me
   Cannot reach me here.
Though the earth be shaking,
Every heart be quaking,
   God dispels our fear ;
Sin and hell in conflict fell
With their heaviest storms assail us :
   Jesus will not fail us.

3.

Hence, all thoughts of sadness !
For the Lord of gladness,
   Jesus, enters in :
Those who love the Father,
Though the storms may gather,
   Still have peace within ;
Yea, what'e'er we here must bear,
Still in Thee liest purest pleasure,
   Jesus, priceless treasure !

Trans. CATHERINE WINKWORTH (1829-1878).

38

JOHANN CRÜGER (1598-1662).

Je - su, mei - ne Zu - ver - sicht Und mein
Je - sus Christ, my sure de - fence And my
Mon Ré - demp - teur est vi - vant Et c'est

Hei - land, ist im Le - ben. Die - ses weiss ich, Sollt ich
Sav - iour, ev - er liv - eth; Know - ing this, my con - fi -
en lui que j'es - pè - re! Je l'ai con - tem - plé mou -

nicht Da - rum mich zu - frie - den ge - ben, Was die
dence Rests up - on the hope it giv - eth, Though the
rant, Pour mes pé - chés, au Cal - vai - re; Mais par

lan - ge To - des - nacht Mir auch für Ge - dan - ken macht.
night of death be fraught Still with many an anx - ious thought.
un su - prême ef - fort Jé - sus a vain - cu la mort.

2.

Jesus, er, mein Heiland, lebt :
　Ich werd auch das Leben schauen,
Sein, wo mein Erlöser schwebt ;
　Warum sollte mir denn grauen ?
Lässet auch ein Haupt sein Glied,
　Welches es nicht nach sich zieht ?

3.

Ich bin durch der Hoffnung Band
　Zu genau mit ihm verbunden,
Meine starke Glaubenshand
　Wird in ihn gelegt befunden,
Dass mich auch kein Todesbann
　Ewig von ihm trennen kann.

4.

Ich bin Fleisch und muss daher
　Auch einmal zu Asche werden,
Das gesteh' ich, doch wird er
　Mich erwecken aus der Erden,
Dass ich in der Herrlichkeit
　Um ihn sein mög allezeit.

L. H. v. BRANDENBURG (1653).

* * *

2.

Jesus, my Redeemer, lives !
　I, too, unto life must waken,
He will have me where He is.
　Shall my courage then be shaken ?
Shall I fear ? or could the head
　Raise and leave His members dead ?

3.

Nay, too closely am I bound
　Unto Him by hope for ever ;
Faith's strong hand the rock hath found,
　Grasped it and will leave it never;
Not the ban of death can part
　From its Lord the trusting heart.

4.

Saviour, draw away our heart
　Now from pleasures base and hollow,
Let us there with Thee have part
　Here on earth Thy footsteps follow.
Fix our hearts beyond the skies,
　Whither we ourselves would rise.

Trans. CATHERINE WINKWORTH (1829-1878).

* * *

2.

Je ne crains rien désormais :
　La tombe a rendu sa proie ;
Je puis m'endormir en paix
　Pour m'éveiller avec joie.
Celui qui m'a racheté,
　Jésus, est ressuscité.

3.

Alors, je remporterai,
　Avec Jésus, la victoire,
Et je le contemplerai
　Face à face dans sa gloire ;
J'exalterai sa bonté
　Jusque dans l'éternité.

4.

Dans les liens du trépas,
　J'en ai la ferme espérance,
Christ ne me laissera pas.
　Mon corps même a l'assurance
D'être à son corps glorieux,
　Semblable, un jour, dans les cieux.

Trad. dans Psalmodie morave (1846).
Remaniée dans Recueil de Vaud, Neuchâtel
et Genève (1866).

— 39 (88) —

Vorreformatorisch
Johann Walther Gesangbuch (1524).

Nun bit - ten wir den hei - li - gen Geist, Um den
Es - prit de Dieu, crée en nous tous la foi. Tou - te
Thou Ho - ly Spi - rit, We pray to Thee, Strength' our

rech - ten Glau - ben al - ler - meist, Dass er uns be-
puis - san - ce nous vient de toi. Si dans la dé-
faith and in - crease it al - way; Com - fort Thou our

hü - te an un - serm En - de, Wenn wir heim - fahr'n
tres - se Le mal nous pres - se, Af - fer - mis nos
hearts in our ad - vers - i - ty With true be-

aus die - sem E - len - de. Ky - ri - e - leis.
cœurs Et les rends vain - queurs. Ky - ri - e - leis.
lief by night and by day. Ky - ri - e - leis.

2.

Du süsse Lieb', schenk uns deine Gunst,
Lass uns empfinden der Liebe Brunst,
Dass wir uns von Herzen einander lieben
Und im Frieden auf einem Sinn bleiben.
    Kyrieleis.

3.

Du höchster Tröster in aller Not,
Hilf, dass wir nicht fürchten Schand' noch Tod,
Dass in uns die Sinne nicht gar verzagen,
Wenn der Feind wird das Leben verklagen.
    Kyrieleis.

MARTIN LUTHER (1483-1546).
Strophe 1 aus dem 13. Jahrhundert.

★ ★ ★

2.

Esprit de Dieu, mets en nous chaque jour
De notre Sauveur le saint amour.
Allume en notre âme la vive flamme
De la vérité dans la charité.
    Kyrieleis.

3.

Esprit de Dieu, ranime en nous l'espoir.
Quand sur notre route tout est noir,
Viens, et nous éclaire de ta lumière.
Rends-nous confiants, toujours vigilants.
    Kyrieleis.

Trad. JAMES SIORDET (1932).

★ ★ ★

2.

Thou sweet Love, grant us all together
Enchanted to be unfeignedly;
That we may all have love for one another,
And of one mind now and always be.
    Kyrieleis.

3.

Be Thou our Comforter in all need,
Make us to fear neither death nor shame
But in holy truth to be established,
That Satan should put us not to blame.
    Kyrieleis.

Trans. MILES COVERDALE (16th Century).
(Adapted.)

« Battle »
HENRY LAWES (1596-1662).

Spir - it of God, de - scend up - on my heart; Wean it from
Komm, Got-tes Geist, komm du, ich bin so schwach, So arm, wie-
Viens, Es-prit Saint, ha - bi - ter dans mon cœur; Daigne ins-pi-

earth, thro' all its puls - es move; Stoop to my weak-ness, might-y
wohl viel fal-scher Freu - den voll! Die nimm du fort, ein Feu - er
rer et bé - nir ton en - fant, Viens jus-qu'à moi dans tou - te

as Thou art, And make me love Thee as I ought to love.
mir ent - fach, Dass ich dich lie - be, wie ich lie - ben soll.
ta splen - deur, Veuil - le m'ai - der à t'ai - mer ar - dem - ment.

2. I ask no dream, no prophet ecstasies;
No sudden rending of the veil of clay;
No angel visitant, no op'ning skies;
But take the dimness of my soul away.

3. Teach me to feel that Thou art always nigh;
   Teach me the struggles of the soul to bear,
   To check the rising doubt, the rebel sigh;
   Teach me the patience of unanswered prayer.

4. Teach me to love Thee as Thine angels love,
   One holy passion filling all my frame;
   The baptism of the heaven-descended dove,
   My heart an altar, and Thy love the flame.

GEORGE CROLY (1780-1860).

★ ★ ★

2. Erschienst Propheten du im Traumgesicht,
   Und gingen Engel aus mit deinem Wort
   Vom Himmel her : dies, Herr, erbitt ich nicht.
   Doch nimm die Nacht von meiner Seele fort.

3. Belehre mich, dass du mich nie verlässt,
   Ja, nah mir bleibst in aller meiner Schuld,
   Brich Trotz und Zweifel, Seufzer und Protest,
   Und wenn du schweigst, so schenke mir Geduld.

4. Lehr' mich dich lieben, wie die Engel tun,
   Mit starkem, heiligen Willen füll mich an,
   Und lass den Geist des Himmels auf mir ruh'n,
   Den Geist, durch den allein ich lieben kann.

Übers. JOHANN CHRISTOPH HAMPE (1950).

★ ★ ★

2. Je ne veux point de grandes visions
   Ni de saints anges pour me visiter,
   De ta clarté, Esprit-Saint, fais-moi don,
   Viens m'éclairer en mon obscurité.

3. A mon côté tu es toujours présent,
   Tu veux m'aider à lutter vaillamment,
   Fais que je sache attendre patiemment
   De mes prières ton exaucement.

4. Toi, qui jadis au monde fus donné,
   Fais que je t'aime d'un céleste amour.
   Fais que mon cœur soit un autel sacré
   Et que ta flamme y brûle tous les jours.

Trad. FLOSSETTE DU PASQUIER (1951).

« Enchiridion » — Martin Luther (1524)
Nach einer gregorianischen Melodie.

Ve - ni Cre - a - tor Spi - ri - tus, Men -
Komm, Schöp - fer Geist, Kehr bei uns ein, Und
Come, Ho - ly Ghost, our souls in - spire, And
O, viens Saint - Es - prit cré - a - teur, Vi -

tes tu - o - rum vi - si - ta: Im - ple su - per - na
lass uns dei - ne Woh - nung sein; Er - füll die Her - zen,
light - en with ce - les - tial fire; Thou the an - oint - ing
si - te - nous dans ton ar - deur! De grâ - ces com - ble

gra - ti - a Quae tu cre - as - ti pec - to - ra.
dein Ge - bild, Mit dei - nen Him - mels - ga - ben mild.
Spi - rit art, Who dost Thy sev'n - fold gift im - part.
le pé - cheur Et ré - gé - nè - re tous les cœurs.

2.

Accende lumen sensibus,
Infund' amorem cordibus,
Infirma nostri corporis
Virtute firmans perpeti.

3.

Hostem repellas longius,
Pacemque dones protinus ;
Ductore sic te praevio,
Vitemus omne noxium.

4.

Per te sciamus da Patrem,
Noscamus atque Filium,
Teque utriusque Spiritum
Credamus omni tempore.

* * *

2.

Ein Tröster kommst du uns herab,
Du bist des Höchsten höchste Gab',
Der Lebensquell', die Liebessonn',
Der Seele Salbung, Lieb und Wonn'.

3.

Gib uns'rer Leuchte klaren Schein,
Flöss Liebesglut den Herzen ein !
Stärk unsern Mut, dass er besteh'
Des schwachen Leibes Not und Weh.

4.

Den Vater und den Sohn, O lehr
Sie uns erkennen immer mehr.
Du heil'ger Geist, in alle Zeit
Sei'n uns're Herzen dir geweiht.

Dichter unbekannt.

* * *

2.

Thy blessèd unction from above
Is comfort, life, and fire of love.
Enable with perpetual light
The dullness of our blinded sight.

3.

Anoint and cheer our soilèd face
With the abundance of Thy grace ;
Keep far our foes, give peace at home ;
Where Thou art guide no ill can come.

4.

Teach us to know the Father, Son,
And Thee, of both, to be but One ;
That through the ages all along
This may be our endless song.

Trans. J. Cosin (1594-1672).

* * *

2.

Aux hommes donne ta clarté,
Règne en nos cœurs par ta bonté,
Soutiens nos corps par ton amour
Pour que nous te suivions toujours.

3.

Au loin, repousse l'ennemi,
Donne la paix et nous bénis,
Au jour du danger, garde-nous,
Quand nous luttons, protège-nous !

4.

Par toi nous connaissons le Fils,
Et le Père, à toi réunis ;
Tu règnes, Sainte Trinité
Pour le temps et l'éternité.

Trad. Flossette Du Pasquier (1951).

Le premier verset du texte français est d'Hélène J. Kocher.)

— 42 —*

Psalterium Chorale
Constance (1510).

Be - a - ta no - - bis gau - di - a An - ni re-
Re - joice ! the year up - on its way Has brought a-
O un - er - mess' - - ne Se - lig - keit, Ge - wen - det
Le monde en - tier se ré - jou - it Car Dieu don-

dux - it or - bi - ta, Cum Spi - ri-
gain that bless - èd day When on the
wur - de al - les Leid ! Kaum dass ent-
na son Saint - Es - prit Aux dis - ci-

tus pa - ra - cli - tus Il - lap - sus est dis-
cho - sen of the Lord The Ho - ly Spi - rit
rückt der Hei - land war, Schenkt er den Geist der
ples de Jé - sus - Christ, Et nous fê - tons ce

* From the English Hymnal, by permission of the Oxford University Press.

ci - - - pu - lis.
was out poured.
Jün - - - ger - Schar.   A - - - - men!
jour bé - ni.

2.

Ignis vibrante lumine
Linguae figuram detulit.
Verbis ut essent proflui,
Et charitate fervidi.

3.

Te nunc, Deus piissime
Vultu precamur cernuo :
Illapsa nobis coelitus
Largire dona Spiritus.

4.

Dudum sacrata pectora
Tua replesti gratia,
Dimitte nostra crimina,
Et da quieta tempora !

* * *

2.

On each the fire, descending, stood
In quivering tongues' similitude [prove,
Tongues, that their words might ready
And fire, to make them flame with love.

3.

And now, O Holy God, this day
Regard us as we humbly pray,
And send us, from Thy heavenly seat
The blessings of the Paraclete.

Trans. RICHARD ELLIS ROBERTS (1878-1940).

4.

As then, O Lord, Thou didst fulfil,
Each holy heart to do Thy will,
So now do Thou our sins forgive
And make the world in peace to live.

Trans. PERCY DEARMER (1867-1936).

* * *

2.

Wie es des Feuers Flamme tut,
So kam hernieder seine Glut :
Er macht die stummen Zungen frei,
Er wohnt mit Liebeseifer bei.

3.

Sieh, treuer Gott, uns vor dir stehn,
Zu dir mit heissem Herzen flehn :
Mögst reichlich uns den Geist verleih'n
Und alle Tage bei uns sein !

4.

Herr, über deine Heil'gen breit'
Den Mantel deiner Heiligkeit,
Die Sünden zähle uns nicht zu
Und gib dem Leib, der Seele Ruh !

Übers. JOHANN CHRISTOPH HAMPE (1950).

* * *

2.

Sur chacun d'eux descend des cieux,
Brillante, une langue de feu
Qui fait brûler leur cœur d'amour
En inspirant tous leurs discours.

3.

Et toi, Seigneur, Dieu tout-puissant,
Nous t'en prions bien humblement,
Fais descendre du haut des cieux
Sur nous ton Esprit radieux.

4.

Jadis tu donnas aux anciens
La grâce de ton Esprit Saint ;
Pardonne, ô Dieu, tous nos péchés
Et procure au monde la paix.

Trad. FLOSSETTE DU PASQUIER (1951).

— 43 —

Prière au Saint-Esprit.*
Orthodoxe.

Цa-рю не-бес-ный у-те-ши-те-лю ду-ше и-сти-ный
O Him-mels Kö-nig, Un-ser Trös-ter, Du Geist der Wahr-heit
O Roi cé-les-te, Con-so-la-teur, Es-prit de vé-ri-té,
O heav-en-ly King, The Com-for-ter Spi-rit of truth

и-же вез-де.... сый и вся ис-пол-ня-яй
All-ge-gen-wär-ti-ger, Al-les Er-fül-len-der
Qui es par-tout pré-sent Et qui rem-plis tout;
Who fill-est all things, Who art in all pla-ces;

* Voir la note précédant la table des matières.
See note preceding the general index.
Vergleiche die Vorbemerkung vor dem Inhaltsverzeichnis.

— 44 —

« Down Ampney » *
RALPH VAUGHAN WILLIAMS
(1872-).

Moderately slow

Come down, O Love di - vine, Seek Thou this soul of
O Got - tes - lieb', er - schein Und nimm die See - le
Des-cends, Es - prit de Dieu, Et de tes dons pré - ci-

mine, And vis - it it with Thine own ar - dour glow - ing;
ein, Ent - flam- me sie mit dei - nem rei - nen Glü - hen.
eux Veuille a - pai - ser nos peu - reu - ses pri - è - res.

O Com - for - ter, draw near, With - in my heart ap-
O na - he er - den- wärts, Geist - Trös - ter in dies
Es - prit con - so - la - teur Vi - si - te no - tre

* From the English Hymnal, by permission of the Oxford University Press.

pear, And kind - le it, Thy ho - ly flame be - stow - ing.
Herz, Lass al - le mü - de Halb - heit dar - aus flie - hen.
cœur, Fais - y bril - ler ta cé - les - te lu - miè - re.

2.

O let it freely burn,
Till earthly passions turn
To dust and ashes in its heat consuming;
And let Thy glorious light
Shine ever on my sight,
And clothe me round, the while my path illuming.

3.

Let holy charity
Mine outward vesture be,
And lowliness become mine inner clothing;
True lowliness of heart,
Which takes the humbler part,
And o'er its own shortcomings weeps with loathing.

4.

And so the yearning strong,
With which the soul will long,
Shall far outpass the power of human telling;
For none can guess its grace,
Till he become the place
Wherein the Holy Spirit makes His dwelling.

BIANCO DI SIENA (1434).
Trans. R. F. LITTLEDALE.

★ ★ ★

2.

Entbrenn' es ohne Mass
Zu hellem Brand, bis dass
Der Erde Sucht wie Asche sich verloren.
Dein göttlich helles Licht
Erleuchte mein Gesicht
Und weise mir den Weg zu deinen Toren.

3.

Gib heil'ge Milde mir
Stets zu Gewand und Zier
Und Demut mach zu meines Herzens Kleide,
Damit ich immerdar
Bleib falschen Stolzes bar
Und, wo er durchbricht, ihn mit Schmerz bestreite.

4.

Kein Menschenwort mehr kann
Erzählen, wie sich dann
Die Seele lässt von deiner Sehnsucht treiben.
Denn was hülf' all ihr Ruhm,
Würd' sie nicht Eigentum
Dir, Heil'ger Geist, d'rin du kannst wohnen bleiben.

Übers. Erwin Kleine (1950).

* * *

2.

Brûle nos passions,
Que nos affections
Soient terre et cendre au regard de ta grâce,
Que toute vérité
Brille de ta clarté,
Que toute paix de ta paix soit la trace.

3.

Viens en nous susciter
La sainte charité,
Qui nous sera vêtement et parure,
Et ce cœur humble et doux
Qui nous fasse à genoux
Servir le Christ et pleurer nos souillures.

4.

Descends, Esprit divin,
Car tout langage est vain
Pour dire notre amère et grande histoire.
Seul ton vivant amour
Nous gardera toujours
Dans la douceur, l'allégresse et la gloire.

Trad. Henri Capieu (1950).

— 45 (82) —

« Dominica » *
Sir Herbert Stanley Oakeley
(1830-1903).

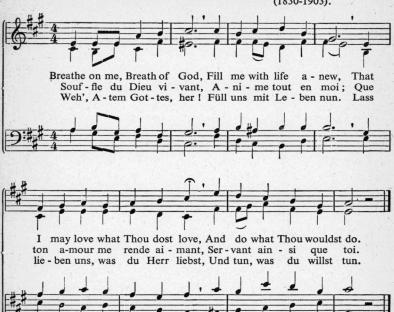

Breathe on me, Breath of God, Fill me with life a - new, That
Souf - fle du Dieu vi - vant, A - ni - me tout en moi ; Que
Weh', A - tem Got - tes, her ! Füll uns mit Le - ben nun. Lass

I may love what Thou dost love, And do what Thou wouldst do.
ton a-mour me rende ai - mant, Ser - vant ain - si que toi.
lie - ben uns, was du Herr liebst, Und tun, was du willst tun.

2.
Breathe on me, Breath of God,
Until my heart is pure ;
Until with Thee I will one will
To do and to endure.

3.
Breathe on me, Breath of God,
Till I am wholly Thine ;
Until this earthly part of me
Glows with Thy fire divine.

4.
Breathe on me, Breath of God,
So shall I never die,
But live with Thee the perfect life
Of Thine eternity.

EDWIN HATCH (1878).

★ ★ ★

2.
Souffle du Dieu vivant,
Viens purifier ma foi ;
Que ce soit ton vouloir puissant
Qui s'accomplisse en moi.

3.
Souffle du Dieu vivant,
Mets ton feu dans mon cœur ;
Que tout en moi soit rayonnant
De ton éclat, Seigneur.

4.
Souffle du Dieu vivant,
Ecarte enfin la mort ;
Que pour jamais, dès maintenant,
J'appartienne au Dieu fort.

Trad. SUZANNE BIDGRAIN (1937).

★ ★ ★

2.
Weh', Atem Gottes, her,
Und mach mein Herze rein,
Bis all mein Tun und Willen geht
In deinen Willen ein.

3.
Weh', Atem Gottes, her,
Bis ich bin völlig dein,
Und bis mein irdisch Teil erglüht
In Gottes Feuerschein.

4.
Weh', Atem Gottes, her !
Dann sterb' ich nimmermehr.
Dann trägt mich zur Vollkommenheit
Der Ewigkeiten Meer.

Übers. HANNS LILJE (1938).

— 46 —

« Hamburg »
LOWELL MASON (1792-1872).

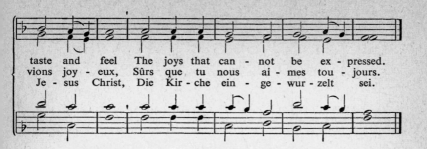

taste and feel The joys that can - not be ex - pressed.
vions joy - eux, Sûrs que tu nous ai - mes tou - jours.
Je - sus Christ, Die Kir - che ein - ge - wur - zelt sei.

2. Come, fill our hearts with inward strength,
   Make our enlarged souls possess
   And learn the height and breadth and length
   Of Thine unmeasurable grace.

3. Now to the God whose power can do
   More than our thoughts or wishes know,
   Be everlasting honours done
   By all the Church, through Christ His Son.

ISAAC WATTS (1674-1748).

★ ★ ★

2. Remplis-nous d'une sainte ardeur,
   Révèle-nous ta vérité
   Et la hauteur, la profondeur
   De ton immense charité.

3. Dieu tout-puissant, dont le pouvoir
   Surpasse tout pouvoir humain,
   Nous mettons en toi notre espoir
   Par Jésus-Christ, ton Fils divin.

Trad. EVA DUBSKA-KUSCHNER (1950).

★ ★ ★

2. Zeig' ihr die Liebe ihres Herrn,
   Die Liebe, die kein Aug' erreicht,
   Ob es sie sucht in Himmelsfern',
   Ob es in Höllentiefen streicht.

3. Es kann durch deinen Geist gescheh'n,
   Mehr als wir bitten und versteh'n.
   Dich preise heut' und alle Zeit
   Durch deinen Sohn die Christenheit.

Übers. JOHANN CHRISTOPH HAMPE (1950).

— 47 (65) —

Hussisches Graduale (1512).

Ot - če náš, mi - lý Pa - ne, Dejž-nám Du-cha sva - té - ho, Pro-
Vat'r un - ser, lie - ber Her - re, Dein Geist woll uns er - fül - len ; Wir
O Dieu, pour te con - naî - tre, Et t'ai-mer comme un Pè - re, Il
O Lord of all, our Fa - ther, For Christs's sake, we im - plore Thee, Be-

si - me, at' se sta - ne Pro Kri - sta, Sy - na tvé - ho, At'
bit - ten, das ge - sche-he Um Chris - ti, dein's Sohn's, wil - len, Dass
faut qu'en nous pé - nè - tre L'Es-prit qui seul o - pè - re. Sans
stow Thy Ho - ly Spi - rit On us who here a - dore Thee: To

nás u - či Bož-ské - ho Prav - du zá - ko - na zná - ti, Pro-
er die gött - lich Wahr-heit Uns leh - re un - ter - schei - den Und
lui, nos cœurs s'é - ga - rent, La nuit é - treint nos â - mes. Al-
teach Thy faith - ful peo - ple Thy truth to seek un - swerv - ing, From

roct - vi fa - leš - né - ho Pil - ně se vy - stří ha - ti.
fal - sche Kunst und Weis - heit Uns sorg - sam hel - fe mei - den.
lume en nous du pha - re La ray - on - nan - te flam - me.
false and ly - ing pro-phets Our minds and souls pre - serv - ing.

2. Kriste, jenž jsi věrným svým
   Seslal Ducha svatého,
   Před věky vyvoleným
   Od Otce nebeského;
   Račiž nám této chvíle
   Téhož Ducha seslati.
   Abychom tebe mile
   Mohli v slovech poznati.

3. Ó milý Duchu svatý,
   Rač naším hostem býti,
   Jenž jsi v dařích bohatý,
   Nemeškej k nám přijíti,
   Spravuj jazyk k mluvení,
   Dej dobré naučení,
   Nachyl uši k slyšení,
   Zapal srdce k věření.

KLIMENT BOSÁK (XVI. Jahrhundert).

* * *

2. Christ, der du dein'n Getreuen
   Den Heil'gen Geist gesendet,
   Die zum himmlischen Vater
   Von Ewigkeit gewendet,
   Auch uns zu unsern Zeiten
   Denselben Geist wollst geben,
   Damit wir dir mit Freuden
   In deinen Worten leben.

3. O Heil'ger Geist, lieb' Tröster,
   Als Herr wollst in uns thronen;
   Der du an Gaben reich bist,
   Säum nicht, bei uns zu wohnen.
   Die Zunge lös zum Sprechen,
   Und gute Lehr' ergründe;
   Die Ohren neig zum Hören,
   Das Herz zum Glaub'n entzünde!

Übers. H. LAEPPLE (1930).

* * *

2. O Christ, divin modèle,
   Quand descendit la nue,
   Tu promis aux fidèles
   De l'Esprit la venue.
   Accomplis ta promesse
   Pour nous qui, dans ce monde,
   Crions à toi sans cesse,
   Pour que tu nous répondes.

3. Esprit saint, sois notre hôte,
   Tout, en nous, te réclame:
   Instruis, purifie, ôte
   Ce qui souille notre âme.
   Puis verse les richesses
   De tes dons innombrables;
   Supplée à nos détresses,
   D'aimer, rends-nous capables.

Trad. H. ECUYER (1930).

* * *

2. O Christ, who to the faithful
   By God the Father chosen
   Didst send the Holy Spirit,
   When Thou from earth hadst risen:
   We pray Thee pour upon us
   In this our day of testing,
   The Spirit's gift of power,
   Thy word of truth attesting.

3. O Holy Spirit, guide us,
   The comfortless befriending:
   Approach, Thou bounteous Giver,
   Thy grace to us extending:
   Thy truth to speak, inspire us,
   Thy counsels just proclaiming:
   Compel our ears to heed Thee,
   Our hearts with faith enflaming.

Trans. FRANCIS HOUSE (1950).

Moderately fast

« University »
C. COLLIGNON (1725-1785).

The Church of God a King-dom is, Where
Die Kir - che ist des Her - ren Reich Da
Oui, sur ta sainte E - glise, ô Dieu, Christ

Christ in power doth reign ; Where spi - rits yearn till,
Chri - stus herrscht in Macht, Und Her - zen har - ren,
ré - gnant, plein d'a - mour, Les cœurs é - mus, trem-

seen in bliss, Their Lord shall come a - gain.
dass zu - gleich Er wie - der - kehrt in Pracht.
blants, joy - eux Es - pè - rent son re - tour.

2.

Glad companies of saints possess
   This Church below, above :
And God's perpetual calm doth bless
   Their paradise of love.

3.

An altar stands within the shrine
   Whereon, once sacrificed,
Is set, immaculate, divine,
   The Lamb of God, the Christ.

4.

There rich and poor, from countless lands,
   Praise God on mystic rood :
There nations reach forth holy hands
   To take God's holy food.

5.

There pure, life-giving streams o'erflow
   The sower's garden-ground :
And faith and hope fair blossoms show,
   And fruits of love abound.

6.

O King, O Christ, this endless grace
To us and all men bring,
To see the vision of Thy face
In joy, O Christ, our King.

L. MUIRHEAD (1845-1925).

* * *

2.

Es schützt der Heil'gen sel'ges Heer
Die Kirche hier und dort,
Und Gottes Friede weht einher
Von jenem sel'gen Ort.

3.

Ein Altar ragt und in dem Schrein
Steht Christus, Gottes Lamm,
Das Opfer Gottes, klar und rein,
In heil'ger Gluten Flamm.

4.

Und reich und arm aus jedem Land
Singt Gottes Lob zumal.
Und Völker strecken aus die Hand
Nach Gottes Abendmahl.

5.

Des Lebens klare Ströme geh'n
Durch Gottes Gartengrund,
Und Glaub' und Hoffnung blühen schön,
Der Liebe Frucht wird kund.

6.

O König Christus, gnadenreich,
Schenk uns das ew'ge Heil,
Und lass uns schau'n in deinem Reich
Der ew'gen Freude Teil.

Übers. HANNS LILJE (1938).

* * *

2.

Et là, tes saints, toujours unis,
S'assemblent chaque jour,
Sans fin, ta paix, ô Dieu, bénit
Leur paradis d'amour.

3.

Là, sur l'autel, il gît couché,
Immaculé, divin,
Livré, meurtri pour nos péchés,
L'agneau, le Christ, le Saint.

4.

Et tous les peuples, sans faillir,
Louant le Dieu des cieux,
Tendant la main, vont pour saisir
Le saint repas de Dieu.

5.

L'eau vive qui jaillit, Seigneur
Féconde nos jardins,
La Foi, l'espoir offrant leurs fleurs,
L'amour, ses fruits divins.

6.

Donne à nous tous, Christ, en tous lieux
La grâce et la faveur
D'avoir sans fin devant les yeux
Ta face, ô Roi sauveur !

Trad. PAULINE MARTIN (1951).

49

Allant

Recueil de Jean A. Freylinghausen (1704).

Sur ton E - glise u - ni - ver - sel - le, Ob - jet cons-
Up - on Thy great Church u - ni - ver-sal, The cons - tant
Du hast ve - reint in al - len Zo-nen Uns, die du

tant de ton a - mour, Oh ! que ta grâ - ce pa - ter - nel - le,
ob - ject of Thy love, May Thine a - bun-dant grace pa - ter - nal
lieb - test je und je, Wir bit - ten, Herr, lass bei uns woh-nen

Sei - gneur, se ré - pande en ce jour. Tes en - fants, a - vec
Be poured out free - ly from a - bove. Thy chil - dren trust - ing
Den Geist der Gna - de aus der Höh ! Sieh an, es beu - gen

con - fi - an - ce, Par - tout flé - chis - sent les ge-
in Thy mer - cy In ev' - ry place ex - pec - tant
voll Ver - trau - en All' dei - ne Kin - der ih - re

noux; Ne con - fonds pas leur es - pé - ran - ce:
pray; Grant that their hopes be not con - found - ed,
Knie, Du wol - lest ih - re Hoff - nung schau - en:

Sei - gneur, sois au mi - lieu de nous.
O Lord, be in our midst to - day.
Tritt, Va - ter, heu - te un - ter sie!

2.
Des promesses de ta Parole
  Daigne, Seigneur, te souvenir :
Que ton Esprit saint nous console
  Et nous apprenne à te bénir !
Ouvre nos yeux à ta lumière,
  Change et maîtrise notre cœur,
Et que ton Eglise en prière
  Par toi triomphe de l'erreur !

3.
Que l'Evangile se répande
  De l'aurore jusqu'au couchant ;
Que de tous côtés l'on entende
  Monter vers toi le même chant !
Que, sur les plus lointains rivages,
  Les peuples, rangés sous la croix,
Viennent tous rendre leurs hommages
  A Jésus-Christ, le Roi des rois !

J. M. DE CARBON-FERRIÈRE (1823).

* * *

2.
O God, be mindful of Thy promise
  Made to Thy people through Thy Word,
Thy Holy Spirit give us comfort,
  And teach us how to call Thee Lord.
Open our eyes to see Thy glory,
  In transformed hearts allegiance win,
And may Thy Church in instant prayer
  Through Thee triumphant conquer sin.

3.
Spread Thy good news to all Thy people
  From rising unto setting sun :
And let us hear the myriad voices
  In theme and music raised as one !
And on the farthest distant beaches
  The nations all their tribute bring,
And there beneath the Cross assembled
  Praise Jesus Christ their Lord and King.

Trans. MARGARET HOUSE (1949).

* * *

2.
Und der Verheissungen gedenke,
  Vereinige uns durch den Geist,
Und schaffe, dass er Frieden schenke,
  Und lehr, wie man dich Vater heisst.
Mach uns're blinden Augen sehen,
  Mach uns're toten Herzen neu,
Gib Stimmen du zu Lob und Flehen
  Und ein Bekenntnis, wahr und treu.

3.
Verbreite deine frohe Kunde
  Vom Aufgang bis zum Niedergang,
Mach alle uns zu einem Munde,
  Aus tausenden ein Lobgesang !
Dein starker Arm zusammenbringe
  Die Völkerwelt von nah und fern,
Dass sie am Kreuz ihr Loblied singe,
  Dir, Jesus Christus, ihrem Herrn !

Übers. JOHANN CHRISTOPH HAMPE (1950).

50

Korean
TAI JUN PARK.

구 주 의 보 혈 로 온 세 상 나 라 들 한

The Sav-iour's prec-ious blood, Hath made all na-tions one. U-
In dei - nem Blut Herr Christ, Nun eins die Mensch-heit ist. Sie
Par son sang ré - demp-teur Christ sau-va les pé-cheurs, Et

형 제 자 매 되 엿 네 그 사 랑 찬 송 해

ni - ted let us praise this deed The Fa-ther's love hath done.
soll ein Volk von Brü-dern sein, Dein' Lieb' zu be-ne-dein.
tous les peu-ples s'u-ni-ront Pour a-do-rer son nom.

4.
주 님 의 새 계 명
사 랑 하 라 섰 네
온 세 게 만 민 합 하 야
그 뜻 을 따 르 세

3.
싸 홈 의 세 상 에
평 화 가 오 려 나
주 예 수 사 랑 아 니 면
참 평 화 없 으 리

2.
죄 악 이 관 영 한
이 인 간 세 상 에
하 나 님 나 라 임 하 기
늘 소 원 이 로 세

TAI JUN PARK.

* * *

2. In this vast world of men,
     A world so full of sin,
   No other theme can be our prayer
     Than this — Thy Kingdom come.

3. In this sad world of war
     Can peace be ever found ?
   Unless the love of Christ prevail
     True peace will not abound.

4. The Master's new Command
     Was — love each other well.
   O brothers, let us all unite
     To do His holy will.

Trans. Dr. WILLIAM SCOTT and Miss YUNG OON KIM (1950).

★ ★ ★

2. Du hast so je geliebt,
     Wie bös sich Bosheit gibt.
   Dein Thron ist bei uns aufgestellt,
     Nun herrsche in der Welt !

3. Welt hat den Frieden nicht,
     Sie weiss nur Kriegsgeschrei,
   An deiner Liebe ihr's gebricht,
     Nur sie legt Kriege bei.

4. O höret, was euch lehrt
     Die Lieb', euch zugekehrt !
   Auf keinem andern Weg ist Heil ;
     In ihr wird's euch zuteil !

Übers. JOHANN CHRISTOPH HAMPE (1951).

★ ★ ★

2. Le monde est perverti :
     Supplions Jésus-Christ
   Que son royaume soit présent
     Partout et en tout temps.

3. Ce monde ensanglanté
     Connaîtra-t-il la paix ?
   Quand Dieu sera le seul berger
     La paix pourra régner.

4. Aimez vos ennemis
     Nous a dit Jésus-Christ ;
   Prions Dieu pour que dans la foi
     Tous, nous suivions sa loi.

Trad. FLOSSETTE DU PASQUIER (1951).

— 51 (29) —

BARTHOLOMÄUS GESIUS (1555-1613).
Harm. by J. S. BACH (1685-1750).

The Chur-ch's one found - a - tion Is Je - sus Christ her
L'E - glise u - ni - ver - sel - le A pour roc Jé - sus
Der Kir - che Grund hie - nie - den, Der Fels, auf dem sie

Lord; She is His new cre - a - tion By wa - ter and the
Christ; Elle est l'œu-vre nou - vel - le Que sa pa - ro - le
ruht, Ihr Le - ben, Heil und Frie - den, Ist Chris - tus und sein

Word; From Heav'n He came and sought her To
fit. Ha - bi - tant le ciel mê - me, Il
Blut. Durch Lei - den und durch Ster - ben Hat

be   His   ho - ly   Bride; With His   own   Blood He
vint   se   l'at - ta - cher,   Et, par   un   don su-
er   sich   ihr   ver - mählt,   Ihr Le - ben   zu   er-

bought   her, And   for   her   life   He   died!
prê -   me, Mou - rut   pour   la   sau - ver!
wer -   ben, Den   Kreu - zes - tod   er - wählt!

2. Elect from every nation,
    Yet one o'er all the earth,
Her charter of salvation
    One Lord, one Faith, one Birth;
One holy Name she blesses,
    Partakes one holy Food,
And to one hope she presses,
    With every grace endued.

3. Mid toil and tribulation
    And tumult of her war,
She waits the consummation
    Of peace for evermore;
Till with the vision glorious
    Her longing eyes are blest,
And the great Church victorious
    Shall be the Church at rest.

4. Yet she on earth hath union
    With God the Three in One,
And mystic sweet communion
    With those whose rest is won.
O happy ones and holy!
    Lord, give us grace that we,
Like them, the meek and lowly,
    On high may dwell with Thee.

S. J. STONE (1839-1900).

* * *

2. L'Eglise en sa prière
   Unit à leur Sauveur
Les peuples de la terre
   Soumis au seul Seigneur.
C'est son nom qu'elle acclame,
   Son pain qui la nourrit ;
Elle verse à toute âme
   L'espoir qui la guérit.

3. Honnie et méconnue,
   Menant de durs combats,
Elle attend la venue
   De la paix ici-bas.
Contemplant par avance
   La fin de son tourment,
La grande délivrance,
   Le repos permanent.

4. Aujourd'hui, sur la terre,
   Elle est unie à Dieu,
Et, par un saint mystère,
   Aux élus du saint lieu.
Rends-nous, comme eux, fidèles,
   Et reçois-nous, Seigneur,
Dans la vie éternelle,
   Dans l'éternel bonheur !

Trad. F. BARTH (1923).

★ ★ ★

2. Aus aller Völker Scharen
   Erkor er sich die Braut,
Die Güter treu zu wahren,
   Die er ihr anvertraut.
Ein Herr, ein Ziel, ein Hoffen,
   Ein himmlisch Wasserbad,
Ein Heil, das allen offen,
   Ein Geist, ein Glaubenspfad.

3. Verkannt, verschmäht, gemieden,
   In Kämpfen leidensvoll,
Erwartet sie den Frieden,
   Der einst ihr werden soll ;
Bis, durch die Ewigkeiten,
   Ihr Siegeslied ertönt,
Und, nach vollbrachtem Streiten,
   Sie stolze Ruhe krönt.

4. Doch eint sie schon hienieden
   Ein heilig Band mit Gott
Und denen, die geschieden
   Aus aller Angst und Not,
Den sel'gen Gotteskindern.
   Herr, mach uns, ihnen gleich,
Auch einst zu Überwindern,
   Und nimm uns in dein Reich !

Übers. C. LECHLER (1923).

« Hummel »
HEINRICH CHRISTOPH ZEUNER (1795-1857).

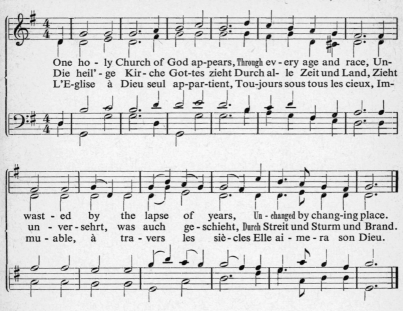

One ho - ly Church of God ap-pears, Through ev - ery age and race, Un-
Die heil' - ge Kir - che Got-tes zieht Durch al- le Zeit und Land, Zieht
L'E-glise à Dieu seul ap-par-tient, Tou-jours sous tous les cieux, Im-

wast - ed by the lapse of years, Un - changed by chang-ing place.
un - ver-sehrt, was auch ge - schieht, Durch Streit und Sturm und Brand.
mu - able, à tra - vers les siè - cles Elle ai - me - ra son Dieu.

2.

From oldest time, on farthest shores,
 Beneath the pine or palm,
One unseen presence she adores,
 With silence or with psalm.

3.

Her priests are all God's faithful sons,
 To serve the world raised up ;
The pure in heart, her baptized ones ;
 Love, her Communion-cup.

4.

The truth is her prophetic gift,
 The soul her sacred page ;
And feet on mercy's errands swift
 Do make her pilgrimage.

5.

O living Church, thine errand speed,
 Fulfil thy task sublime,
With bread of life earth's hunger feed,
 Redeem the evil time !

SAMUEL LONGFELLOW (1819-1892).

★ ★ ★

2.

Wie's unverwandt seit alters währt,
 Bleibt's je und überall :
Den Unsichtbaren sie verehrt,
 Hier still, dort froh mit Schall.

3.

Kein andern Dienst der Welt sie kennt
 Als gottgetreu zu steh'n —
Und nichts, das sie ihr eigen nennt,
 Drin nicht der Herr zu seh'n.

4.

Die Wahrheit ihre Prophetie,
Das Herz ihr Heiligtum.
Mit Gnadenbotschaft spät und früh
Vermehrt sie Gottes Ruhm.

5.

O halte fest des Herrn Gebot,
Erfüll es erdenweit,
Du Kirche, spende Lebensbrot
Und hilf der armen Zeit.

Übers. ERWIN KLEINE (1950).

* * *

2.

De l'orient jusqu'au couchant
Toujours l'on entendra
Louer la présence invisible
De Dieu, du Roi des rois.

3.

Ses prêtres, fils du Dieu vivant,
Le servent chaque jour,
S'approchant de la Table Sainte
Le cœur rempli d'amour.

4.

Ses reins sont ceints de vérité,
Son glaive, c'est l'esprit,
Et la justice est son armure,
La foi son bouclier.

5.

Vivante Eglise, hâte-toi,
Accomplis ton destin
Et donne-nous le pain de vie,
Assouvis notre faim.

Trad. FLOSSETTE DU PASQUIER (1951).

— 53 —

JOHAN CRÜGER (1647).

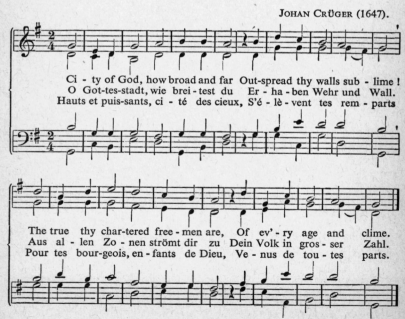

Ci - ty of God, how broad and far Out-spread thy walls sub - lime !
O Got-tes-stadt, wie brei - tes du Er - ha - ben Wehr und Wall.
Hauts et puis-sants, ci - té des cieux, S'é - lè - vent tes rem - parts

The true   thy char-tered free - men are, Of ev' - ry age and   clime.
Aus al - len Zo - nen strömt dir zu Dein Volk in gros - ser   Zahl.
Pour tes bour-geois, en - fants de Dieu, Ve - nus de tou - tes   parts.

2.

One holy Church, one army strong,
  One steadfast high intent,
One working band, one harvest song,
  One King omnipotent.

3.

How purely hath thy speech come down
  From man's primeval youth !
How grandly hath thine empire grown
  Of freedom, love, and truth !

4.

How gleam thy watchfires through the
  With never-fainting ray !   [night,
How rise thy towers, serene and bright,
  To meet the dawning day !

5.

In vain the surge's angry shock,
  In vain the drifting sands ;
Unharmed, upon th' Eternal Rock,
  Th' eternal city stands.

SAMUEL JOHNSON (1822-1882).

* * *

2.

O Kirche Gottes, starke Schar,
  O heilighoher Plan,
O Saat und Ernte immerdar,
  O Herr, der alles kann !

3.

Wie lauter kam herab dein Wort
  Und tränkt uns Jahr für Jahr.
Wie wächst dein Reich nun fort und fort,
  In Liebe frei und wahr.

4.

Wie glüh'n die Feuer durch die Nacht
Mit ungedämpftem Schein.
Wie ragt der Türme stille Macht
  In frühe Dämmern ein !

5.

Was kann der Wogen Schreckgewalt,
  Der Sturm, der wütend weht :
Auf ew'ger Felsen Hort und Halt
  Die ew'ge Stadt besteht.

Übers. ERWIN KLEINE (1950).

* * *

2.

O vous, soldats du Dieu vainqueur,
  Eglise du Seigneur,
Chantez l'amour, chantez l'honneur
  Du Roi dominateur.

3.

Clair et vibrant aux premiers jours
  Son verbe a retenti.
Vrai, fort et libre, dans l'amour,
  Son empire a grandi.

4.

Phares divins, feux éternels
  Percez l'obscurité.
Tours, haussez-vous jusques au ciel,
  Vers l'aube et sa clarté.

5.

Malgré les vagues en courroux
  Et les terrains mouvants
Toi, Cité, sur le roc, debout,
  Brave l'assaut des vents !

Trad. PAULINE MARTIN (1951).

JOHANN CRÜGER (1649).

Schmü-cke dich, O lie - be See - le, Lass die dun-kle Sün-den-
Deck thy-self my soul with glad-ness, Come in - to the day-light's
Pa - re - toi, mon âme heu-reu - se, Fuis la rou-te té - né-

höh - le, Komm ans hel - le Licht ge - gan - gen, fan - ge
splen - dor, Leave the gloom-y haunts of sad - ness, There with
breu - se, Et, mon - tant dans la lu - miè - re, Bril - le

herr - lich an zu pran - gen; Denn der Herr voll Heil und
joy thy prais-es rend - er Un - to Him whose grace un-
d'u - ne flam-me clai - re. Oui, le Dieu de tou - te

Gna - den Will dich jetzt zu Gas - te la - den; Der den
bound - ed Hath this won-drous ban-quet found-ed : High o'er
grâ - ce A sa ta - ble te fait pla - ce; Lui, le

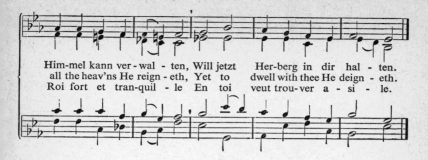

Him-mel kann ver - wal - ten, Will jetzt Her-berg in dir hal - ten.
all the heav'ns He reign - eth, Yet to dwell with thee He deign - eth.
Roi fort et tran-quil - le En toi veut trou-ver a - si - le.

2.

Jesu, meine Lebenssonne,
Jesu, meine Freud und Wonne,
Jesu, du mein ganz' Beginnen,
Lebensquell und Licht der Sinnen,
Hier fall' ich zu deinen Füssen;
Lass mich würdiglich geniessen
Dieser deiner Himmelsspeise,
Mir zum Heil und dir zum Preise.

3.

Jesu, wahres Brot des Lebens,
Hilf, dass ich doch nicht vergebens
Oder mir vielleicht zum Schaden
Sei zu deinem Tisch geladen.
Lass mich deine Gnade finden,
Mich auf ewig dir verbinden,
Dass ich auch, wie jetzt auf Erden,
Mög dein Gast im Himmel werden.

JOHANN FRANK (1618-1677).

* * *

2.

Now I bow before Thee lowly,
Filled with joy most deep and holy;
As with trembling awe and wonder
On Thy mighty works I ponder;
How by mystery surrounded,
Depths no man has ever sounded,
None may dare to pierce unbidden
Secrets that with Thee are hidden.

3.

Sun, who all my life dost brighten;
Light, who dost my soul enlighten;
Joy, the sweetest man e'er knoweth;
Fount, whence all my being floweth:
At Thy feet I cry, my Maker,
Let me be a fit partaker
Of this blessèd food from Heaven
For our good, Thy glory, given.

Trans. C. WINKWORTH (1820-1878).

* * *

2.

Christ, brillant soleil de gloire,
Christ, ma joie et ma victoire,
Christ, lumière de mon âme,
Source vive, ardente flamme !
A tes pieds, mon divin Frère,
Je m'abats dans la poussière
Pour goûter, dans ma faiblesse,
Au repas de la promesse.

3.

O Jésus, vrai pain de vie,
Aide-moi, je t'en supplie,
A me déclarer coupable
Quand j'approche de ta table.
Laisse-moi trouver ta grâce ;
Et qu'au ciel, devant ta face,
Comme aujourd'hui sur la terre
Je sois l'hôte de ton Père.

Trad. PAULINE MARTIN (1951).

— 55 (84) —

Wittenberg (1541-1543).

Er - halt uns, Herr, bei dei - nem Wort, Und steu - re dei - ner Fein - de Mord, Die Je - sum Chris - tum dei - nen Sohn, Wol - len stür - zen von dei - nem Thron.

Lord, keep us stead - fast in Thy Word; Curb those who fain by craft or sword Would wrest the King - dom from Thy Son; And set at naught all He hath done.

Dieu, gar - de - nous par ton Es - prit. Perds et con - fonds notre en - ne - mi. Ils vont ci - fi - er ton Fils Et ren - ver - ser ton trône aus - si.

2.

Beweis dein' Macht, Herr Jesu Christ,
  Der du Herr aller Herren bist,
Beschirm dein' arme Christenheit,
  Dass sie dich lob' in Ewigkeit.

3.

Gott heil'ger Geist, du Tröster wert,
  Gib dein'm Volk ein'rlei Sinn auf Erd
Steh bei uns in der letzten Not,
  G'leit uns ins Leben aus dem Tod.

MARTIN LUTHER (1483-1546).

★ ★ ★

2.

Lord Jesus Christ, Thy power make known,
  For Thou art Lord of lords alone;
Defend Thy Christendom, that we
  May ever more sing praise to Thee.

3.

O Comforter of priceless worth
  Send peace and unity on earth;
Support us in our final strife,
  And lead us out of death to life.

Trans. CATHERINE WINKWORTH (1863).

★ ★ ★

2.

Montre ton droit, Jésus, Sauveur,
  Toi le Seigneur de tous seigneurs.
Viens protéger tes serviteurs
  Qu'ils chantent tous à ton honneur.

3.

Toi, Saint-Esprit, en ce beau jour,
  Donne à ton peuple un seul amour.
Quand devant nous sera la mort
  Tu nous guideras vers le port.

Trad. PAULINE MARTIN (1951).

— 56 —

O. ÅHLSTRÖM (1756-1835).

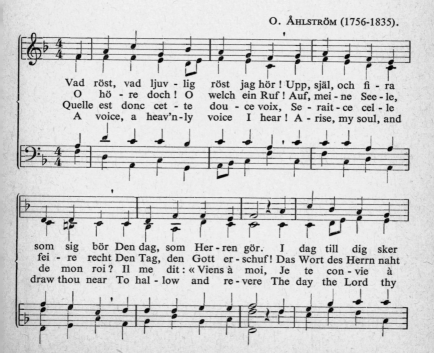

Vad röst, vad ljuv - lig röst jag hör! Upp, själ, och fi - ra
O hö - re doch! O welch ein Ruf! Auf, mei - ne See - le,
Quelle est donc cet - te dou - ce voix, Se - rait - ce cel - le
A voice, a heav'n - ly voice I hear! A - rise, my soul, and

som sig bör Den dag, som Her - ren gör. I dag till dig sker
fei - re recht Den Tag, den Gott er - schuf! Das Wort des Herrn naht
de mon roi? Il me dit : « Viens à moi, Je te con - vie à
draw thou near To hal - low and re - vere The day the Lord thy

Her - rens ord: Kom i min famn, Kom till mitt bord.
heut zu dir: Zu mei - nem Tisch, komm her zu mir.
mon re - pas, Ma Table est prête, ap - pro - che - toi. »
God doth make, And of the Bread of Life par - take.

2.
Jag kommer, Jesu, på ditt bud,
Men kläd mig själv i helig skrud,
Min Herre och min Gud.
Ikläd mig din rättfärdighet,
Att jag må se din salighet.

3.
Så kom att i mitt hjärta bo.
Till dig jag sätter all min tro,
Hos dig jag finner ro.
Med dig jag lugn till målet går
Och trygg på Herrens dag består.

JOHAN OLOF WALLIN (1813).

★ ★ ★

2.
Ich komme, Christ, auf dein Gebot,
Doch schenk' du selbst das heil'ge Kleid,
Mein Herr, du, und mein Gott.
Bekleid' mich mit Gerechtigkeit,
Dass ich seh' deine Seligkeit.

3.
Komm, lass mein Herz dir Wohnung sein
Mein Glaube blickt ganz fest auf dich,
Bei dir ist Ruh' allein.
In Fried' kann ich zum Ziel dann geh'n,
Furchtlos am Tag des Herrn besteh'n.

Übers. GISELA VAN SPANKEREN (1950).

★ ★ ★

2.
Je viens à toi, Sauveur aimant,
Revêts-moi de saints vêtements,
O Seigneur tout-puissant,
Prends-moi au nombre des élus,
Fais-moi contempler ton salut.

3.
Seigneur, viens habiter en moi
Car en toi seul j'ai mis ma foi,
Je me repose en toi.
Efface mon iniquité
Je marcherai dans tes sentiers.

Trad. FLOSSETTE DU PASQUIER (1951).

★ ★ ★

2.
I come, dear Jesus, at Thy word,
A guest unworthy to Thy board,
My Saviour and my Lord.
O clothe me with Thy righteousness,
My soul with Thy salvation bless.

3.
Come Thou, o come, abide in me,
For all my trusting is in Thee
And my tranquillity.
With Thee I walk upon my way,
Safely to stand on God's great Day.

Trans. Evangelical
Lutheran Augustana
Synod Hymnbook (1925).

Trans. MARGARET P. BARCLAY
(1951).

Slow and dignified

Melody in Neu-Leipziger Gesangbuch (1682).
Harm. by J. S. Bach (1685-1750).

Strength-en for ser - vice, Lord, the hands That ho - ly
Zu dei - nem Dienst, Herr, stärk die Hand, Die Heil' - ges
Sei - gneur, daigne af - fer - mir ma main, Car à la

things have tak - en; Let ears that now have
durft' be - rüh - ren'; Das Ohr, das dich im
Sain - te ta - ble J'ai pris le pain a-

heard Thy songs To cla - mour nev - er wak - en.
Lied er - kannt, Lass kein Ge - schrei ver - füh - ren!
vec le vin, Sa - cre - ment a - do - ra - ble.

2.
Lord, may the tongues which 'Holy' sang
    Keep free from all deceiving ;
The eyes which saw Thy love be bright,
    Thy blessèd hope perceiving.

3.
The feet that tread Thy hallowed courts
    From light do Thou not banish ;
The bodies by Thy spirit fed
    With Thy new life replenish.

Liturgy of Malabar, Trans.
Percy Dearmer and C. W. Humphreys. *

2.

Und mach die Zung', die ' Heilig ! ' sang,
Herr, frei von aller Lüge.
Das Aug', das deine Lieb' durchdrang,
In Hoffnung auf dich blicke !

3.

Und wer dein Heiligtum begehrt,
Soll nicht dem Licht entstreben.
Den Leib, von deinem Geist genährt,
Füll' ihm mit neuem Leben !

Übers. WILHELM HORKEL (1950).

* * *

2.

Christ, que la voix qui t'a chanté
Répugne à tout mensonge,
Par ton amour, viens dissiper
Le doute qui me ronge.

3.

Quand nos pieds foulent tes parvis
Accueille-nous, ô Père ;
Nourris nos corps de ton Esprit,
Exauce nos prières.

Trad. VIOLETTE DU PASQUIER (1950).

— 58 —

LOYS BOURGEOIS (1558).
Harm. d'après GOUDIMEL (1565).

Bread of the world in mer - cy bro - ken, Wine
Brot, für die Welt aus Gnad ge - ge - ben, Ver-
Pain vi - vant don - né pour nos â - mes, Vin

of the soul in mer - cy shed, By whom the words of
gos - sen Blut, im Kelch ge - reicht, Du hei - lig Wort, von
pour nos ê - tres ré - pan - du, Pa - ro - les d'a - mour

life were spo-ken, And in Whose death our sins are dead : Look
dem wir le-ben, O Tod, vor dem der uns-re weicht ! Wir
et de flam-mes, Mort où l'es-poir nous est ren - du ; Vois

on the heart by sor-row bro - ken, Look on the
bit-ten : wol - lest uns ver-ge - ben, Dass un - ser
no - tre des - tin mi - sé - ra - ble, Les pleurs ver-

tears by sin - ners shed, And by Thy feast to us the
Herz in Reu - e schweigt Und wir noch vor dem Dun-klen
sés sur nos mal-heurs, Nour - ris - nous à ta sain - te

to - ken That by Thy grace our souls are fed.
be - ben, Ob - gleich dein Licht uns längst er - reicht !
Ta - ble Par ta bon - té, par tes dou - leurs.

English text : Bishop R. HEBER (1783-1826).
Deutsche Übers. : HELGA RUSCHE (1950).
Trad. française : HENRI CAPIEU (1950).

« Duke Street »
JOHN HATTON (? -1793).

Je - sus shall reign wher - e'er the sun Does his suc -
Tant que le mon - de du - re - ra Christ no - tre
Je - sus hat sein' Herr - schaft be - stellt Bis an das

cess - ive jour - neys run; His king - dom stretch from
Maî - tre ré - gne - ra, Tant que les as - tres
En - de die - ser Welt, Sein Kö - nig - reich wird

shore to shore, Till moons shall wax and wane no more.
glo - ri - eux Ray - on - ne - ront du haut des cieux.
nicht ver - gehn, So - lan - ge sich die Son - nen drehn.

2. People and realms of ev'ry tongue
   Dwell on His love with sweetest song,
   And infant voices shall proclaim
   Their early blessings on His name.

3. Blessings abound where'er He reigns ;
   The pris'ner leaps to lose his chains ;
   The weary find eternal rest,
   And all the sons of want are blest.

4. Let every creature rise and bring
   Peculiar honours to our King;
   Angels descend with songs again,
   And earth repeat the long amen.

Isaac Watts (1674-1748).

* * *

2. Les peuples chanteront toujours
   Les grands bienfaits de son amour;
   Les voix d'enfants proclameront
   La majesté de son Saint Nom.

3. Il a soumis le monde entier,
   Rompu les liens des prisonniers,
   Donné la paix aux malheureux.
   Et béni tous les miséreux.

4. Frères, levons-nous avec foi
   Pour rendre hommage à notre roi;
   Les anges chantent dans les cieux
   Glorifiant le seul vrai Dieu.

Trad. Flossette Du Pasquier (1950).

* * *

2. Kein Volk so fremd, kein Land so fern,
   Es priese nicht den lieben Herrn,
   Die Kindlein haben seiner Macht
   Ein stammelnd Loblied dargebracht.

3. Wo er regiert, wird alles neu,
   Dort springen die Gefangnen frei,
   Den Müden schenkt er Ruhestatt
   Und die, die hungern macht er satt.

4. Ein jed' Geschöpf ihn preisen soll,
   Den König, aller Ehren voll!
   Er hat den Himmel aufgetan,
   Die Erde stimmt ihr Loblied an.

Übers. Johann Christoph Hampe (1950).

— 60 (31) —

Allegro

Brüdergemeinde (1745).

Herz und Herz ver-eint zu-sam-men, Sucht in Got-tes Her-zen
Christ-ian hearts in love u - ni-ted, Seek a - lone in Je - sus
Au-jour-d'hui peu-ple de frè-res, A - ni-més d'un même es-

Ruh, Las - set eu - re Lie-bes-flam-men Lo-dern auf den Hei - land
rest. Has He not your love ex - ci - ted! Let His love ins - pire your
prit, Fai-sons mon-ter nos pri - è - res A ton trô - ne Jé - sus-

zu! Er das Haupt, wir sei-ne Glie-der; Er das Licht und wir der
breast. Members on our Head de - pending, Lights re - flect - ing Him, our
Christ. Jé - sus, chef de notre ar - mé - e, Jé - sus, tout puis-sant Sau-

Schein; Er der Meis-ter, wir die Brü-der; Er ist un-ser, wir sind sein.
Sun, Breth-ren, His com-mands at - tending, We in Him, our Lord, are one.
veur, Sur notre œu-vre bien - ai - mé-e, Fais re - po - ser ta fa-veur.

2. Tragt es unter euch, ihr Glieder,
   Auf so treues Lieben an,
   Dass ein jeder für die Brüder
   Auch das Leben lassen kann.
   So hat uns der Freund geliebet,
   So vergoss er dort sein Blut ;
   Denkt doch, wie es ihn betrübet,
   Wenn ihr selbst euch Eintrag tut !

3. Liebe, hast du es geboten,
   Dass man Liebe üben soll,
   O so mache doch die toten,
   Trägen Geister lebensvoll.
   Zünde an die Liebesflamme,
   Dass ein jeder sehen kann ;
   Wir, als die von einem Stamme,
   Stehen auch für einen Mann !

4. Lass uns so vereinigt werden,
   Wie du mit dem Vater bist,
   Bis schon hier auf dieser Erden
   Kein getrenntes Glied mehr ist.
   Und allein von deinem Brennen
   Nehme unser Licht den Schein ;
   Also wird die Welt erkennen,
   Dass wir deine Jünger sein.

N. L. VON ZINZENDORF (1700-1760).

* * *

2. Come then, come, O flock of Jesus,
   Covenant with Him anew ;
   Unto Him, who conquered for us,
   Pledge we love and service true.
   And should our love's union holy
   Firmly linked no more remain,
   Wait ye at His footstool lowly,
   Till He draw it close again.

3. Grant Lord, that with Thy direction:
   'Love each other' we comply,
   Aiming, with unfeigned affection,
   Thy love to exemplify.
   Let our mutual love by glowing ;
   Thus will all men plainly see
   That we, as on one stem growing,
   Living branches are in Thee.

4. Oh, that such may be our union
   As Thine with the Father is,
   And not one of our communion
   E'er forsake the path of bliss.
   May our light 'fore men with brightness
   From Thy light reflected shine.
   Thus the world will bear us witness
   That we, Lord, are truly Thine.

Trans. J. MILLER (1789).

* * *

2. Enrôlés dès la jeunesse
   Sous la croix du Rédempteur,
   Nous voulons l'aimer sans cesse,
   Le servir d'un même cœur.
   Et si notre foi vacille,
   Ranimons-la chaque jour
   A l'autel où toujours brille
   L'ardent feu de son amour.

3. De l'amour dont je vous aime,
   Aimez-vous, nous dit Jésus ;
   Aimez ! c'est l'ordre suprême
   Que je laisse à mes élus.
   Aimons donc, aimons encore,
   Sans compter et chaque jour ;
   O toi, que notre âme adore,
   En nos cœurs mets ton amour.

Trad. E. BUDRY (1902).

4. Comme le Fils avec le Père
   Sont parfaits dans l'unité,
   Jésus veut sur cette terre
   Une seule chrétienté.
   Que soumis à notre maître
   Et témoins obéissants,
   Notre amour fasse connaître
   Que nous sommes ses enfants.

Trad. CHARLES WESTPHAL (1938).

— 61 (27) —

Unison — Risoluto

« Little Cornard »
Martin Shaw (1876).

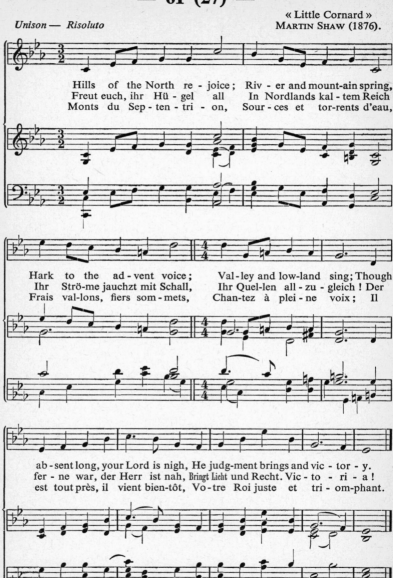

Hills of the North re - joice; Riv - er and mount-ain spring,
Freut euch, ihr Hü - gel all In Nordlands kal - tem Reich
Monts du Sep - ten - tri - on, Sour - ces et tor-rents d'eau,

Hark to the ad - vent voice; Val - ley and low-land sing; Though
Ihr Strö-me jauchzt mit Schall, Ihr Quel-len all - zu - gleich ! Der
Frais val-lons, fiers som - mets, Chan-tez à plei - ne voix; Il

ab - sent long, your Lord is nigh, He judg-ment brings and vic - tor - y.
fer - ne war, der Herr ist nah, Bringt Licht und Recht. Vic - to - ri - a !
est tout près, il vient bien-tôt, Vo - tre Roi juste et tri - om-phant.

Copyright : By permission of J. Curwen and Sons, Ltd. London.

2.

Isles of the Southern seas,
  Deep in your coral caves
Pent be each warring breeze,
  Lulled be your restless waves :
He comes to reign with boundless sway,
And make your wastes His great highway.

3.

Lands of the East, awake,
  Soon shall your sons be free,
The sleep of ages break,
  And rise to liberty :
On your far hills, long cold and grey,
Has dawned the everlasting day.

4.

Shore of the utmost West,
  Ye that have waited long,
Unvisited, unblest,
  Break forth to swelling song :
High raise the note, that Jesus died,
Yet lives and reigns, the Crucified.

5.

Shout, while ye journey home ;
  Songs be in every mouth ;
Lo, from the North we come,
  From East, and West, and South :
City of God, the bond are free ;
We come to live and reign in Thee.

C. E. OAKLEY (1832-1865).

* * *

2.

Ihr Südsseeinseln steigt
  Aus der Korallen Tor !
Ihr wilden Wogen schweigt !
  Still sei der Wellen Chor !
Er kommt mit Königspracht heran,
Macht Land und Meer sich untertan.

3.

Erwach, du östlich Land !
  Dein Retter kommt herbei.
Vom Schlaf, der dich gebannt,
  Macht seine Hand dich frei,
Dass über dir und deiner Nacht
Sich ewgen Lichtes Glanz entfacht.

4.

Ihr fremden Ufer auch
  Im fernsten Westen dort,
Die nie ein Gnadenhauch,
  Nie traf ein Segenswort :
Jauchzt laut, dass der am Kreuze starb,
Lebt, herrscht und Leben euch erwarb.

5.

Singt alle hier und dort,
  Die er berufen hat
Von West, Ost, Süd und Nord,
  In seine Gottesstadt :
« Dir Herr, der du uns frei gemacht,
Dir sei Lob, Ehr und Preis gebracht. »

Übers. C. LECHLER (1924).

* * *

2.

Iles des mers du Sud,
  Vos rocs nus vont fleurir !
Tempêtes, taisez-vous !
  Océan, calme-toi !
En y passant, il va changer
Vos déserts en chemin royal.

3.

Terres de l'Orient,
  Voici la liberté :
L'appel a retenti ;
  Vos fils ouvrent les yeux :
Dans vos ténèbres luit enfin
L'aurore du jour éternel !

4.

Rives de l'Occident,
  Vous attendrez toujours...
Votre morne abandon
  Maintenant a pris fin.
Chantez bien haut votre Sauveur,
Jésus mort et ressuscité.

5.

Ils viennent, à présent,
  Et sur tous les chemins
Eclate, triomphant,
  L'hymne des rachetés.
Cité de Dieu, voici tes fils,
Tes affranchis qui vont régner.

Trad. H. ECUYER (1924).

— 62 (78) —

Adapted from CHRISTOPHER TYE
(1497-1572).

In Christ there is no East or West, In
En toi, Jé - sus, sous tous les cieux, Mal-
In Chris - tus ist nicht Ost noch West, Nicht

Him no South or North, But one great fel - low - ship of
gré race et cou - leur, Ai - més du même a - mour de
Sü - den o - der Nord, Nur ei - ne gros - se Brü - der-

love Through-out the whole wide earth. In Him shall true hearts
Dieu Nous for-mons un seul cœur. Ve - nus des bouts de
schaft Die gan - ze Er - de fort. Die wah - ren Her - zen

ev - ry - where Their high com-mun-ion find: His serv - ice is the
l'ho - ri - zon Nous tous, tes ou - vri - ers, Joi - gnons nos mains en
fin - den all In ihm die heil' - ge Statt; Er ist es, der das

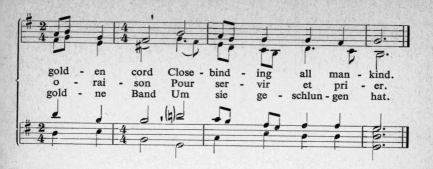

gold - en cord Close - bind - ing all man - kind.
o - rai - son Pour ser - vir et pri - er.
gold - ne Band Um sie ge - schlun - gen hat.

2.

Join hands then, brothers of the faith,
    What'er your race may be !
Who serves my Father as a son
    Is surely kin to me.
In Christ now meet both East and West,
    In Him meet South and North,
All Christly souls are one in Him,
    Throughout the whole wide earth.

JOHN OXENHAM (1908).

* * *

2.

Celui qui sert Dieu comme un fils
    Devient ton frère à toi :
Lien parfait des cœurs conquis
    Unis-nous par la foi !
Du Nord au Sud, en tout pays,
    De tout peuple ou tribu
Nous sommes frères bien unis
    En toi, Seigneur Jésus !

Trad. F. DE ROUGEMONT (1930).

* * *

2.

Drum, Glaubensbrüder, schliesst den Bund
    Welch Stamm euch auch gesandt !
Wer meinem Vater dient als Sohn,
    Ist wahrlich mir verwandt.
In Christus eint sich Ost und West
    Und eint sich Süd und Nord,
Die Seelen sein sind eins in ihm
    Die ganze Erde fort.

Übers. M. Liesegang (1924).

— 63 (4) —

St. Anne C.M.
WILLIAM CROFT (1678-1727).

Slow and dignified

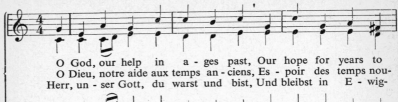

O God, our help in a - ges past, Our hope for years to
O Dieu, notre aide aux temps an - ciens, Es - poir des temps nou-
Herr, un - ser Gott, du warst und bist, Und bleibst in E - wig-

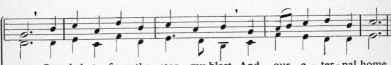

come, Our shel - ter from the stor - my blast, And our e - ter - nal home.
veaux, Aux jours mau-vais, puis-sant sou-tien, Notre é - ter - nel re - pos.
keit; Du bist's der uns'-re Hoff - nung ist In uns' - rer Pil - ger - zeit.

2.

Under the shadow of Thy throne
  Thy saints have dwelt secure ;
Sufficient is Thine arm alone,
  And our defence is sure.

3.

Before the hills in order stood,
  Or earth received her frame,
From everlasting Thou art God,
  To endless years the same.

4.

A thousand ages in Thy sight
  Are like an evening gone,
Short as the watch that ends the
  Before the rising sun. [night

5.

Time, like an ever rolling stream,
  Bears all its sons away ;
They fly forgotten, as a dream
  Dies at the opening day.

6.

O God, our help in ages past,
  Our hope for years to come,
Be Thou our guard while troubles last,
  And our eternal home.

ISAAC WATTS (1674-1748).

* * *

2.

A l'ombre de ton trône, assis,
  Tes saints ont habité.
Ton bras vaillant nous garde aussi
  En toute sûreté.

3.

Quand les collines et les flots
  Se confondaient mêlés,
Seul, tu régnais sur le chaos
  De toute éternité.

4.

Mille ans, Seigneur, sont à tes yeux
  Plus brefs qu'un soir enfui,
Plus brefs que l'aube dans les cieux
  Lorsque prend fin la nuit.

5.

Le temps comme un torrent fougueux
  Emporte ses enfants.
Ils passent, comme un rêve heureux
  S'envole au jour naissant.

6.

O Dieu notre aide aux temps anciens
  Espoir des temps nouveaux,
Aux jours mauvais, puissant soutien,
  Notre éternel repos.

Trad. Pauline Martin (1950).

★ ★ ★

2.

Wenn uns dein Schatten überdeckt,
  Bleibt fern uns Angst und Harm.
Und wenn der Feind uns droht und
  Hilft uns dein starker Arm. [schreckt,

3.

Du warst, eh' deines Mundes Hauch
  Schuf Himmel, Meer und Welt,
Und wirst derselbe bleiben auch,
  Wenn alles stürzt und fällt.

4.

Denn tausend Jahre Erdenzeit
  Sind vor dir wie ein Tag,
Ein Atemzug der Ewigkeit,
  Ein kurzer Flügelschlag.

5.

Und reisst der Zeiten Strom wie Schaum
  Hinweg — wir bleiben nicht.
Die Namen sterben, wie ein Traum
  Verbleicht im Morgenlicht.

Übers. Wilhelm Horkel (1950)
(nur für den 5. Vers.).

6.

Gott, der du immer warst und bist,
  Leit uns an deiner Hand,
Und bring, wenn uns're Wallfahrt schliesst,
  Uns heim ins Vaterland !

Übers. C. Lechler (1923).

★ ★ ★

Psalm XXIII
« Crimond »
Scottish Psalter (1650).

The Lord's my Shep - herd, I'll not want. He
Gott ist mein Hort, was will ich mehr? Er
L'E - ter - nel seul est mon ber - ger, De

makes me down to lie In past - ures green; He
schenkt mir Rast und Statt In rei - chem Land und
rien ne man - que - rai. Il me con - duit pour

lead - eth me The qui - et wa - ters by.
rich - tet her An Was - sern mei - nen Pfad.
mon re - pos Vers l'herbe et vers les eaux.

2.
My soul He doth restore again;
  And me to walk doth make
Within the paths of righteousness,
  Even for His own Name's sake.

3.
Yea, though I walk in death's dark vale,
  Yet will I fear none ill;
For Thou art with me; and Thy rod
  And staff me comfort still.

4.

My table Thou hast furnishèd
  In presence of my foes ;
My head Thou dost with oil anoint,
  And my cup overflows.

5.

Goodness and mercy all my life
  Shall surely follow me :
And in God's house for evermore
  My dwelling-place shall be.

Scottish Psalter (1650).

★ ★ ★

2.

Er gibt der Seele neue Kraft
  Und führet meinen Fuss,
Dass die gewisse Wanderschaft
  Sein Heil bezeugen muss.

3.

Und wär's auch in der Finsternis,
  Blieb doch die Furcht mir fern.
Er geht ja mit, das ist gewiss.
  Gott is mein Stab und Stern.

4.

Er hält mir Dach und Tisch bestellt
  Vor meiner Feinde Blick,
Er schenkt mir, was das Herz erhellt,
  Und überschwänglich Glück.

5.

Erbarmen bleibt und Gutes mir,
  Solang ich leb, zur Seit.
In deinem Hause dank ich dir,
  Herr, einst in Ewigkeit.

Übers. ERWIN KLEINE (1950).

★ ★ ★

2.

Il vient guérir, il vient bénir
  Mon âme et l'affermir
Pour me guider sur son chemin,
  Mon Dieu saisit ma main.

3.

Marchant au long du sombre val
  Craindrais-je encor le mal ?
Toujours il reste près de moi
  Mon sûr appui, mon Roi.

4.

Pour moi la table il a dressé,
  Face à qui me fait front !
Ma coupe est pleine à déborder
  Car il oindra mon front.

5.

Bonheur et grâce, ô Dieu d'amour,
  Me garderont toujours ;
J'habiterai, suprême honneur
  Dans ta maison, Seigneur !

Trad. PAULINE MARTIN (1951).

— 65 (6) —

Psaume 42
Mélodie Loys Bourgeois (1551).
Harmonisé d'après Cl. Goudimel (1565).

Comme un cerf al - té - ré bra - me, Pour - chas - sant
Wie der Hirsch nach fri - scher Quel - le Schreit mit lech-
As the hind, dis - tressed and pan - ting, Bays for streams

le frais des eaux, O Sei - gneur, ain - si mon
zen - der Be - gier, Al - so schreit auch mei - ne
of wa - ter cool, So my soul, its Sav - iour

â - me Sou - pire a - près tes ruis - seaux.
See - le voll Ver - lan - gen, Gott, nach dir.
want - ing, Sighs for liv - ing foun - tains full.

Elle a soif du Dieu vi - vant, Et s'é - crie
Nur nach dir, le - bend' - ger Gott, Dürs - tet sie
For the liv - ing God a - thirst, Forth her tears

en le sui - vant: O   mon Dieu, quand donc sein ih - rer Not.   Ach, wann wird   es   doch ge-
and sor-rows burst: "O   my God, when shall   it

ra - ce   Que mes yeux ver-ront ta fa - ce?
sche - hen,   Dass ich, Herr, vor dir kann ste - hen?
be   That mine eyes Thy face may see?"

2.

Mon seul pain, ce sont mes larmes ;
  Et, nuit et jour, en tout lieu,
Chaque fois qu'en mes alarmes
  On me dit : que fait ton Dieu ?
Je regrette la saison
  Où j'allais, dans ta maison,
Chanter avec les fidèles
  Tes louanges immortelles.

3.

Tous les flots de ta colère
  Sur moi, Seigneur, ont passé,
Et pourtant mon cœur espère
  Que l'orage va cesser.
Chaque jour, tu m'aideras ;
  Et, la nuit, tu me feras
Célébrer, l'âme ravie,
  Ta bonté, Dieu de ma vie.

4.

Mais pourquoi, mon âme, encore
  Frémis-tu d'un tel effroi ?
Quand, déjà, paraît l'aurore
  Et que Dieu prend soin de moi ?
Un regard, dans sa faveur,
  Me dit qu'il est mon Sauveur.
Il te faut louer, mon âme,
  Ce grand Dieu que je réclame.

THÉODORE DE BÈZE (1551). CONRART (1677).

★ ★ ★

2.

Angst und Pein die Seele nagen,
 Tränen sind mein täglich Brot,
Wenn die Spötter zu mir sagen :
 Lass uns sehn, wo ist dein Gott ?
Alsdann schütt' ich aus mein Herz
 Und gedenke voller Schmerz,
Wie der Festgesang erschallte,
 Da ich noch zum Tempel wallte.

3.

Alle deine Wasserwogen,
 Deine Wellen allzumal,
Über mir zusammenschlagen ;
 Doch tröst ich mich in Trübsal,
Dass du helfen wirst bei Tag,
 Dass des Nachts ich singen mag,
Dich als meinen Heiland preise,
 Anruf' und anbet' mit Fleisse.

4.

Was betrübst du dich, O Seele,
 Und bist banger Unruh voll.
Harr auf Gott, sei still und wähle
 Ihn zum Trost, er meint es wohl.
Hoff auf ihn mit Zuversicht.
 Bald wirst du sein Angesicht
Leuchten sehn, ihn fröhlich preisen
 Und ihm Lob und Dank erweisen.

Übers. AMBROSIUS LOBWASSER (1515-1585).

* * *

2.

Bitter tears have been my measure
 Night and day in ev'ry place ;
Scoffing foes have found their pleasure
 Saying : "Where's thy God of grace?"
How I miss those happy days !
 When my voice joined in the praise
Where the thronging pilgrims trod,
 In Thy courts, blest House of God !

3.

Floods of wrath, like raging torrents,
 Lord, upon my soul have passed :
In Thy pity, stem the currents,
 Bid me hope : give peace at last.
Thou wilt guide me day by day,
 Nightly fears Thou wilt allay,
While I praise, with thankful songs,
 God, to whom my soul belongs.

4.

Why then, soul, be vexed with sorrows ?
 Hope in God : thy woes shall cease.
He will give thee glad to-morrows,
 Thou shalt pass thy days in peace.
He will send thee saving grace,
 Thou shalt see His smiling face :
All thy woes He will remove,
 They reveal His chast'ning love.

Trans. R. BIRCH HOYLE (1923).

— 66 —

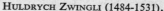

HULDRYCH ZWINGLI (1484-1531).

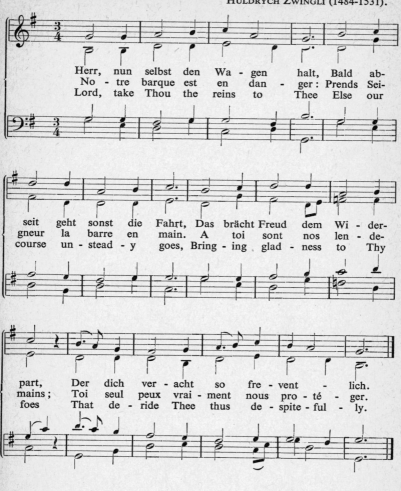

Herr, nun selbst den Wa - gen halt, Bald ab-
No - tre barque est en dan - ger: Prends Sei-
Lord, take Thou the reins to Thee Else our

seit geht sonst die Fahrt, Das brächt Freud dem Wi - der-
gneur la barre en main. A toi sont nos len - de-
course un - stead - y goes, Bring - ing glad - ness to Thy

part, Der dich ver - acht so fre - vent - lich.
mains; Toi seul peux vrai - ment nous pro - té - ger.
foes That de - ride Thee thus de - spite - ful - ly.

2.

Gott, erhöh deins Namen's Ehr,
Wehr und straf der Bösen Grimm,
Weck die Schaf mit deiner Stimm,
Die dich lieb haben inniglich.

3.

Hilf, dass alle Bitterkeit
Scheid, O Herr, und alte Treu
Wiederkehr und werde neu,
Dass wir ewig lobsingen dir.

HULDRYCH ZWINGLI (1529).

* * *

2.

Notre barque est en danger,
Viens chasser nos ennemis,
Veille, ô Dieu sur tes brebis ;
Sois toujours, ô Dieu, leur bon berger.

3.

Notre barque est en danger :
Aimons mieux de jour en jour ;
Notre force est dans l'amour,
Et le tien, Seigneur, ne peut changer !

Trad. Daniel Meylan (1930).

* * *

2.

Thy most glorious name extol,
Bring the powers of ill to fall,
Rouse Thy people with Thy call
That exalt Thee with their heart and soul.

3.

Help us banish disaccord,
And restore old kindliness,
That we evermore may bless
And adore the name of God our Lord.

Margaret Barclay (1951).

— 67 —

« Mornington »
Garret Wellesley (1735-1831).

Teach me, my God and King, In all things Thee to see,
Lehr mich, mein Gott und Herr, In al - lem dich zu seh'n !
En - sei - gne-moi, Sei - gneur Tou - jours et en tous lieux,

And what I do in an - y - thing To do it as for Thee.
Und was ich wir - ke und be - gehr, Es sei für dich ge - scheh'n !
A t'a - do - rer de tout mon cœur, A voir ton œuvre, ô Dieu.

2.

A man that looks on glass,
  On it may stay his eye ;
Or if he pleaseth, through it pass,
  And then the heaven espy.

3.

All may of Thee partake ;
  Nothing can be so mean,   [sake,»
Which with this tincture, For Thy
  Will not grow bright and clean.

4.

A servant with this clause
  Makes drudgery divine ;
Who sweeps a room, as for Thy laws,
  Makes that and the action fine.

5.

This is the famous stone
  That turneth all to gold ;
For that which God doth touch and own
  Cannot for less be told.

GEORGE HERBERT (1593-1633).

* * *

2.

Wer traut auf splitternd Glas,
  Such' dort sein gläsern Glück !
Geh', wie's gefällt, des Wegs fürbass —
  Ihm winkt kein Himmelsblick !

3.

Du wohnest allem ein.
  Kein Ding willst du verschmäh'n.
Es hat die Art von dir allein ;
  Sonst kann's nicht herrlich steh'n.

4.

Sag' dir, du Knecht, zum Trost :
  Die Plage wird Gewinst.
Gott hat die Mühsal dir erlost !
  Dein Dienst ist Gottesdienst.

5.

So aus geringem Stein
  Schmilzt man das Gold heraus.
Gott fasst dich, darfst sein eigen sein.
  Kein Lied je sagt es aus !

Übers. WILHELM HORKEL (1950).

* * *

2.

Ne nous dérobe pas
  Tes cieux et leur splendeur.
Nous ne pouvons vivre ici-bas
  Sans ta clarté, Seigneur.

3.

Nous sommes appelés
  A vivre sous ta loi,
Et ta lumière peut briller
  Sous les plus humbles toits.

4.

Aussi tout serviteur
  S'il a compris cela
Fait son travail avec ardeur
  Malgré son peu d'éclat.

5.

Ton amour merveilleux
  Rayonne et resplendit,
Tout t'appartient, ô notre Dieu,
  Et tu nous éblouis.

Trad. FLOSSETTE DU PASQUIER (1951).

Japanese.
IMAYO.

よ　も　に　く　も　き　り　た　ち

Mist　and　dark - ness　all　a - round, Dark clouds
Dunst　und　Dun - kel　rings　um - her, Wol - ken
Par　la　nuit　en - vi - ron - né, Sous　un

ふ・さ　ぎ　た　づ　き　し　ら　れ　ぬ

o - ver - head, Doubt - ing　how　to　find　the　path
nur　zu　sehn; Zwei - felnd　find　ich　nicht　den　Pfad,
ciel　obs - cur　J'erre　au　ha - sard　du　che - min,

お　ほ　の　は　ら　ま　よ　ひ　つ

Which　my　feet　should　tread; Guide　my　wand - 'ring,
Den　mein　Fuss　soll　gehn; Lenk　den　mü - den,
Je　ne　suis　pas　sûr. Gui - de　mes　pas

かるるよわきみをまも
wea - ry steps, Guard me in my road Through the
Wan - der-schritt, Halt mich in der Not, In der
trop crain - tifs Et di - ri - ge - moi. Gar - de-

りたまひねわがみかみ
track - less wil - der - ness, O my Lord and God.
Wild - nis oh - ne Weg, O mein Herr und Gott!
moi dans le dé - sert Mon Sei - gneur, mon Roi!

四ヨルダンがはに　　　　三くもの　みはしら　　　二あめの　みかてを　　　一よもに　くもきり　たちふさぎ
こゝろの　おそれ　　　　いまも　あらはし　　　いのちの　いづみ　　　たづき　左られぬ　大野原
みくにの　きしに　　　　みち　あきらけく　　　うゑ　かわきたる　　　まよひ　つかるる　おほのはら
われらしめてよ　　　　みちびき　たまへ　　　やしなひ　たまへ　　　まもり　たまひね　わがみかみ
　　わがみかみ　　　　　わが　みかみ　　　　　おどろへを　　　　　めぐみの　みかてを
　　　　　　　　　　雲　　　　　　　　　　　火　わが　みかみ　　　　　　御糧　　降下
たひらげて慈　　　　　われの　ゆく　　　　　わき　いだし
つゝがなく　　　　　　てらしつゝ　　　　　御糧　ふりくだし
いたる　とき　　　　　ひの　はしら　　　　　りくだし

＊　＊　＊

2. Give me, Lord the Bread of life, — Manna from above;
   Living waters from the rock — Send me in Thy love.
   In my hunger and my thirst — Meat and drink afford;
   In my weakness strengthen me, — O my God and Lord.

3. By Thy cloudy pillar, Lord, — Lead me day by day;
   By Thy pillar bright of fire — Nightly show my way;
   Thus Thy chosen flock of old — Knew the way they trod;
   Make me thus to know my way, — O my Lord and God.

4. When I come to Jordan's banks, — And death draweth near,
   Fill my heart with peace and hope, — Drive away all fear.
   That I may the bliss attain — Promised in Thy Word,
   Bring me to the heavenly shore, — O my God and Lord.

Trans. Bishop HUGH JAMES FOSS (1930).

* * *

2. Gib mir, Herr, das Lebensbrot, — Himmelsmanna send;
   Lebenswasser aus dem Fels — Deine Liebe spend.
   Mir in Hunger und in Durst — Speis und Trank gewähr;
   In der Schwachheit stärke mich, — O mein Gott und Herr!

3. Deine Wolkensäule Herr, — Tags den Weg mich leit;
   Deiner Feuersäule Glanz — Nachts Licht um mich spreit.
   So wusst einst dein wertes Volk — Weg, Ziel und Gebot;
   So weis' mir auch meinen Weg, — O mein Herr und Gott!

4. Komm ich an des Jordans Rand, — Naht heran der Tod,
   Füll mein Herz mit Fried und Licht, — Weg sei Furcht und Not!
   Seligkeit verheisst dein Wort, — Wo kein Dunkel mehr:
   Die gib mir, da bring mich hin, — O mein Gott und Herr!

Übers. H. LAEPPLE (1930).

* * *

2. Fais jaillir de ce rocher — Les vivantes eaux;
   De ta manne nourris-moi — C'est le pain d'en-haut.
   Tu apaiseras ma soif, — Je n'aurai plus faim,
   Tu soutiens mon faible corps, — O Dieu souverain.

3. Ta nuée, ô Dieu puissant, — Le jour me conduit,
   Et ta colonne de feu — Brille dans la nuit,
   Comme au peuple élu jadis — Montrant le chemin,
   Vers le port dirige-moi, — O Dieu souverain.

4. Quand j'atteindrai le Jourdain — Quand viendra la mort
   Donne à mon esprit ta paix — Pour que je sois fort;
   Fais-moi la grâce, ô mon Dieu — De voir tes parvis,
   De connaître le bonheur — Que tu m'as promis.

Trad. FLOSSETTE DU PASQUIER (1951).

Moderato animato

Psaume 68
MATTHIEU GREITER (?) (1525)

Que Dieu se mon - tre seu - le - ment, Et l'on ver-
Let God a - rise and show His face, And all that
Wenn Gott er - hebt sein Au - ge nur, So ist ver-

ra dans un mo - ment A - ban - don - ner la pla - ce;
hate Him shall give place, And all His foes shall scat - ter;
weht der Fein - de Spur Wie Rauch vor schnel-len Win - den;

Le camp des en - ne - mis é - pars, E - pou - van-
Just as the smoke a - way doth blow, So shall His
Und wie im Feu - er Wachs zer - rinnt, So, Herr, vor

té, de tou - tes parts Fui - ra de - vant sa fa - ce.
arm dis - perse the foe, And all op - po - nents ban - ish;
dir die Frev - ler sind: Ein Nu macht sie ver-schwin - den.

On ver - ra tout ce camp s'en - fuir Com - me l'on
And as the wax be - com - ing warm Melts, leav - ing
Es ist kein Schutz-wall auf der Welt, Da nicht dein

voit s'é - va - nou - ir Une é - pais - se fu - mé - e;
nei - ther shape nor form, So shall th'un-god - ly van - ish;
Zorn sie trifft und fällt, Wie du es zu - ge - mes - sen.

Com - me la ci - re fond au feu, Ain - si des
Be - fore His face they can - not stand, But fall a -
Sie lau - fen auf Ver - der - bens Bahn, Und was sie

mé-chants de - vant Dieu La force est con - su - mé - e.
side on ev - ery hand, And at His pre - sence per - ish.
tun, es ist ver - tan, Und was ge - sagt, ver - ges - sen.

2.

Mais, en présence du Seigneur,
Les justes chantent sa grandeur
Et sa gloire immortelle ;
Car sur la nue il est porté ;
Son nom est plein de majesté,
L'Eternel il s'appelle.
Réjouissez-vous devant lui :
Il est de la veuve l'appui,
Des orphelins le père ;
Aux captifs il porte secours,
Et de l'affligé, tous les jours,
Il entend la prière.

3.

Grand Dieu, toi qui nous as fait voir
Et ton amour et ton pouvoir
Dans mainte délivrance,
Seigneur, montre encore en ce jour,
De ce pouvoir, de cet amour,
L'immuable constance.
A toi, dont le nom glorieux
Est révéré dans les saints lieux
Qu'honore ta présence,
A toi qui fais notre bonheur,
A toi, grand Dieu, soit tout honneur,
Force et magnificence.

THÉODORE DE BÈZE (1562).
Arr. par CONRART (1677).

* * *

2.

But let the righteous all rejoice,
Be glad and raise a merry voice,
And sing His fame supernal ;
Upon the heavens rideth He,
His name is full of majesty,
Jehovah the Eternal.
He takes the orphan for His own,
Companions them who are alone,
Defends the widows' causes ;
He makes the household to agree,
Releases from captivity
The prisoner in bondage.

3.

O God, to us whose fathers told
Thy love and power in days of old,
In many a time of danger,
Show yet again in this new hour
Thy loving kindness and Thy power,
Still constant and unchanging ;
Come, all ye kingdoms of the earth,
Extol His honour and His worth
With all your myriad voices.
All worship, honour, praise be given
To Thee, O God, in highest heaven,
In Whom my soul rejoices.

Trans. MARGARET HOUSE (1949).

* * *

2.

Die Frommen aber weichen nicht,
Sie singen Gottes Angesicht
Das Loblied Tag um Tage.
Denn Gott sie wie auf Wolken trägt,
Ein Vater so die Kindlein hegt
Und schützt vor aller Plage.
So hat's der Herr seit je gemeint,
Der Witwen und der Weisen Freund,
Der Schützer aller Schwachen.
Er bringt die Irrenden nach Haus,
Lässt die Gefangenen heraus
Und macht sie wieder lachen.

3.

O Herr, du hast es oft gezeigt,
Dass deine Liebe sich geneigt,
In Liebe uns zu leiten !
Erweise diese Lieb' aufs Neu,
Heb deinen Arm, dein Volk befrei
Wie zu der Väter Zeiten !
Und uns, die du dir auserwählt,
Dass unser Mund dein Lob erzählt,
Aufs Neu' zu dir bekehre,
Dass unser Wort und Werk dir zollt,
Wie du's in Ewigkeit gewollt,
Durch Wohltun Preis und Ehre !

Übers. JOHANN CHRISTOPH HAMPE (1950).

— 70 (50) —

JOHANN WALTHER (1524) oder
MARTIN LUTHER (1529).

Allegro maestoso

Ein fe - ste Burg ist un - ser Gott, Ein gu - te
Er hilft uns frei aus al - ler Not, Die uns jetzt
A safe strong-hold our God is still, A trust - y
He'll help us clear from all the ill That hath us
C'est un rem - part que no - tre Dieu, Une in - vin-
No - tre dé - li - vrance en tout lieu, No - tre dé-

Wehr und Waf - fen, ⎱ Der alt bö - se Feind, Mit
hat be - tro - fen. ⎰
shield and weap - on; ⎱ The an - cient prince of hell Hath
now o'er - tak - en. ⎰
cible ar - mu - re, ⎱ L'en - ne - mi con - tre nous Re-
fen - se sû - re. ⎰

Ernst er es jetzt meint; Gross Macht und viel List Sein grau-
ris'n with pur - pose fell; Strong mail of craft and power He wear-
dou - ble de cour-roux... Vai - ne co - lè - re! Que pour-

sam Rü - stung ist, Auf Erd ist nicht seins-glei - chen.
eth in this hour; On earth is not his fel - low.
rait l'ad - ver - sai - re? L'E - ter - nel dé - tour - ne ses coups.

2. Mit unsrer Macht ist nichts getan,
   Wir sind gar bald verloren;
   Es streit't für uns der rechte Mann,
   Den Gott selbst hat erkoren.
      Fragst du nun, wer der ist?
      Er heisset Jesus Christ,
      Der Herr Zebaoth,
      Und ist kein andrer Gott;
   Das Feld muss er behalten.

3. Und wenn die Welt voll Teufel wär
   Und wollt uns gar verschlingen,
   So fürchten wir uns nicht so sehr,
   Es soll uns doch gelingen.
      Der Fürste dieser Welt,
      Wie sauer er sich stellt,
      Tut er uns doch nichts;
      Das macht, er ist gericht't,
   Ein Wörtlein kann ihn fällen.

4. Das Wort sie sollen lassen stahn
   Und kein Dank dazu haben;
   Er ist bei uns wohl auf dem Plan
   Mit seinem Geist und Gaben.
      Nehmen sie uns den Leib,
      Gut, Ehre, Kind und Weib,
      Lass fahren dahin,
      Sie habens kein Gewinn,
   Das Reich muss uns doch bleiben.

MARTIN LUTHER (1483-1546).

* * *

2. With force of arms we nothing can,
   Full soon were we down-ridden;
   But for us fights the proper Man,
   Whom God Himself hath bidden.
      Ask ye, who is this same?
      Christ Jesus is His name,
      Of Sabaoth the Lord,
      Sole God to be adored,
   'Tis He must win the battle.

3. And were this world all devils o'er,
   And watching to devour us,
   We lay it not to heart so sore;
   Not they can overpower us.
      And let the prince of ill
      Look grim as e'er he will,
      He harms us not a whit;
      For why? his doom is writ;
   A word shall quickly slay him.

4. God's word, for all their craft and force,
   One moment will not linger,
   But, spite of hell, shall have its course;
   'Tis written by His finger.
      And, though they take our life,
      Goods, honour, children, wife,
      Yet is their profit small;
      These things shall vanish all,
   The city of God remaineth.

Trans. THOMAS CARLYLE (1795-1881).

* * *

2. Seuls, nous bronchons à chaque pas,
   Notre force est faiblesse ;
   Mais un héros, dans les combats,
   Pour nous lutte sans cesse.
       Quel est ce défenseur ?
       C'est toi, divin Sauveur,
       Dieu des armées,
       Tes tribus opprimées
   Connaissent leur libérateur.

3. Que les démons forgent des fers
   Pour accabler l'Eglise,
   Ta Sion brave les enfers,
   Sur son rocher assise.
       Constant dans son effort,
       En vain, avec la mort,
       Satan conspire :
       Pour briser son empire,
   Il suffit d'un mot du Dieu fort.

4. Dis-le, ce mot victorieux,
   Dans toutes nos détresses ;
   Répands sur nous du haut des cieux
   Tes divines largesses.
       Qu'on nous ôte nos biens,
       Qu'on serre nos liens,
       Que nous importe !
       Ta grâce est la plus forte,
   Et ton royaume est pour les tiens.

Trad. H. LUTTEROTH (1802-1892).

— 71 (79) —

Traditional Chorale Strophe.
HARRINGTON SHORTALL.*

God be in my head, and in my un-der-stand-ing;
Dieu soit en mon front et mon in-tel-li-gen-ce;
Gott, re-gie-re du al-lein in Haupt und Glie-dern;

God be in mine eyes, and in my look-ing; God be in my
Dieu soit en mes yeux et leur lu-miè-re ; Dieu soit en ma
Gott, mit dei-nem Licht mein Aug durch-leuch-te ! Gott, von dir er-

mouth, and in my speak-ing; God be in my
voix et mon lan - ga-ge; Dieu donne à mon
füllt sei Mund und Re - de! Gott, in Herz und

heart, and in my think-ing; God - - - be at mine
cœur force et cou - ra - ge; Dieu - - - - soit mon re-
Sinn wollst du nur wal - ten! Gott, - - - in dir am

end, and at my de - part - ing.
cours, au der - nier pas - sa - ge. } A - men!
End' lass micht einst ab - schei - den!

Old Saxon Primer — Trad. CLAIRE JULLIEN (1930).
Übers. C. LECHLER (1930).

72

Korean
LA WOON HYUNG.

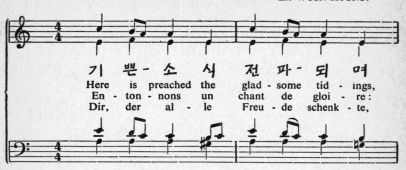

기 쁜 - 소 식 전 파 - 되 며
Here is preached the glad-some tid - ings,
En - ton-nons un chant de gloi - re:
Dir, der al - le Freu - de schenk - te,

제 - 물 이 반 - 혀 지 고 성 삼 - 위 께
Off - ered here our sac - ri - fice. Here the Tri - une
Jé - sus-Christ par son a - mour Vint pour sau - ver
schen-ken, Herr, wir uns' - re Lieder. Drei - ge - stal - ter

찬 송 - 드 려 속 죄 사 랑 감 사 하 니
God is wor-shipped, Prais-ing His re - deem - ing love.
tous les hom - mes: of - frons-nous à lui tou - jours.
Gott der Lie - be, heil - ger, dich er - hebt das Lied.

하 늘 - 영 광 그 윽 - 다　　하 늘 - 영 광
Glo - ry from the Heav'ns a - bove　　Makes our church a
Gloire au Pè - re dans les cieux !　　Gloire au Pè - re
Al - le Him - mel rüh - men dich,　　al - le Him - mel

그 윽 - 다 거 룩 - 한 곳 우 리 교 - 회
ho - ly place. Glo - ry full of awe and love
dans les cieux ! L'E - glise ap - par - tient à Dieu.
rüh - men dich. Und auf Er - den preist dich laut

거 룩 - 한 곳 우 리 교 - 회
Sanc - ti - fy our ho - - ly place.
L'E - glise ap - par - tient à Dieu.
die Ge - mein - de dei - - ne Braut.

3.

하늘나라 땅에심어
자라는 생명나무
아드님이 본체되고
우리들은 그가지라
날마다 달마다
날마다 달마다
열매맺는 우리교회
열매맺는 우리교회

어둔사회 빛이되고
썩은맘에 소금되어
가루속에 누룩같이
소리없이 변화시켜
새사람 새나라
새사람 새나라
길러내는 우리교회
길러내는 우리교회

KIM CHAI CHOON.

* * *

2.

Planted here is God's own kingdom,
  Growing like a tree of life ;
Jesus Christ the central body,
  We the branches stemming from Him.
Day by day throughout the year,
  Bearing fruit — our holy church ;
Week by week throughout the year,
  Fruit in season — this our church.

3.

Like light within a darkened world,
  Like salt within a sordid mind,
Like leaven in a peck of flour —
  Silently it changes all.
Bringing new life to the people,
  Like a mother at her task ;
Making new our men and nation,
  Thus our church fulfils her task.

Trans. Dr. WILLIAM SCOTT and Miss YUNG OON KIM (1950)

* * *

2.

Ton royaume, sur la terre
  Tel un arbre poussera ;
Ses racines : le Messie,
  Ses rameaux : nous ici-bas.
  Chaque jour et chaque mois (*bis*)
  Notre Eglise grandira. (*bis*)

3.

Dans ce monde de ténèbres
  Sa lumière brillera :
Notre Eglise sans relâche
  Poursuivra son bon combat,
  Renouvelant nos esprits (*bis*)
  Transformant notre pays.(*bis*)

Trad. FLOSSETTE DU PASQUIER (1951).

* * *

2.

Herr, dein Reich wächst hier auf Erden
  Wie des Lebens ew'ger Baum :
Gottes Sohn ist Stamm und Wurzel,
  Wir die Zweige dieses Baums.
  Tag um Tage, Jahr um Jahr, (*bis*)
  Bringt er Frucht in Fülle dar. (*bis*)

3.

Herr, dein Licht macht Todesschatten,
  Deine Gnade Sünder neu.
Wunder wirkst du, weil du willst, dass
  Die Gemeinde heilig sei.
  Menschen, die dir wohlgefall'n, (*bis*)
  Einst in deiner Kirche du. (*bis*)

Übers. JOHANN CHRISTOPH HAMPE (1951).

73

Moderato

Psaume 36
MATHIEU GREITER (?) (1525).

E - ter - nel, ta fi - dé - li - té Va jus-qu'aux
O like the deep Thy judg-ments are, Thy mer - cy
O Va - ter, dei - ne Gü - te reicht, Wo - hin kein

cieux et ta bon - té Dé - pas - se tou - te ci - me!
stretch-eth wide and far, Up to the clouds of heav - en;
A - dler - fit - tich streicht Mit Wol - ken und mit Win - den!

Ta jus - tice est pa - reille aux monts, Et tes ju -
O Lord, let not the foot of pride Come forth a -
Und wie die Ber - ge sind ge - reiht, So si - cher

ge - ments sont pro - fonds Com - me le grand a - bî - me.
gainst me, or de - ride Thy serv - ant who hath stri - ven
wird Ge - rech - tig - keit Ein je - der bei dir fin - den.

O Seigneur, qu'ils sont précieux
Les biens que tu répands des cieux
Sur les âmes fidèles !
Les fils de l'homme, en leur effroi,
Ont un refuge auprès de toi,
A l'ombre de tes ailes !
Ils trouvent, en toute saison,
Leur nourriture en ta maison ;
Ta grâce les abreuve ;
Et dans leur cœur, de jour en jour,
Les délices de ton amour
S'épanchent comme un fleuve.

Oh ! répands sur nous ta faveur !
En toi seul se trouve, Seigneur,
La source de la vie.
Tu dissipes l'obscurité :
Sans ta lumière, la clarté
A notre âme est ravie.
Donne ta force aux hommes droits
Qui, connaissant tes saintes lois,
Marchent devant ta face ;
Et que, malgré tes ennemis,
Par ton peuple heureux et soumis
Ta volonté se fasse !

CLÉMENT MAROT (1543). Arr. par CONRART (1677).

★ ★ ★

Beneath the shadow of Thy wing
Children of men Thy praises sing,
In happy songs united.
But he that loveth not the Lord
In misery doth walk abroad,
In doubt and care benighted.
For with Thee is the well of life
Whose waters stay me in the strife,
Whose enemies would slay me.
For in Thy light shall we see light,
Turning to day from darkest night
The shadows that dismay me.

Trans. Mrs. K. W. SIMPSON.
In Terry Calvin's First Psalter
(1539).

O may we be to grace restored !
In Thee alone we find, dear Lord,
The spring of all our living.
The darkness Thou dost roll away ;
Without Thy light, the light of day
From all our souls is driven.
Give strength to every upright heart
By holy wisdom led apart
To walk steadfast before Thee,
That so, withstanding hostile shock,
Thy happy and devoted flock
May serve Thee and adore Thee.

Trans. MARGARET HOUSE
(1950).

★ ★ ★

Du weisest deine Güte aus
In jedem Land, in jedem Haus,
In jedem Herz hienieden.
Treibt überall die Furcht uns fort,
So haben wir doch Zufluchtsort
In deiner Flügel Frieden.
Und Speise steht zu aller Zeit
An deinem Tische uns bereit
Und Trank aus deinen Krügen.
Du machst in deiner reichen Stadt
Die Menschenkinder alle satt,
Du stillest all Genügen.

Bevor dein heilig Licht uns traf,
War unser Dasein Nacht und Schlaf,
Du kamst und es ward helle.
Und wer dich schmeckt hat nimmermehr
Nach anderm Tranke noch Begehr,
Du bist des Lebens Quelle.
Steh' uns mit Kraft des Geistes bei,
Dass wir gehorsam, fromm und treu
Vor deinem Antlitz gehen,
Und deinen heil'gen Willen lass,
Entgegen aller Feinde Hass,
Durch uns, dein Volk, geschehen !

Übers. JOHANN CHRISTOPH HAMPE (1950).

— 74 (23) —

Old Indian Song.
Harm. arr. par FRÉDÉRIC MATHIL (1950).

Grant me to give to men what they de - sire, And
Ser - viable ain - si que ton a - mour l'ins - pi - re, Con-
Gib, dass der Men - schen Sehn - sucht sei mein Ziel Und

for my por - tion take what they do slight. Grant
tent pour moi des re - liefs du fes - tin, Je
wenn sie schla - gen mich, mach du mich still. Ver-

me, my Lord, a mind that doth as - pire To
veux, Sei - gneur, que mon es - prit n'as - pi - re A
leih mir, Herr, dass auf - wärts fliegt mein Sinn Und

less than it may claim of pro - per right, To
trou - ver son bon - heur qu'en ne dé - si - rant rien, A
dass das Eig - ne gern ich le - ge hin, Und

less than it may claim of pro - per right.
trou - ver son bon - heur qu'en ne dé - si - rant rien.
dass das Eig - ne gern ich le - ge hin.

2.

Rather, the lowest place, at all men's feet,
   That do Thou graciously reserve for me.
This only bounty I would fain entreat,
   That Thy will, O my God, my will may be. (*bis*)

NARAYAN VAMAN TILAK (1862-1919).*
Trans. J. C. WINSLOW (1920).

* * *

2.

Aux pieds de tous, à la plus humble place,
   Que ta bonté me garde dans la paix !
Je ne demande, ô Dieu ! que cette grâce :
   N'avoir de volonté que la tienne à jamais. (*bis*)

Trad. CHARLES WESTPHAL (1930).

* * *

2.

Zu aller Menschen Füssen sei mein Ort,
Die Gnade, die von dir, mein Ruheport ;
Das sei mein einz'ger Will, dass mein Ziel,
   Dass nur dein Will, O Gott, auch werd' mein Will. (*bis*)

Übers. FRANZ SPEMANN (1930).

Published with the kind permission of the Rev. J. C. Winslow.

M. Teschner (1613).
Harm. J. S. Bach (Johannes Passion, 1724).

Animato

Ich weiss an wen ich glau - be, Ich weiss, was fest be-
I know with full as - sur - ance In whom I place my
Je sais en qui j'es - pè - re, Je sais en qui je

steht, Wenn al - les hier im Stau - be Wie Staub und Rauch ver-
trust: What proves its firm en - dur - ance, When this world turns to
crois; E - tran - ger sur la ter - re, Je mar - che par la

weht. Ich weiss was e - wig blei - bet, Wo al - les wankt und
dust. I know what bides e - ter - nal Where all else shakes and
foi. Je sais ce qui de - meu - re Quand le fu - nè - bre

fällt, Wo Wahn die Wei - sen trei - bet Und Trug die Klu-gen hält.
falls, When fraud from foes in - fer - nal Earth's shrewd-est wits en - thrals.
glas Ap-pel - le, d'heure en heu - re, Les sa - ges d'i - ci - bas.

2. Ich weiss, was ewig dauert,
   Ich weiss, was nie verlässt.
Auf ew'gem Grund gemauert
   Steht diese Schutzwehr fest.
Es sind des Heiland's Worte,
Die Worte fest und klar,
An diesem Felsenhorte
Halt ich unwandelbar.

4. Er, den man blutbedecket
   Am Abend einst begrub ;
Er, der von Gott erwecket
   Sich aus dem Grab erhub ;
Der meine Schuld versöhnet,
Der seinen Geist mir schenkt,
Der mich mit Gnade krönet
Und ewig mein gedenkt.

3. Auch kenn ich wohl den Meister,
   Der mir die Feste baut :
Es ist der Herr der Geister,
   Auf den der Himmel schaut.
Vor dem die Seraphinen
Anbetend niederknien,
Um den die Heil'gen dienen :
Ich weiss und kenne ihn.

5. Drum weiss ich, was ich glaube,
   Ich weiss, was fest besteht
Und in dem Erdenstaube
   Nicht mit als Staub verweht.
Es bleibet mir im Grauen
Des Todes ungeraubt ;
Es schmückt auf Himmelsauen
Mit Kronen einst mein Haupt.

ERNST MORITZ ARNDT (1769-1860).

* * *

2. I know what never faileth,
   But evermore endures ;
A fort, when Hell assaileth,
   In safety me secures :
The words of Christ my Saviour
My refuge are and tower,
They show His grace and favour
And shield in danger's hour.

4. My Lord was slain, abasèd
   By those He died to save :
But God His Son upraisèd
   Victorious o'er the grave.
My guilt He has forgiven,
He crowns me with His grace,
His spirit comes from Heaven
To lead me to His face.

3. My Rock and my Defender
   Right well my soul doth know :
All Heav'n glows with His splendour,
   He rules His Church below.
Him, seraphs, with love burning,
Adore, on bended knee :
His Saints on earth are yearning
For His Epiphany.

5. And so, with full assurance,
   In Him I place my trust :
I'll prove His firm endurance
   When this world turns to dust.
When death's dark shades are o'er me
He'll keep me in His hand,
Till, crowned with those in glory,
Beside His throne I stand.

Trans. R. BIRCH HOYLE (1923).

* * *

2. Je sais ce qui ne cesse,
   Ce qui ne trompe pas,
Et quelle forteresse
   Dieu m'offre dans ses bras.
Je crois à la Parole
Que rien n'effacera ;
Tout fuit et tout s'envole,
Elle est et restera.

4. Par un dur sacrifice
   Il assura ma paix
Du joug de l'injustice
   Me sauva pour jamais
Sur la croix d'infamie
   Christ fut cloué pour moi
Sa mort sera ma vie,
   Je le sais, je le crois.

3. Je sais à quel bon maître
   J'ai remis mon destin
Et pourquoi je puis être
   Tranquille pour demain.
Dieu règne sur la terre,
Il règne dans les cieux,
Il est, profond mystère,
Et mon Père et mon Dieu !

5. Je sais ce qui demeure
   Et m'est un sûr appui,
Je sais une demeure,
   Un éternel abri.
Vers la sombre vallée
Je marche sans frayeur :
Pour l'âme rachetée
Il est un sûr bonheur.

Trad. J. VINCENT (1934).

76

Irish Traditional Melody.
SLANE.*

Be Thou my vi - sion, O Lord of my heart; Naught be all
Herr mei - nes Her-zens, Gib du auf mich acht! Oh - ne dich
Qu'en toi je vi - ve, Sei - gneur bien - ai - mé, O sour - ce

else to me Save that Thou art, Thou my best tho't, By
bleib ich in Ne - bel und Nacht! Oh - ne dich sind die Ge-
vi - ve de fé - li - ci - té, Qu'à toi je pen - se Le

day or by night, Wak-ing or sleep-ing, Thy pre-sence my light!
dan-ken ver-wirrt. Sei ge-gen-wär - tig, Mein Hei - land und Hirt!
jour et la nuit, Car ta clé-men - ce Tou - jours me bé - nit.

2.

Be Thou my wisdom,
   Thou my true word
I ever with Thee,
   Thou with me, Lord;
Thou my great Father,
   I Thy true son;
Thou in me dwelling,
   And I with Thee one.

3.

Be Thou my battle-shield,
   Sword for the fight;
Be Thou my dignity,
   Thou my delight,
Thou my soul's shelter,
   Thou my high tow'r;
Raise Thou me heav'nward,
   O pow'r of my pow'r.

* *Tune :* From Dr. Joyce's Ancient Irish Music. By permission of Educational Company of
   Ireland Ltd.
   Harmony : By permission of Oxford University Press.
   Words : By permission of the Executors of Miss E. Hull.

4. Riches I heed not,
    Nor man's empty praise,
Thou mine inheritance,
    Now and always:
Thou and Thou only,
    First in my heart,
High King of heav'n,
    My treasure Thou art.

5. High King of heaven,
    After victory won
May I reach heaven's joys,
    O bright heav'n's son!
Heart of my own heart,
    Whatever befall
Still be my vision,
    O Ruler of all.

Ancient Irish. Transl. MARY BYRNE;
Versified by ELEANOR HULL.

★ ★ ★

2. Ewige Weisheit,
    Wahrhaftiges Wort!
Heiliger Vater,
    Mein Herr hier und dort!
Hilf uns zur Kindschaft
    Und eine die Welt,
Die mit sich selber
    In Feindschaft zerfällt.

3. Gib uns die Würde,
    Die jeder verlor!
Führ uns zur Heimat
    Und öffne das Tor;
Zuflucht gewähre
    Dem, den du befreit!
Herr, mein Erretter,
    Mein Schutzherr im Streit!

4. Kostbar ist, König,
    Was du uns getan!
Mit neuen Augen
    Seh'n wir es jetzt an.
Leer ist dagegen,
    Was Menschen erdacht,
Reichtum und Ehre
    Vergeh'n über Nacht.

5. Herrscher der Himmel,
    Bei dem aller Krieg
Unter dem Wort sich
    Verwandelt in Sieg!
Herr meines Herzens,
    Wie gern bin ich dein!
Ohne dich wär' ich
    Verwirrt und allein.

Übers. HELGA RUSCHE (1950).

★ ★ ★

2. Dieu, ta sagesse
    Rayonne sur moi:
Le mal me presse,
    Toujours garde-moi;
Père, fais grâce,
    Pardonne à ton fils,
Montre ta face,
    Vis en mon esprit.

3. Lorsque je ploie
    Sois mon ferme appui,
Donne ta joie,
    Sois mon sûr abri,
Ma forteresse,
    Mon seul bouclier,
De la détresse
    Tu sais me garder.

4. Fuir la richesse,
    Les propos flatteurs,
Dans l'allégresse
    Servir le Seigneur:
Mon bien suprême
    C'est lui, mon Sauveur,
Car si je l'aime,
    Il vit dans mon cœur.

5. A toi la gloire,
    Seigneur notre Dieu,
Car ta victoire
    Nous ouvre les cieux.
Fais, ô bon Maître,
    Toujours, en tous lieux,
A tous connaître
    Ton nom glorieux.

Trad. FLOSSETTE DU PASQUIER (1951).

77

Melodie EISLEBEN (1598).
Satz : 1939.

Aus mei - nes Her - zens Grun - de, Sag' ich dir Lob und
D'un cœur con - trit j'ex - ha - le Ma vie et mon sou-
My in - most heart now rais - es In this fair mor - ning

Dank In die - ser Mor - gen - stun - de, Da - zu mein Le - ben
ci. A l'heu - re ma - ti - na - le Je crie à Dieu mer-
hour, A song of thank - ful prais - es To Thine Al - might - y

lang, O Gott, in dei - nem Thron, dir zu Lob, Preis und Eh-
ci. Quand sur son trône as - sis, Il règne en sa vic - toi-
pow'r; And as I have be - gun This day, my God, my life shall

ren durch Chri-stum un - sern Her - ren, dein' ein - ge - bor-nen Sohn.
re Je loue et chan - te gloi - re Par Christ, Jé - sus, son Fils.
be Be-gun and closed with praise to Thee, Through Christ Thy on - ly Son.

2.

Dass du mich hast aus Gnaden
  In der vergang'nen Nacht
Vor G'fahr und allem Schaden
  Behütet und bewacht.
Ich bitt' demütiglich,
Wollst mir mein Sünd'vergeben,
  Womit in diesem Leben
  Ich hab'erzürnet dich.

3.

Gott will ich lassen raten,
  Denn er all'Ding vermag.
Er segne meine Taten,
  Mein Vornehmen und Sach';
  Ihm hab'ich heimgestellt
Mein Leib, mein Seel', mein Leben,
Und was er sonst gegeben ;
  Er mach's, wie's ihm gefällt.

4.

Darauf so sprech ich Amen
  Und zweifle nicht daran,
Gott wird es all's zusammen
  In Gnaden sehen an ;
  Und streck nun aus mein' Hand,
Greif an das Werk mit Freuden,
Dazu mich Gott bescheiden
  In mein Beruf und Stand.

GEORG NIEGE (1525-1588).

* * *

2.

Ta grâce, aux nuits d'orage,
  Aux sombres jours passés,
Du mal, de tout dommage,
  Toujours m'a su garder.
Je t'ai fort irrité
Au long de cette vie.
Je prie, ô Dieu, supplie,
  Pardonne mon péché.

3.

Je prête à Dieu l'oreille
  Car tout me fait défaut,
Lui seul toujours conseille
  Guidant projets, travaux.
Il est mon souverain,
Oui, tout ce qu'il réclame :
Mon corps, mon sang, mon âme,
  Qu'il prenne tout en main.

4.

Je crois, Seigneur, j'espère,
  Que craindre auprès de toi ?
Ta grâce salutaire
  Prend soin de tout pour moi.
Je vais offrir mes mains,
A l'œuvre plein de joie,
Car Dieu choisit ma voie
  Et fixe mon destin.

Trad. PAULINE MARTIN (1950).

* * *

2.

For Thou from me hast warded
  All perils of the night ;
From every harm hast guarded
  My soul till morning's light ;
  Humbly to Thee I cry,
Do Thou in grace the sins forgive
That anger Thee each day I live,
  Have mercy, Lord most high !

3.

And keep me of Thy kindness
  From every harm today ;
Nor let me in my blindness
  To Satan fall a prey,
  My cup with good o'erflows,
My soul and body, goods and life,
My home and friends, my child and wife,
  Thy bounteous hand bestows.

4.

Amen ! I say, not fearing
That God rejects my prayer,
I doubt not He is hearing
And granting me His care ;
And so I go my way,
And joyfully put forth my hands
To do the work that He commands,
And serve Him through the day.

Trans. CATHERINE WINKWORTH (1829-1878).

— 78 —

Scottish Psalter (1615).
As given in Ravenscroft Psalter (1621).

Moderately slow

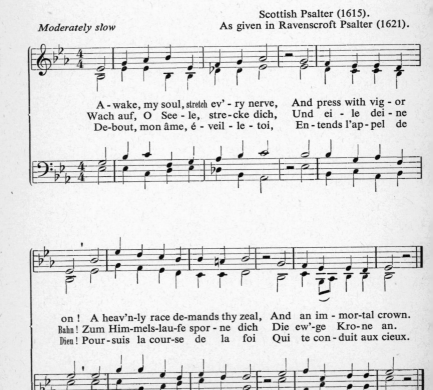

A - wake, my soul, stretch ev' - ry nerve, And press with vig - or
Wach auf, O See - le, stre - cke dich, Und ei - le dei - ne
De-bout, mon âme, é - veil - le - toi, En - tends l'ap - pel de

on ! A heav'n-ly race de-mands thy zeal, And an im - mor-tal crown.
Bahn ! Zum Him-mels-lau-fe spor - ne dich Die ew'-ge Kro-ne an.
Dieu ! Pour-suis la cour-se de la foi Qui te con - duit aux cieux.

2.

A cloud of witnesses around
  Hold thee in full survey :
Forget the steps already trod,
  And onward urge thy way !

3.

'Tis God's all-animating voice
  That calls thee from on high ;
'Tis His own hand presents the prize
  To thine aspiring eye, —

4.

That prize with peerless glories bright
  Which shall new lustre boast
When victors' wreaths and monarchs' gems
  Shall blend in common dust.

PHILIP DODDRIDGE (1702-1751).

* * *

2.

Der Zeugen Wolke um dich her
  Schaut deinem Jagen zu.
Vergiss den Schritt, den du getan,
  Und vorwärts dränge du !

3.

S'ist Gottes Stimme, die dich ruft,
  Die alle Welt belebt,
S'ist seine Hand, die dir den Preis
  Hoch vor die Augen hebt.

4.

Das Kleinod, dessen Strahlenglanz
  Auf's Neue triumphiert,
Wenn Diadem und Herrscherkranz
  Sich längst im Staub verliert.

Übers. KURT WIEGERING (1950).

* * *

2.

Vois-tu, vivant à tes côtés
  La foule des témoins ;
Libère-toi de ton passé
  Suis un nouveau chemin.

3.

Entends la voix du Dieu vivant
  Qui vient du haut des cieux ;
Il tend le prix à son enfant,
  Un trésor précieux.

4.

Aucun trésor du genre humain
  Ne sera éternel.
Préfère-leur ce prix divin,
  Lui seul est immortel.

Trad. EVA DUBSKA-KUSHNER (1951).

Psaume 25
Recueil Pierre Attaignant, Paris (1530)
et Recueil d'Anvers (1540).

A toi, mon cœur, O Dieu Sau - veur, En qui seul
Nur dein soll sein Das Her - ze mein, Herr Gott, du
Its on - ly joy, Sav - iour and Lord, To Thee my

est ma joi - e! Tu m'as re - mis, Tu m'as con-
mei - ne Freu - de. Dein Wort mich weist, Dein Gnad' mich
heart dis - clo - ses; Thy hand re - stores me to the

duit Dans u - ne jus - te voi - e. Ni les fa-
speist Und gibt mir das Ge - lei - te. Denn al - le
way, And ev - ery step dis - po - ses. Nei - ther de-

veurs, Ni les ter - reurs Du mon - de qui s'ef - fa - ce Ne
Macht Und gros - se Pracht Der Welt muss doch ver - ge - hen, Du
lights nor ter - rors here Nor this world's tran-sient sto - ry Can

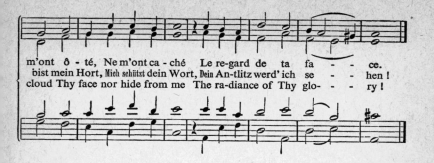

m'ont ô - té, Ne m'ont ca - ché Le re-gard de ta fa - - ce.
bist mein Hort, Mich schützt dein Wort, Dein An-tlitz werd' ich se - - hen!
cloud Thy face nor hide from me The ra-diance of Thy glo- - -ry!

2.	2.
A toi mon cœur,	Nur dein soll sein
Consolateur,	Das Herze mein
Esprit saint que j'adore!	Du Hilf' und Trost der Armen!
Vois les combats	Sieh meinen Streit,
Que pas à pas	Und sieh mein Leid',
Je dois livrer encore.	Und hab' mit mir Erbarmen.
De mes péchés	Des Bösen Kraft,
Veuille arracher	Die in mir schafft,
Jusqu'aux dernières traces.	Wollst gänzlich du zerstören.
Pour mon bonheur	Zu deiner Ehr'
Et pour l'honneur	Den Glauben mehr'!
De la foi que j'embrasse.	Lass mich nur dir gehören!

LÉON JUDAE (1483-1542).

Übers. KURT WIEGERING (1950)
und WOLFGANG SCHWEITZER (1950).

* * *

2.

O Holy Spirit, Comforter,
Possess I now implore Thee
This sinner still by conflicts torn
And falling down before Thee;
In mercy come to loose my chains,
The bonds of sin to sever,
That I by faith Thy grace receive,
Thy name to praise forever.

Trans. NANSIE ANDERSON (1949).

— 80 (2) —

Nederlandsche Gedenck-Clanck.
ADRIANUS VALERIUS (1626).

Risoluto

Wilt he - den nu tre - den voor God den
Wir tre - ten zum Be - ten vor Gott den
We ga - ther, dear Fa - ther, in pray'r be-
Sei - gneur, tes en - fants au - jour - d'hui s'u-

Hee - re, Hem bo - ven al lo - ven van her - ten
Her - ren, Ihn dro - ben zu lo - ben mit Herz und
fore Thee; Thee prais - ing, up - rais - ing our joy - ful
nis - sent, Ils veu - lent chan - ter ton a - mour sau-

zeer En ma - ken groot zijns lie - ven na - mens
Mund: So rüh - met froh sein's lie - ben Na-mens
strain; We bless Thy pre - cious Name as we a-
veur, Leurs voix, leurs cœurs, leurs â - mes te bé-

ee - re, Die daar nu on - zen vij - and slaat ter neer !
Eh - ren, Der nun vor uns den Feind warf auf den Grund !
dore Thee; Thine arm o'er Sa-tan's realm doth vict' - ry gain.
nis - sent O Dieu, car de Sa - tan tu es vain - queur.

2. Ter eeren ons Heeren wilt al uw dagen
   Dit wonder bijzonder gedenken toch;
   Maackt u, o mensch, voor God steeds wel te dragen;
   Doet ieder recht en wacht u voor bedrog.

3. Bidt, waket en maket, dat g'in bekoring
   En 't kwade met schade toch, niet en valt.
   Uw vroomheid brengt den vijand tot verstoring,
   Al waar' zijn rijk nog eens zoo sterk bewald.

Danklied uit 1597.

★ ★ ★

2. Zu Ehren des Herren wollt, weil ihr lebet,
   Ihm danken, ohn' wanken, dies Wunder gross;
   Vor seinem Aug' stets rein zu wandeln strebet,
   Tut recht und sagt von Lug und Trug euch los!

3. Wacht, flehet, bestehet im guten Streite,
   Mit Schande in Bande der Sünd nicht fallt!
   Dem frommen Volk gibt Gott den Feind zur Beute,
   Und wär noch eins so gross sein's Reich's Gewalt!

Übers. KARL BUDDE (1896).

★ ★ ★

2. Soul, ponder each wonder the Lord is working.
   Unfailing, prevailing He holdeth thee fast.
   Walk neath His eye, no charge He gives thee shirking;
   Do right, speak truth, keep pure while life shall last.

3. Unsleeping, be keeping what God bestoweth;
   Be pray'rful and careful from sin to keep free.
   Through God's sure help, each faithful soldier knoweth
   O'er foes of hell he shall triumphant be.

Trans. R. BIRCH HOYLE (1929).

★ ★ ★

2. Seigneur, nous voulons célébrer ta gloire,
   O Dieu trois fois saint, nous te bénissons,
   Et nous voulons proclamer la victoire
   Du Dieu qui de son Fils nous a fait don.

3. Je veux, Eternel, rechercher tes voies,
   Toujours je t'implore, aide-moi, Seigneur;
   Oh! daigne me donner enfin ta joie
   Et fais que du péché je sois vainqueur.

Trad. FLOSSETTE DU PASQUIER (1951).

— 81 (86) —

« Kings Lynn » *
English Traditional Melody.

To be sung in unison

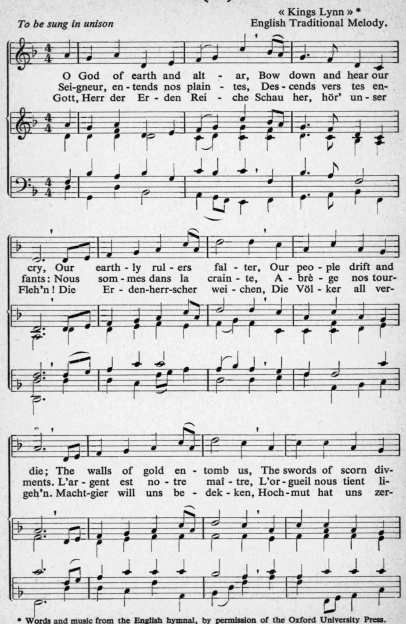

O God of earth and alt - ar, Bow down and hear our
Sei-gneur, en - tends nos plain - tes, Des - cends vers tes en -
Gott, Herr der Er - den Rei - che Schau her, hör' un - ser

cry, Our earth - ly rul - ers fal - ter, Our peo - ple drift and
fants: Nous som - mes dans la crain - te, A - brè - ge nos tour -
Fleh'n! Die Er - den-herr-scher wei - chen, Die Völ - ker all ver -

die; The walls of gold en - tomb us, The swords of scorn div -
ments. L'ar - gent est no - tre maî - tre, L'or - gueil nous tient li -
geh'n. Macht-gier will uns be - dek - ken, Hoch-mut hat uns zer -

* Words and music from the English hymnal, by permission of the Oxford University Press.

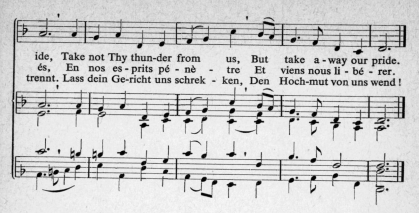

ide, Take not Thy thun-der from us, But take a - way our pride.
és, En nos es-prits pé - nè - tre Et viens nous li - bé - rer.
trennt. Lass dein Ge-richt uns schrek - ken, Den Hoch-mut von uns wend !

2.

From all that terror teaches,
    From lies of tongue and pen,
From all the easy speeches
    That comfort cruel men,
From sale and profanation
    Of honour and the sword,
From sleep and from damnation,
    Deliver us, good Lord !

3.

Tie in a living tether
    The prince and priest and thrall,
Bind all our lives together,
    Smite us and save us all ;
In ire and exultation
    Aflame with faith, and free,
Lift up a living nation,
    A single sword to Thee.

GILBERT KEITH CHESTERTON (1874-1936).

*   *   *

2.

Si la terreur nous ronge,
    Seigneur, rassure-nous.
Du mal et du mensonge,
    Seigneur, délivre-nous.
De profaner ta gloire,
    Oh ! garde-nous, Seigneur,
Toi seul as la victoire
    Et donnes le bonheur.

3.

Les grands de cette terre
    Aux humbles sont égaux,
Et pour toi, tendre Père,
    Il n'est qu'un seul troupeau ;
Seigneur, toi qui pardonnes
    Au cœur qui se repent,
Inspire tous les hommes
    Par ton amour ardent.

Trad. FLOSSETTE DU PASQUIER (1951).

*   *   *

2.

Die Allgewalt der Lügen,
    Die Macht der Tyrannei
Und was uns will betrügen
    Durch dich bezwungen sei.
Was leichthin mag verraten
    Die Ehre und das Schwert,
Trägheit und Missetaten
    Sei, Herr, von dir gewehrt !

3.

Bind Fürst und Volk zusammen,
    Die Kirche und das Reich ;
Lass unser Leben flammen
    Und hilf uns allzugleich.
In Zorn und Glück, im Leben
    Und Glauben gleich geehrt,
Lass uns zu dir erheben
    O Herr, ein einig Schwert !

Übers. HANNS LILJE (1938)

— 82 (91) —

« Picardy » *
French Traditional Carol
Arr. by GUSTAV HOLST (1874-1934).

Let all mort-al flesh keep sil - ence, and with fear and
Oh ! que tou-te chair se tai - se, fré-mis-sant d'un
Mensch-lich We - sen müs - se schwei - gen und in Furcht und

trembl - ing stand; Pon - der noth - ing earth - ly - mind - ed,
saint es - poir; Pen - sées é - phé - mè - res, vai - nes
Zit - tern stehn. Ir - disch Den - ken müs - se en - den,

for with bless - ing in His hand, Christ our God to
ah ! quit - tez l'â-me et le cœur. Le Sei - gneur des-
wenn mit Se - gen aus der Höh'n Chri - stus kommt, und

earth de - scen - deth, our full hom-age to de - mand. ———
cend sur ter - re, Dieu lui don - ne tout pou - voir. ———
wir ge - hor - sam un-serm Herrn ent-ge - gen - geh'n. ———

* Printed by permission of Messrs Stainer and Bell Ltd.

2. King of kings, yet born of Mary, as of old on earth He stood,
   Lord of lords, in human vesture — in the Body and the Blood —
   He will give to all the faithful His own Self for heavenly Food.

3. Rank on rank the host of heaven spreads its vanguard on the way,
   As the Light of light descendeth from the realms of endless day,
   That the powers of hell may vanish as the darkness clears away.

4. At His feet the six-winged Seraph ; Cherubim with sleepless eye,
   Veil their faces to the Presence, as with ceaseless voice they cry,
   Alleluia, Alleluia, Alleluia, Lord most high.

Liturgy of St. James. Trans. G. MOULTRIE (1829-1885).

★ ★ ★

2. Roi des rois, ton Fils, Marie, aux jours de sa chair il vint
   Dans le pauvre corps des hommes, des seigneurs pourtant Seigneur,
   Nourrir et sauver le monde, dont il est le pain divin.

3. O Prince de paix, de grâce, toi qui sais calmer la mer,
   Fais triompher la lumière, fais tomber du ciel Satan !
   Dans nos tristes cœurs, si lâches, Christ, fais reculer l'enfer !

4. Tandis que le chœur des anges chante, en se voilant les yeux :
   Gloire à celui qui se donne, qui se rend obéissant
   Jusques à la mort infâme ; gloire au Christ venu des cieux !

Trad. SUZANNE BIDGRAIN (1937).

★ ★ ★

2. Grosser König, Sohn der Jungfrau, wie er einst auf Erden ging.
   Herr der Herren, den auf Erden irdisch Fleisch und Blut umfing —
   Gab sich selbst dem frommen Herzen, das im Glauben an ihm hing.

3. Aller Himmel heil'ge Heere hielten Wacht auf seiner Bahn.
   Licht vom ungeschaffnen Lichte brach der ew'ge Morgen an,
   Und die Höllenmächte wankten als die Nacht sie schwinden sah'n.

4. Die Seraphen mit sechs Flügeln und der Cherubinen Wacht
   Haben mit verhülltem Antlitz unermüdlich Lob gebracht :
   Halleluja, Halleluja, sein ist Preis und Ehr und Macht !

Übers. HANNS LILJE (1937).

83

« Picardy » *
French Traditional Carol
Harm. GUSTAV HOLST (1874-1934).

Judge e - ter - nal, thron'd in splen-dour, Lord of lords and
Herr, um den die En - gel sin - gen, Herr, vor dem die
E - ter - nel, aux cieux tu rè - gnes Ray - on - nant dans

King of kings, With Thy liv - ing fire of judg - ment
Her - ren knien, Lass dein Feu - er uns durch - drin - gen,
ta splen - deur, Roi des rois, Sei - gneur su - prê - me,

Purge this land of bit - ter things ; Sol - ace all its wide dom-
Un - ser ar - mes Land durch-glühn, Strei - che mit des Geis - tes
Donne au mon - de le bon - heur ; No - tre mi - sère est ex-

in - - - ion With the heal - ing of Thy wings.
Schwin - - - gen Hei - lend ü - ber uns da - hin.
trê - - - me, Viens con - so - ler nos dou - leurs.

2.

Still the weary folk are pining,
  For the hour that brings release ;
And the city's crowded clangour
  Cries aloud for sin to cease ;
And the homesteads and the woodlands
  Plead in silence for their peace.

3.

Crown, O God, Thine own endeavour :
  Cleave our darkness with Thy sword :
Feed the faint and hungry people
  With the richness of Thy word :
Cleanse the body of this nation
  Thro' the Glory of the Lord.

HENRY SCOTT HOLLAND (1847-1918) *.

★ ★ ★

2.

Wann ist uns der Tag beschieden,
  Welcher Rettung bringen kann ?
All die Armen, all die Müden
  In den Städten Mann bei Mann,
Gnade wollen sie und Frieden :
  Sieh' die Not der Sünder an !

3.

Weinen wendest du in Lachen,
  Durch ein Wort kann es gescheh'n !
Herr, du wirst ein Ende machen,
  Vor der Welt als Sieger steh'n,
Dass wir Armen, dass wir Schwachen
  Deine Herrlichkeiten seh'n !

Übers. JOHANN CHRISTOPH HAMPE (1950).

★ ★ ★

2.

Tes enfants, dans leur faiblesse,
  Sans relâche t'ont prié ;
Dans les cités ils se pressent
  Sans repos, ni liberté.
Les champs et les bois se taisent,
  Implorant pour eux la paix.

3.

Daigne tenir tes promesses,
  Brille en notre obscurité,
Donne aux tristes l'allégresse,
  Et soutiens les opprimés.
Viens soulager nos détresses,
  Seigneur Dieu, par ta bonté.

Trad. FLOSSETTE DU PASQUIER (1951).

* Words from the English Hymnal. By permission of the Oxford University Press.

84

Danish Folk Song.

Vi - dun - der - ligst af alt på jord Er
Most won - drous is of all on earth The
Die schöns - te Zier auf die - ser Welt, Ist
Oui ton roy - aume, ô Christ vi - vant, Ex-

Je - su Kris - ti ri - ge; Dets her - lig - hed er
King - dom Je - sus found - ed, Its glo - ry, peace and
Je - sus Reich so präch - tig, Das Dun - kel ward vom
is - te sur la ter - re, Sa gloire et son ray-

og så stor, At det har in - gen li - ge.
pre - cious worth No tongue has ev - er sound - ed.
Licht er - hellt, Durch Got - tes Wort all mäch - tig.
on - ne - ment Ne sont pas é - phé - mè - res.

2.

Usynligt vel som sjæl og sind
  Det nemt dog er at kende,
Alt som en stad på bjergetind,
  Der ses til verdens ende.

3.

Dets gåde er et guddoms-ord,
  Som skaber, hvad det nævner,
Som fylder dale trindt på jord
  Og klipperne udjævner.

4.

Lad hvisle kun i ormegård,
  At riget er lagt öde,
Gud kroner lige fuldt dets år
  Med frugtbarhed og gröde.

5.

Dets glans opstår som aks i vang,
  Som maj i bögeskove,
Ja, prægtig under fuglesang
  Som gylden-sol af vove.

6.

Det er den store konges glans,
  Som kun på korset döde,
For at med livets rosenkrans
  Jordklimpen ham kan möde.

7.

Ja, når han kommer i det blå,
  Er kristnes kamp til ende,
Hvad troende i spejlet så,
  Skal salige erkende.

8.

Da riget er med sole-kår
  Til syne og til stede
I evighedens gyldenår :
  Med ret og fred og glede !

N. F. S. GRUNDTVIG (1783-1872).

* * *

2.

As breath of wind invisible,
  Its signs are yet revealèd ;
A city set upon a hill
  From men is not concealèd.

3.

Its secret — God's almighty word
  Which heav'n and earth created,
The valleys when His voice they heard
  Were filled, the floods abated.

4.

The tempter by his evil power
  The Kingdom is distressing,
God crowns in His appointed hour
  With joy and fruitful blessing.

5.

It shines like golden harvest ear,
  Or leaves of beechwood springing;
Like waves in sun it will appear
  While birds in flight are singing.

6.

Its glorious King is He who died
  Upon the Cross to save us,
New joy unto the world to bring
  His very life He gave us.

7.

And when He comes again to reign
  The strife will have an ending ;
What yet to faith was not made plain
  The bless'd are comprehending.

8.

Then comes the year of Jubilee,
  Fulfilled the agelong story ;
The heavenly reign shall all men see
  Of justice, peace and glory.

Trans. JEAN FRASER (1951).

* * *

2.

Wie Geist und Seele unsichtbar,
So ist es doch zu sehen,
Wie eine Stadt wird offenbar
Auf steilen Berges Höhen.

3.

Beschlossen war's in Gottes Rat
Bereits von Ewigkeiten,
Er wird in seiner Schöpfungstat,
Unebenheiten gleichen.

4.

« Zerstört wird sein des Herren Reich »,
Mag auch die Schlange höhnen,
Er segnet doch die Erde reich,
Und wird die Jahre krönen.

5.

Sein' Pracht ist wie ein Ernte Rain,
Wie Buchengrün im Lenze,
Mit Vögel Singen — wird's erschein
Ein Meer im Sonnenglanze.

6.

Die Glorie ist's des grossen Gott,
Für uns am Kreuz gestorben,
Dem Mensch in seiner tiefsten Not,
Hat Leben er erworben.

7.

Der Kampf der Christen hat ein End',
Wenn Christ der Herr wird kommen,
Die gläubig waren doch geblend't
Der Schleier wird genommen.

8.

Wenn einst die Zeiten sind erfüllt,
Das helle Reich wird kommen,
Dann allen Augen wird's enthüllt,
Freude and Fried' den Frommen.

Übers. ANNE-MARIE SCHAEFER (1951).

★ ★ ★

2.

Nos yeux ne peuvent pas le voir,
Mais sur la terre entière
Nos âmes peuvent percevoir
L'éclat de sa lumière.

3.

Ton verbe est saint, ô Dieu très bon,
Sa puissance est divine
Et pourra soulever les monts,
Aplanir les collines.

4.

Au jeu maudit des passions
Le royaume est en butte,
Mais Dieu bénira sa moisson,
Il gagnera la lutte.

5.

Il est comme un épi des champs
Ou comme un bois de hêtres,
Comme un soleil étincelant
Lorsqu'il vient de paraître.

6.

C'est la splendeur d'un très grand roi
Mort d'une mort infâme,
Mais en mourant il nous sauva
Et racheta nos âmes.

7.

Oui, quand il descendra des cieux,
Nous verrons face à face
Le Fils de l'homme et notre Dieu,
Eclairés par la grâce.

8.

Et ce royaume éblouissant,
Dans la joie éternelle,
Accueillera tous ses enfants,
Tous ses sujets fidèles.

Trad. FLOSSETTE DU PASQUIER (1951).

— 85 (92) —

楊蔭瀏 詞

Air chinois ancien.
Harmonisé par ROGER VUATAZ (1951).

(一) 愛之泉源救世神曾將十架奠南
針解決人生諸矛盾入世廣佈救拯
多恩感謝仁愛慈悲主真理光采啟幽昏

O Dieu, de ton corps bles - sé L'a - mour se ré - pand sur
Dank sei dir, Hei - land der Welt, Der das Kreuz uns auf - ge-
God the love that saved man-kind Raised the Cross our sure land-

nous. Par nos pro-pres mains fi - xé Ton bras nous me - su - re
stellt, Ziel und Lö-sung uns - rer Not. Lie - bes - born, durch dei - nen
mark, Gui-ding us through wind - ing ways. Praise we Him Who brought the

tous. Sur nos fronts hon-teux, ploy - és, Fais des-cen - dre ta pi - tié.
Tod Hast du in die Er-den-nacht Dei - ner Wahr-heit Licht ge-bracht.
blind Grace that doth dis - pel the dark By di-vine truth's liv - ing blaze.

南　針　歌

(二) 呼號時代煩悶中　不知生命真意義
(三) 世事反覆多變更　理想終歸成泡影
(四) 紛歧路口久徬徨　萬般主義擾心腸
(五) 主在黑暗世塵中　賞賜自由救墮落

(二) 周圍但覺滿陰沉　目倦身污心厭世
(三) 因所希望皆虛空　枯水無源樹無本
(四) 左右皆非何所擇　欲求息足無地方
(五) 主在紛歧道路間　指點迷羊示歸宿

(二) 求主舉起希望光　瞻見樂園景美麗
(三) 求主佈賜救恩霖　潤澤栽培真生命
(四) 求主伸出扶助手　引上正道使安康
(五) 求引萬眾進窄門　到主面前同喜樂

* * *

2.
Tant de crainte et de combats
 Nous font vite perdre cœur ;
Seules montent de là-bas
 Les ténèbres de la peur.
Devant nos yeux éblouis
 Fais briller ton paradis.

3.
Mais bien vains sont nos efforts
 Dieu, toi seul peux nous aider ;
Viens nourrir nos pauvres corps,
 Revêts-nous de ta clarté,
Nous recevrons à genoux
 Et la manne et l'eau sur nous.

4.
Notre cœur est partagé
 De désirs par trop humains.
Par ta grâce protégé
 Il prendra les vrais chemins.
Oh ! étends sur nous ton bras,
 Viens guider nos faibles pas.

5.
Parmi notre obscurité,
 Seigneur, sur notre horizon,
Resplendisse ton été
 Et se montre la maison,
Où nous pourrons à jamais
 Vivre avec toi dans la paix.

Trad. HENRI CAPIEU (1938).

* * *

2.
Zeit der Ängste, Zeit des Kriegs,
 Unsichtbar das Ziel des Siegs.
Sinnlos alles, ohne Glut...
 Spül' mit deiner Gnadenflut
Uns're trüben Augen aus,
 Führ die müde Seel' nach Haus.

3.
Wahn ist alles, eitler Traum,
 Unser Streben leerer Schaum,
Wurzellos ist unser Herz,
 Nichts in uns ragt himmelwärts.
Netze, feuchte mein Gemüt,
 Dass die dürre Seele blüht.

4.
Irr am Kreuzweg stehen wir,
 Ach wo ist der Weg zu dir ?
Zeig, O Herr, der Seele an,
 Wo sie sicher ruhen kann.
Hebe deinen starken Arm,
 Gib uns Frieden, schütz vor Harm !

5.
Gott belohnet den, der frei,
 Stehet dem Gefall'nen bei.
Hoffe drum, verirrter Mut,
 Christ am Kreuzweg führt dich gut
Durch das enge Himmelstor
 Zu der Seligkeit empor.

Übers. CONSTANTIN SCHWANN (1938).

* * *

2.
Babel voices round us rise ;
 Grief and torment, blood and dust
Hide all meaning and all light.
 Burdened hearts and aching eyes
Seek their Lord in love and trust,
 Praying that He end their night.

3.
Quiet from the earth is fled ;
 Vain is hope, and striving vain,
Like dead water and dead wood
 Severed from the fountainhead.
Send Thou down like healing rain
 Grace that brings forth truth and
 [good.

4.
Where a cross-road comes, we stand
 Rent by inner questioning,
Aims that differ and delude.
 Stretch Thou forth Thy guiding hand,
And Thy wandering people bring
 Into peace and plenitude.

5.
Free the vanquished and enslaved,
 And those sunk in pain and hate,
By Thy glorious sacrifice.
 Lead Thou them whom Thou hast
Upward through the narrow gate [saved
 To the joy of Paradise.

Trans. MARGARET BARCLAY (1951).

— 86 (53) —

Orthodoxe Kirchen-Musik.*

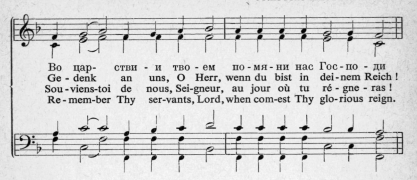

Во цар - стви - и тво - ем по - мя - ни нас Гос - по - ди
Ge - denk an uns, O Herr, wenn du bist in dei - nem Reich!
Sou - viens-toi de nous, Sei-gneur, au jour où tu ré - gne - ras!
Re - mem-ber Thy ser-vants, Lord, when com-est Thy glo-rious reign.

Бла - жен - ни ни - щи - и ду-хом я-котех есть царство не-бесно-е.
Se - lig sind die geist-lich Ar-men; denn das Him-mels-kö - nig-reich ist ihr.
Heu-reux sont en Dieu les pau-vres, car c'est pour eux que s'ou-vri-ront les cieux.
Bless-èd are the poor in spir - it; for the heav-en-ly King-dom is theirs.

2.

Блаженни плачущии яко тии утешатся.

Блаженни кротции яко тии наследят землю.

Блаженни алчущшии и жаждущшии правды яко тии насытятся.

Блаженни милостивии яко тии помилованы будут.

Блаженни чистии сердцем яко тии Бога узрят.

Блаженни миротворцы яко тии сынове Божии нарекутся.

Блаженни изгнанны правды ради яко тех есть царство небесное.

Блаженни есте егда поносят вас и изженут и рекут всяк зол глагол
на вы лжуще Мене ради.

Радуйтеся и веселитеся яко мзда ваша многа на небеси.

* Vergleiche die Vorbemerkung vor dem Inhaltsverzeichnis.
Voir la note précédant la table des matières.
See note preceding the general index.

2.

Selig sind, die da Leid tragen, denn sie sollen reich getröstet werd'n.
Selig sind die sanften Mutes ; denn der Erde Reich fällt ihnen zu.
Selig, die hungert und dürstet nach Gerechtigkeit ; sie werden satt.
Selig sind alle Barmherz'gen ; denn auch ihnen wird Barmherzigkeit.
Selig sind, die reines Herzens ; denn sie werden Gottes Antlitz schau'n.
Selig sind, die Frieden machen ; Kinder Gottes wird ihr Name sein.
Selig, die verfolget werden um Gerechtigkeit ; das Reich ist ihr.
Selig ihr, wenn man euch schmähet, fälschlich Übles spricht um meinetwill'n ;
Da freut, freut euch überschwenglich : In den Himmeln wart't eu'r grosser Lohn.

Metrisch gesetzt H. LAEPPLE (1930).

* * *

2.

Heureux aussi ceux qui pleurent, Dieu de sa main, essuiera leurs yeux.
Heureux sont les débonnaires, le monde, un jour, reconnaîtra leur loi.
Heureux dans leur faim les justes, les temps viendront où ils n'auront plus faim.
Heureux fils de la promesse : pitié à qui exerça la pitié ;
Heureux ceux dont l'âme est pure, dans sa clarté ils connaîtront leur Dieu.
Heureux dans la paix céleste ceux qui, sur terre, ont procuré la paix.
Heureux ceux qui, pour Christ, souffrent, car le Royaume des cieux est à eux.
Heureux ceux que l'on outrage. Celui qu'ils ont servi les bénira.
Vous tous, tressaillez de joie, la récompense est grande dans les cieux.

Adaptation J. VINCENT (1930).

* * *

2.

Blessed are they that do mourn ; for their Lord shall wipe away their tears.
Blessed in Him are the meek ; for their heritage shall be the earth.
Blessed are they that seek righteousness ; in that great day their thirst shall be
quenched.
Blessed are they that show mercy ; for God shall be merciful unto them.
Blessed are the pure in heart ; for in that day shall they see their God.
Blessed are they that make peace ; for they shall be called children of God.
Blessed those who suffer for Him ; the righteous own the Kingdom of Heav'n.
Blessed ye whom men revile ; this world shall persecute you for me.
Rejoice, be ye glad in God ; for in Heaven great is your reward.

Trans. M. M. GOWEN (1949).

— 87 (37) —

J. S. BACH (1685-1750).

Make me a cap-tive, Lord, And then I shall be
Nimm mich ge-fan-gen, Herr, Dann ist die Frei-heit
Je m'a-bats de-vant toi, Li-bè-re-moi, Sei-

free; Force me to rend-er up my sword, And
mein. Ent-zie-he mei-ner Hand das Schwert, Dann
gneur. Mon glaive est à tes pieds, ô Roi, Tu

I shall con-queror be. I sink in life's a-
werd' ich Sie-ger sein. Auf ei-gne Kraft ge-
me ren-dras vain-queur. Quand je n'ai que mon

larms When by my-self I stand; Im-
stützt, Ver-sink ich ganz und gar; Wenn
bras, L'an-gois-se me sai-sit, Mais

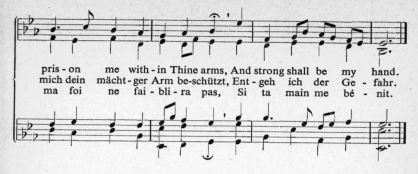

pris - on me with - in Thine arms, And strong shall be my hand.
mich dein mächt - ger Arm be-schützt, Ent - geh ich der Ge - fahr.
ma foi ne fai - bli - ra pas, Si ta main me bé - nit.

2.

My heart is weak and poor
  Until it master find :
It has no spring of action sure,
  It varies with the wind :
It cannot freely move
  Till Thou hast wrought its chain ;
Enslave it with Thy matchless love,
  And deathless it shall reign.

3.

My power is faint and low
  Till I have learned to serve,
It wants the needed fire to glow,
  It wants the breeze to nerve ;
It cannot drive the world
  Until itself be driven,
Its flag can only be unfurled
  When Thou shalt breathe from Heaven.

4.

My will is not my own — Till Thou hast made it Thine ;
If it would reach a monarch's throne — It must its crown resign.
It only stands unbent — Amid the clashing strife,
When on Thy bosom it has leant, — And found in Thee its life.

GEORGE MATHESON (1842-1906).

* * *

2.

Mein Herz, das arm und schwach,
  Verzagt und haltlos ist,
Bleibt unbeständig wie der Wind,
  Bis du sein Herrscher bist.
Es kann sich nicht befrei'n,
  Bis du zerbrichst das Band.
Gefesselt von der Liebe dein
  Ist königlich sein Stand.

3.

Mein Wirken tauget nicht,
  So lang dein Friede fehlt ;
All meine Macht ist Ohnmacht nur,
  Bis mich dein Geist beseelt.
Wenn du mich dienen lehrst,
  Dann wird mein Werk besteh'n
Mein Kreuzesbanner flattert erst,
  Wenn Himmelslüfte weh'n.

4.

Mein Wille ist nicht mein, — Er schwanket her und hin,
Bis du ihn unterworfen hast, — Dann erst beherrsch ich ihn.
Dann wird er stark und still, — Weil deine Kraft ihn hält,
Und er nun anders nicht mehr will, — Als was dir wohlgefällt.

Übers. JOHANNA MEYER († 1921).

* * *

2.

Mon cœur est inconstant,
  Loin du port du salut.
Comme la feuille tremble au vent,
  Il s'agite sans but.
Rends-lui la liberté
  En forgeant ses liens !
Que ton amour illimité
  Lui donne les vrais biens !

3.

Tu me vois sans ardeur,
  Impuissant à servir :
Réchauffe-moi près de ton cœur,
  Ranime mon désir !
Conduis-moi par la main,
  Assure tous mes pas !
Fais-moi sentir l'Esprit divin,
  Que je ne bronche pas !

4.

Je ne m'appartiens plus — Puisque je suis à toi.
Pour régner parmi les élus, — J'abdique, ô Dieu, mon Roi.
Dans mes rudes combats — Je resterai vainqueur,
Si tu me tiens, dès ici-bas, — Tout près de toi, Seigneur.

Trad. FERNAND BARTH (1923).

— 88 —

« Bedford »
Original form of melody
by W. WEALE (d. 1727).

Very slow and dignified

O help us, Lord ! Each hour of need Thy heaven-ly suc-cour
Sei-gneur, que ton cé-leste a-mour Nous garde à tout mo-
Hilf, Herr, der Not, die uns be-trat, Vom Him-mel tritt her

give ; Help us in thought, and word, and deed, Each hour on earth we live.
ment, Qu'il nous pré-ser-ve tous les jours Des maux et des tour-ments.
für ! Hilf in Ge-dan-ken, Wort und Tat, So-lang wir le-ben hier !

2. O help us, when our spirits bleed
      With contrite anguish sore,
   And when our hearts are cold and dead,
      O help us, Lord, the more.

3. O help us through the prayer of faith
      More firmly to believe ;
   For still the more the servant hath,
      The more shall he receive.

4. O help us, Jesu, from on high,
      We know no help but Thee ;
   O help us so to live and die
      As Thine in heaven to be.

H. H. MILMAN (1791-1868).

★ ★ ★

2. Quand nos esprits sont torturés
      Par une affreuse peur,
   Par ton amour et ta bonté,
      Protège-nous, Seigneur.

3. Par la prière et par la foi
      Viens affermir nos cœurs,
   Car nous savons que grâce à toi
      Point n'aurons de malheur.

4. Si nous marchons selon ta loi,
      Tu sauras nous bénir,
   Quand nous mourrons, auprès de toi
      Tu veux nous accueillir.

Trad. FLOSSETTE DU PASQUIER (1950).

★ ★ ★

2. Hilf denen, die in Seelennot,
      In Reu' sich ängsten sehr !
   Und wenn die Herzen kalt und tot,
      Hilf uns nur um so mehr !

3. Hilf, das durch gläubiges Gebet
      Der Glaub' sich in uns mehrt !
   Je höh'r der Knecht im Solde steht —
      Je mehr wird ihm gewährt.

4. Hilf ferner, Heiland, aller Not !
      Wo wär ein Helfer sonst ?
   Hilf uns durchs Leben, durch den Tod
      Bis dahin, wo du thronst !

Übers. WILHELM HÖRKEL (1950).

Moderato   HUUGO NYBERG (1873-).

För Je - su mil - da   ö   gon Jag stäl - ler
De - vant Jé - sus, mon   ju - ge, Je me pré-
Vor Je - su mil - de   Aug - gen Stell ich in
Be - fore Thy eyes, Lord Je - sus, I   look in

mig sä arm jag är. Min skuld och fat - tig - dom jag
sente en l'im - plo - rant. Je me sais pauvre, et viens pour-
mei - ner Ar - mut mich, Und mei - ne Schul-den   tra - ge
all my mis - er - y. My need, my guilt I   bring to

bär För Je - su   mil - da   ö - gon.
tant A ce Jé - sus, mon   ju - ge.
ich Vor Je - su   mil - de   Au - gen.
Thee, Be - fore Thy eyes, Lord Je - sus.

2.

För Jesu milda ögon
Betryckt af synd jag faller ner;
Med längtan i min nöd jag ser
I Jesu milda ögon.

3.

För Jesu milda ögon
Jag syndat har mot Herrens lag;
Min dom däröfver väntar jag
För Jesu milda ögon.

4.

I Jesu milda ögon
Jag ser ; förksjuter han mig, så
Nedsjunkande jag ser ändå
I Jesu milda ögon.

LARS STENBÄCK (1811-1870).

★ ★ ★

2.

Devant Jésus, mon juge,
Je viens, de fautes accablé,
Et je regarde en mon péché
Aux yeux d'un juste juge.

3.

Devant Jésus, mon juge,
Je sais avoir violé la loi,
Mais je m'approche par la foi
De ce Jésus, mon juge.

4.

A ce Jésus, mon juge,
Je viens, du fond de mon malheur,
Et je contemple le Sauveur
Que j'ai pour juste juge.

Trad. L. MONASTIER-SCHROEDER (1923).

★ ★ ★

2.

Vor Jesu milden Augen
Drückt mich darnieder Sünd und Tod.
Mit Sehnsucht seh ich in der Not
In Jesu milde Augen.

3.

Vor Jesu milden Augen
Hab' ich verletzt des Herrn Gebot;
Nun wart' ich, welches Urteil droht
Vor Jesu milden Augen.

4.

In Jesu milde Augen
Seh' ich allzeit. Und will er mich
Verstossen, — sinkend sehe ich
In Jesu milde Augen.

Übers. F. ISRAEL (1923).

★ ★ ★

2.

Before Thy eyes, O Jesus,
Sin-stricken down I prostrate fall,
In agony Thy Name I call,
At Thy bless'd feet, Lord Jesus.

3.

Before Thy eyes, O Jesus,
I often broke God's holy law ;
My soul's sore burden I bring with awe
Before Thy eyes, Lord Jesus.

4.

In Thy tender eyes, O Jesus
I look — to Thee in Faith I cling,
Although to me my doom they bring —
These tender eyes, Lord Jesus.

Trans. unknown.

« Lobt Gott ihr Christen »
NIKOLAUS HERMANN (1485-1561).
Arranged and harm. by J.-S. BACH.

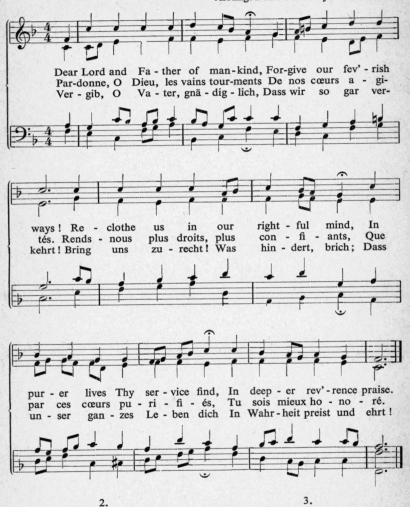

Dear Lord and Fa - ther of man - kind, For - give our fev' - rish
Par - donne, O Dieu, les vains tour - ments De nos cœurs a - gi -
Ver - gib, O Va - ter, gnä - dig - lich, Dass wir so gar ver -

ways ! Re - clothe us in our right - ful mind, In
tés. Rends - nous plus droits, plus con - fi - ants, Que
kehrt ! Bring uns zu - recht ! Was hin - dert, brich ; Dass

pur - er lives Thy ser - vice find, In deep - er rev' - rence praise.
par ces cœurs pu - ri - fi - és, Tu sois mieux ho - no - ré.
un - ser gan - zes Le - ben dich In Wahr - heit preist und ehrt !

2.

In simple trust like theirs who heard,
  Beside the Syrian sea,
The gracious calling of the Lord,
Let us, like them, without a word,
  Rise up and follow Thee.

3.

O Sabbath rest by Galilee,
  O calm of hills above,
Where Jesus knelt to share with Thee
The silence of eternity,
  Interpreted by love !

4.

Drop Thy still dews of quietness,
   Till all our striving cease ;
Take from our souls the strain and stress,
And let our ordered lives confess
   The beauty of Thy peace.

5.

Breathe through the heats of our desire
   Thy coolness and Thy balm ;
Let sense be dumb, let flesh retire ;
Speak through the earthquake, wind and
   O still small voice of calm !   [fire,

J. G. WHITTIER (1807-1892).

* * *

2.

Comme autrefois, au bord des flots,
   Tes premiers serviteurs,
A ton appel fais qu'aussitôt
Nous nous levions vaillants de cœur,
   Pour te suivre, ô Seigneur.

3.

Repos du lac galiléen
   Et de ses doux sommets,
Où Jésus, priant pour les siens,
Rayonnait de l'éclat divin,
   De l'amour, de la paix !

4.

De ce repos profond et doux
   Verse en nous les bienfaits.
Que toute lutte cesse en nous
Et que nous montrions à tous
   La beauté de ta paix.

5.

De notre chair les vains désirs
   Eteins en nous l'ardeur,
A tout péché fais-nous mourir,
Et que ta douce voix, Seigneur,
   Parle seule en nos cœurs.

Trad. E. BUDRY (1930).

* * *

2.

Vertrauend, wie die Jünger dort
   Am See Genezareth,
Lass stracks uns folgen deinem Wort,
Wenn du uns rufst, du unser Hort,
   Wohin dein Weg auch geht !

3.

O Sabbatruhe, hehr und gross
   Auf jener Hügel Kranz,
Da er, der kam aus deinem Schoss,
Sich im Gebete dir ergoss,
   Verklärt von deinem Glanz !

4.

Von solcher Ruhe, Herr, verleih
   Auch uns, was uns gebricht,
Bis — ganz von Müh' und Irrtum frei —
All unser Tun ein Spiegel sei
   Von deines Friedens Licht !

5.

Der Wünsche ungestüme Glut,
   Die wechselnde Begier,
Herr, dämpfe du ; stürmt Fleisch und
Dann züg'le du den wilden Mut,   [Blut,
   Sprich : Friede sei mit dir !

Übers. C. LECHLER (1924).

91

Psaume 137
Mélodie LOYS BOURGEOIS (1542).
Harm. d'après GOUDIMEL (1565).

As - sis au bord du fleuve, à Ba - by - lo - ne,
So sas - sen wir ver - bannt an Ba - bels Was - sern;
Sit - ting be - side the Ba - by - lo - nian wa - ters,

Ter - re d'ex - il où Dieu nous a - ban - don - ne, A - vec
Ver - stos - sen, land - fremd und von Gott ver - las - sen. Da Gram
By God a - ban - doned, where our cap - tors brought us, Sad - ly

dou - leur nous son - gions à Si - on. En ce sé - jour de
uns frass den Tag und nagt' die Nacht, Wir dach - ten Zi - ons,
we thought of Zi - on, longed for home, In this far land of

notre af - flic - ti - on Té - moin des pleurs qu'un jour nous
der ge - stürz - ten Pracht; Und uns' - re Har - fen hin - gen
ex - ile where we roam. Those harps which saw us weep up -

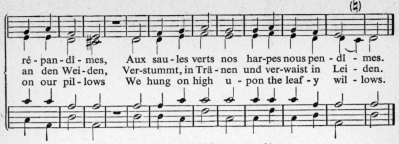

ré - pan - dî - mes, Aux sau - les verts nos har-pes nous pen - dî - mes.
an den Wei - den, Ver-stummt, in Trä - nen und ver-waist in Lei - den.
on our pil - lows We hung on high u - pon the leaf - y wil - lows.

2. Là, nos vainqueurs raillaient notre détresse :
« Chantez-nous donc ces hymnes d'allégresse
Qui remplissaient, jadis, votre cité ! »
Comment, ces chants, pourrions-nous les chanter,
Et profaner sur la terre étrangère
Nos hymnes saints qui louaient Dieu naguère ?

3. Jérusalem, si jamais je t'oublie,
A mon palais que ma langue se lie
Et que m'oublie aussi ma propre main !
O seule joie, espoir qui seul m'étreint,
Que sous mes doigts nulle corde ne vibre,
Jérusalem, tant que tu n'es pas libre.

CLÉMENT MAROT (1539).
CHARLES DOMBRE (1935).

★ ★ ★

2. Die uns besiegten, höhten uns're Qualen.
« Nun singt doch lustig wie zu andern Malen
Und froh, wie ihr's in eurer Stadt getan ! »
Wie stimmen wir die heil'gen Lieder an,
Entweihen in dem fremden Land die Weisen
Die sonst erklangen, Gott den Herrn zu preisen ?

3. Jerusalem, wenn je ich dein vergesse,
So soll die Zunge mir am Gaumen kleben
Und mich vergessen meine eig'ne Hand !
Du einz'ge Hoffnung, liebes Heimatland,
Mein Finger macht die Saiten nimmer klingen,
Bevor sie nicht von deiner Freiheit singen.

Übers. KONRAD JUTZLER (1950).

★ ★ ★

2. Our captors then made mock of all our sadness :
"Sing to us now those songs of simple gladness
Which echoed through your city long ago !"
How can we sing with hearts that break with woe ?
How can we sing amidst an alien nation
Our sacred hymns of praise and jubilation ?

3. Jerusalem, if ever I forget Thee,
Let my tongue cleave for ever to my palate,
And let my own right hand forget its skill !
O only joy, sole hope that holds me still,
That not a string be by my hand vibrated
Till thou, Jerusalem, art liberated.

Trans. MARGARET HOUSE (1950).

92

Psaume 6
LOYS BOURGEOIS (1542).
Harmonisé d'après C. GOUDIMEL (1565).

Vois ma fai - blesse hu - mai - ne, E-
O Fa - ther see my de - so - la - tion, See
Ach, Herr, ich muss ver - ge - hen, Wer

ter - nel, vois ma pei - ne, Et mon an - xi - é - té.
me in my temp-ta - tion And my anx - i - e - ty.
kann vor dir be - ste - hen, Du, E - wi - ger sieh' an !

Dans ta jus - te co - lè - re, Se - ras - tu si sé-
Des - pite Thy jus - tice hear me ! Let not that wrath come
Dein stren - ger Grimm be - droht mich, Dein Zor - nes - brand um-

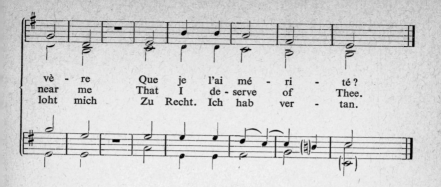

vè - re / Que je l'ai mé - ri - té ?
near me / That I de - serve of Thee.
loht mich / Zu Recht. Ich hab ver - tan.

2.

Parle à ta créature,
Et ranime et rassure
Ses esprits chancelants.
Pitié, mon Dieu, pardonne !
La force m'abandonne
Et mes os sont tremblants.

3.

Mon Dieu, tu vois mes larmes.
Sois tendre à mes alarmes.
Sois doux à mon remords.
Reviens, reviens, mon Père,
Exauce ma prière :
Sauve-moi de la mort !

Arr. RENÉ-LOUIS PIACHAUD (1932)
d'après CLÉMENT MAROT (1541).

✶ ✶ ✶

2.

Speak through the clouds of doubt
           that veil Thee now
Rekindle, reassure me,
For all my courage flees.
In arms of mercy take me
Ere strength shall quite forsake me,
Sustain my trembling knees.

3.

Lord from on high, Who seest
           my bitter passion
The ice of my transgression
Thaw with Thy pitying breath.
Return, return to cheer me,
Father in mercy hear me,
Save me at last from death.

Trans. T. E. LAWRENSON (1950).

✶ ✶ ✶

2.

Du hast mich einst erschaffen ;
Gib Zuversicht dem schlaffen
Und Mut dem schwanken Geist !
Mein Gott, hab' doch Erbarmen ;
Die Kraft verlässt mich Armen,
Und Furcht den Leib zerreisst.

3.

Mein Gott, du siehst die Tränen,
Sei gnädig meinem Sehnen
Und lind're meine Not !
Komm Vater, komm und höre
Mein Beten, ja erhöre :
Errette mich vom Tod !

Übers. KONRAD JUTZLER (1950).

— 93 (68) —

Adagio
Unison

Old Chinese tune.

於穆上……帝憮啟我……民精靈

Grant good Lord, that we serve Thee as we ought, Thee Who
Mach uns, Gott der Huld, So dir dienst-be - reit, Wie du
Toi qui nous com-blas Tou-jours de tes dons, Fais que

感……格誓矢忠……誠樂獻我……躬取義

ev - er dost serve men pa - tient-ly. Teach us all to give And not
in Ge-duld Die-nest uns all-zeit! Lass', des Ziels be-wusst, Käm - pfen
nous sa-chions Te ser - vir en Roi, Que nous nous don-nions A toi

成……仁刀鋸不……避奮發志……身

count the cost, Fight-ing, heed-ing not wounds and in - fa - my.
uns, O Herr! Acht-end nicht Ver-lust, Schmerz nicht noch Be-schwer.
plei - ne - ment, Et que nous lut-tions Pour toi vail - lam - ment.

二

含辛茹苦
克勇克勤
敢歷功利
恬淡存心
帝命不忒
昭事惟馨
念兹在兹
期終吾生

ST. IGNATIUS LOYOLA (1491-1556).
Chinese Trans. Y. T. WU.

* * *

2.

Teach us still to toil
　And not seek for rest ;
Steadfast labouring,
　Asking no reward :
Pressing toward the goal,
　Caring but to know
That we faithfully
　Do Thy will, O Lord.

Metric Version
LILIAN STEVENSON (1930).

2.

Lehr' uns — ob die Müh'
　Hart und herb auch sei —
Wirken spät und früh,
　Deinem Willen treu.
Eins nur hoffend nun,
　Voller Heilsbegier,
Dass uns solches Tun
　Näher führ' zu dir !

Übers. C. LECHLER (1930).

* * *

2.

Daigne nous aider
　A te mieux servir,
Et dans ta bonté
　Veuille nous bénir,
Fais que chaque jour
　Nous t'obéissons,
Car de ton amour
　Tu nous as fait don.

Trad. FLOSSETTE DU PASQUIER (1951).

— 94 (60) —

NIKOLAUS HERMANN (1554).

Allegro

O taenk når en - gang sam - les skal, De frel - stes me - nig -
An je - nem Tag wird Freu - de sein, Der uns zu-sam-men-
What joy to think of that vast host, Of ev' - ry tribe and
La joie, ô Dieu, rem - plit mon cœur, Je pense aux lé - gi-

het, Av al - le fol - ke - sleg - ters tal, I
führt; Dann wird nur ei - ne Her - de sein, Und
tongue, Gath- ered from ev' - ry clime and coast, Who
ons Qui font vers toi mon - ter leurs chœurs, Leur

him - lens her - lig - het, I him - lens her - lig - het.
nur ein' einz' - ger Hirt, Und nur ein' einz' - ger Hirt.
raise in Heav'n their song, Their glad tri - um - phal song.
a - do - ra - ti - on, leur a - do - ra - ti - on.

2.

O tenk, når Herrens vidnehaer,
Hans tienere på jord,
De millioner mötes der
Som hörte deres ord ! (*bis*)

3.

O tenk dog, hvilken jubellyd —
En ström av kjaerlighet !
Tenk hvilken tak kog pris og fryd
Og salighet og fred ! (*bis*)

4.

O Gud, hvos er din nåde stor !
Oss alle til dig drag,
At vi må stå blandt frelstes kor
På denne höitidsdag ! (*bis*)

W. A. WEXELS (1796-1866).

* * *

2.

Schaut an der Zeugen grosse Schar,
Sie kommt von nah und fern,
Und wie es einst verkündet war,
So preisen sie den Herrn. (*bis*)

3.

Und tönt von Tausend, Mann bei Mann,
Nur einer Stimme Schall ;
Ihr Rühmen steigt zum Himmel an
Wie grossen Wassers Schwall. (*bis*)

4.

Dein Arm zieht unser Herz hinan
Dorthin wo Freude ist ;
Wir singen ewiglich im Chor
Den Namen Jesus Christ. (*bis*)

Übers. JOHANN CHRISTOPH HAMPE (1950).

* * *

2.

Glad thought that all who served the
The apostolic band,   [Lord ; —
The myriads trusting in their Word ; —
Shall all together stand,
Redeemed at God's right hand.

3.

What bliss, their loves and joys to tell !
What rapt'rous strains they sing !
Exultant anthems rise and swell
Till Heav'n's high arches ring.
As they adore their King.

4.

Great God, in mercy save us all ;
Raise us to dwell with Thee.
With the redeemed, when Thou shalt call,
Grant that our place may be,
Through all eternity.

Trans. R. BIRCH HOYLE (1923).

* * *

2.

Ils servent tous le Dieu vainqueur,
Louant le Tout-Puissant,
Un seul troupeau qui pour pasteur
Aura le Christ vivant. (*bis*)

3.

Leurs voix par milliers s'uniront
Chantant en ton honneur
Et vers le ciel s'élèveront,
Louant ton nom, Seigneur. (*bis*)

4.

O Dieu d'amour, accueille-nous
A tous les saints unis,
Nous t'en supplions à genoux
Au nom de Jésus-Christ. (*bis*)

Trad. FLOSSETTE DU PASQUIER (1951).

F. F. FLEMMING (1810).
Harm. FRÉDÉRIC MATHIL (1950).

Moderato

Nun - ca Dios mí - o, ce - sa - rá mi la - bio
Nie - mals, O Hei - land, sol - len ruh'n die Lip - pen,
Nev - er, O God, will my lips more be si - lent,
Dieu tout - puis - sant, mes chants di - sent ta gloi - re;

De ben - de - cir - te, de can - tar tu glo - ria, Por - que con -
Dei - ner Hoch-herr - lich-keit Lob-preis zu schen - ken. Denn oh - ne
Nor cease to bless you and to sing your glo - ry, Since in my
Ja - mais ma bou - che ne pour-ra se tai - re Car, en mon

ser - vo de tu amor in-men - so. Gra - ta me-mo - ria.
Mas - sen, Gott, liebst du; Des muss ich im - mer ge-den - ken.
heart I hold the pre-cious me - mory Of your un - bound-ed love.
â - me, je sais ta vic-toi - re, Dieu sa - lu - tai - re.

2. Cuando perdido en mundanal sendero,
   No me cercaba sino niebla obscura,
   Tú me miraste, y alumbróme un rayo
   De tu luz pura.

3. Cuando inclinaba mi abatida frente
   Del mal obrar el oneroso yugo,
   Dulce reposo y eficaz alivio
   Darme te plugo.

4. Cuando los dones malgasté a porfía,
   Con que a mi alma pródigo adronaste,
   « Padre, he pecado », con dolor te dije,
   Y me abrazaste.

5. Oh ! nunca, nunca cesará mi labio
   De bendecirte, de cantar tu gloria :
   Porque conservo de tu amor inmenso
   Grata memoria.

                    JUAN BAUTISTA CABRERA (1837-1916).

★ ★ ★

2. Lange, ach, ging ich auf dunkelem Pfade,
   Du aber sahst mich, in Nächten verloren,
   Und deines Lichtes ein Strahl, Herr, nun hat mich
   Wiedergeboren.

3. Bleibe mir nah, wenn ich zitt're und wanke,
   Niedergebeugt von der Last meiner Sünde,
   Schliess dann den Arm um dein Kind, dass es, Heiland,
   Ruh' bei dir finde.

4. Was du mir gabst, dein Gut, ich hab's verschwendet.
   Erst in der Fremde bereut' ich und weinte :
   « Vater, ich habe gesündigt ! » Du aber
   Breitest die Arme.

5. Niemals, O Heiland, sollen ruh'n die Lippen
   Deiner Hochherlichkeit Lobpreis zu schenken.
   Denn ohne Massen, Gott, liebst du ; des muss ich
   Immer gedenken.

                    Übers. JOHANN CHRISTOPH HAMPE (1950).

★ ★ ★

2. When I was lost in this world's pleasant byways,
   Only surrounded by thick clouds of darkness,
   You looked upon me, shedding on my pathway
   Your beam of pure light.

3. When by the burden of my sinful actions
   I am discouraged and my brow is heavy,
   Rest and refreshment and your own sure healing
   Give me, I pray you.

4. When I had wasted gifts so rich and precious
   Which for my soul's adorning you had given,
   And came to you and said : "Father I have grieved you",
   You did embrace me.

5. O never, never, will I cease to bless you,
   Never will my lips cease to sing your glory
   Since in my heart I hold the precious memory
   Of your unbounded love.

                    Trans. MARGARET HOUSE (1950).

★ ★ ★

2. Lorsque j'avance sans but sur la terre,
   Quand les ténèbres me cachent la voie,
   Tu fais, ô Père, briller ta lumière,
   Donnant la joie.

3. Quand, sous le poids de mon péché, je ploie
   Quand le courage n'est plus dans mon âme,
   Dieu, tu me donnes la paix et la joie
   Et le vrai calme.

4. J'ai oublié les biens que tu me donnes
   Et je gaspille les dons de ta grâce,
   Mais toi, ô Père, toujours tu pardonnes,
   Rien ne te lasse.

5. Dieu tout-puissant, je veux chanter ta gloire,
   Jamais ma bouche ne pourra se taire
   Car en mon âme, je sais ta victoire,
   Dieu salutaire !

Trad. FLOSSETTE DU PASQUIER (1951).

— 96 (94) —

WALD RUDIN (1833-1921).
Harmonisation revue par F. MATHIL (1950).

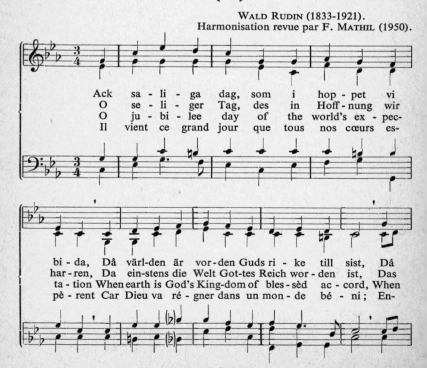

Ack sa - li - ga dag, som i hop - pet vi
O se - li - ger Tag, des in Hoff - nung wir
O ju - bi - lee day of the world's ex - pec-
Il vient ce grand jour que tous nos cœurs es-

bi - da, Då värl-den är vor-den Guds ri - ke till sist, Då
har - ren, Da ein-stens die Welt Got-tes Reich wor - den ist, Das
ta - tion When earth is God's King-dom of bles - sèd ac - cord, When
pè - rent Car Dieu va ré - gner dans un mon - de bé - ni ; En-

män - skor - nas släk - te för - loss - nin - gen fun - nit Och
Men - schen - ge - schlecht zur Be - frei - ung ge - kom-men, Die
man's err - ing race finds the path of sal - va - tion And
fin ap - pa - raît le che - min sa - lu - tai - re Qui

fol - ken be - kän - na, att Her - ren är Krist, Då
Völ - ker be - ken - nen, dass Herr ist: der Christ! Ge -
all shall ac - know-ledge that Christ is the Lord, When
mè - ne tout hom - me au Sau - veur Jé - sus - Christ. Le

dö - den är dö - dad och syn - den för - svun - nen Och
tö - tet der Tod und die Sün - de zer - ron - nen, Er -
sin has been ba - nished and death slain for ev - er And
mal est vain - cu, et la mort a - bo - li - e, La

fräls - nin - gens full - het för e - vigt är vun - nen!
lö - sung in Fül - le für e - wig ge - won - nen.
bles - sèd re - demp - tion will part from us nev - er.
grâ - ce di - vi - ne a sau - vé no - tre vi - e.

2. Han kommer, han kommer, den dag, som vi bida ;
   Dess strålar vi skåda på morgonens sky.
   Än mörkret är mäktigt i dimmiga dälder,
   Men dagen begynner på höjderna gry.
   Han kommer att stilla de sörjandes trängtan,
   Han kommer att fylla de heligas längtan.

3. Han kommer, han kommer, den dag, som vi bida,
   Då folken förenas i kärlek och tro,
   Och himmelens Herre på jorden är konung
   Och de i hans skugga få saliga bo,
   Den dag, som fullkomnar de heligas böner,
   Den dag, som vår tro med beskådande kröner.

4. Han kommer, han kommer, den dag, som vi bida.
   Den ljusaste dag, som i världen har grytt,
   Då Herren allsmäktig allena regerar
   Och Satan och synd för hans anlete flytt
   Och skapelsen, frälsad från synder och strider,
   Förkunnar hans ära till eviga tider.

NATANAEL BESKOW (1865-).

* * *

2. Er kommt ! Ja er kommt jener Tag, des wir harren,
   Auf Morgenrots Wolken sein Licht wir schon schau'n.
   Noch herrschet das Dunkel in nebligen Tälern,
   Doch glänzt auf den Höh'n jungen Tags erstes Grau'n,
   Er kommt, um zu stillen der Trauernden Tränen,
   Er kommt, zu erfüllen der Heiligen Sehnen.

3. Er kommt ! Ja er kommt, jener Tag, des wir harren,
   Da Völker sich finden in Liebe und Treu,
   Der Herr aller Himmel wird König auf Erden
   Und selig die Menschheit sich gründet aufs neu,
   Der Tag, der der Heil'gen Gebete erfüllet,
   Der Tag, der das Suchen im Schauen uns stillet.

4. Er kommt ! Ja er kommt ! Heil dem Tag, des wir harren !
   Der strahlendste Tag, der der Welt je geleucht' !
   Da Er, der Allmächt'ge, alleine regieret,
   Und Satan und Sünde sein Angesicht fleucht' !
   Da sündlos die Schöpfung, erlöst von all'm Streiten,
   Verkündigt sein Lob bis in ewige Zeiten !

Übers. GEORG KEMPFF.

* * *

2. It cometh, it cometh, the day of our longing
   Whose beams we behold in the clouds of the morn.
   Though shades in the mist of the valleys are thronging,
   The day'on the summits already is born.
   It cometh to quiet the tears of the grieving,
   The hopes to fulfil of the faithful believing.

3. It cometh ; not long are the years now remaining.
   All nations, united in love and in peace,
   Shall know heaven's Lord upon earth now is reigning
   And dwell in His shadow, and warfare shall cease.
   The wonders long prayed for shall then be unfolding,
   Our faith shall be crowned with the grace of beholding.

4. It cometh, the day of the old prophets' story,
   Most bright of all days that have dawned on our race
   When, the Lord God Omnipotent reigneth in glory,
   While Satan and Sin shrink in fear from His face ;
   When, saved from the bondage of strife, all Creation
   Proclaims through the ages the joy of salvation.

Trans. CHARLES WHARTON STORCK (1881-).

★ ★ ★

2. Voici poindre enfin l'émouvante journée
   Où luit la clarté d'un soleil éclatant,
   Qui chasse la brume des sombres vallées
   Et nimbe les monts d'un halo flamboyant ;
   Il vient, ce grand jour, pour calmer les alarmes
   De ceux dont les yeux ont versé trop de larmes.

3. Au jour attendu que nos âmes espèrent
   Les peuples vivront dans l'amour et la paix
   Et Dieu régnera tout-puissant sur la terre,
   Des hommes nouveaux chanteront ses bienfaits.
   Ainsi s'accomplit la promesse de grâce,
   Car tous les humains verront Dieu face à face.

4. Il vient, le voici, ce grand jour de victoire,
   Nul autre n'a lui d'un si brillant éclat
   Car Dieu, tout-puissant, va régner dans la gloire
   Et Satan gémit et tressaille d'effroi :
   Le péché succombe et la nature entière
   Proclame de Dieu la bonté salutaire.

Trad. FLOSSETTE DU PASQUIER (1951).

— 97 —

Pre-Reformation tune. Erfurt (1524).
LUKAS OSIANDER.

They whose course on earth is o'er, Think they of their
Die be-freit von ird'-schen Joch Den-ken sie der
Ceux qui nous ont de-van-cés Et nous ont i-

breth-ren more? They be-fore the throne who bow,
Brü-der noch? Wer vorm Thron des Lam-mes kniet,
ci lais-sés, De-vant ton trô-ne cour-bés

Feel they for their breth-ren now?
Fühlt er mit den Brü-dern mit?
Aux vi-vants ont-ils pen-sé?

2. We by enemies distrest —
    They in paradise at rest;
We the captives — they the freed;
    We and they are one indeed:

3. One in all we seek or shun,
    One, because our Lord is one;
One in home and one in love;
    We below, and they above.

4. Saints departed, even thus
    Hold communion still with us;
Still with us, beyond the veil,
    Praising, pleading without fail.

5. So with them our hearts we raise,
    Share their work and join their praise,
Rendering worship, thanks, and love
    To the King of saints above.

J. M. NEALE (1818-1866) and others.

* * *

2. Feindschaft hat uns übermannt —
   Sie ruh'n dort in Gottes Land.
   Ob wir Knechte, jene frei —
   Steh'n wir doch in einer Reih' :

3. Was wir flieh'n, was wir begehr'n,
   Steht ja unter einem Herrn !
   Heimat hier und Liebe dort —
   Wo sie steh'n am sel'gen Ort.

4. Die Vollendeten des Herrn
   Bleiben unserm Lauf nicht fern.
   Seit' an Seite, ungeseh'n
   Sie ob uns'rem Streite steh'n.

5. Unser Herz sehnt sich empor,
   Dass es mit der Heil'gen Chor
   Gott zu Lobe allezeit
   Anzubeten sei bereit !

Übers. WILHELM HORKEL (1950).

* * *

2. Nous, de maux environnés
   Eux, au ciel, du mal gardés,
   Nous captifs, eux libérés,
   Tous, en toi, sont apaisés.

3. Mais pareils nous sommes nés,
   Pour nous tous Christ s'est donné ;
   Tous nous aimons notre Roi :
   Eux, au ciel, nous ici-bas.

4. Vous aussi, saints bienheureux,
   Avec nous, du haut des cieux,
   Vivez en communion,
   Un dans l'adoration.

5. Vers vous, élevant nos cœurs,
   Nous louons le Rédempteur
   Et, nous joignant à vos chœurs
   Nous chantons en son honneur.

Trad. VIOLETTE DU PASQUIER (1951).

— 98 —

Psalm 130
Wittenberg (1524).
JOHANN WALTHER Gesangbuch.
Harm. von J. S. BACH.

Aus tie - fer Not schrei ich zu dir, Herr Gott, er - hör mein
Des lieux pro - fonds je crie à toi, Sei-gneur, en ma dé-
Out of the depth I cry to Thee, Lord God, Oh hear my

Ru - fen. Dein gnä-dig Oh - ren kehr zu mir, Und mei-ner Bitt' sie
tres - se. En-tends ma plainte, é - cou - te-moi, Dis - si - pe ma tris-
wail - ing! Thy gra-cious ear in - cline to me, And make my prayer a-

öff - ne. Denn so du willst das se - hen an, Was Sünd und Un-recht
tes - se! De-vant toi je ne puis te - nir Si tu gar-des le
vail - ing. On my mis-deeds in merc - y look, Oh deign to blot them

ist ge - tan: Wer kann, Herr, vor dir blei - ben?
sou - ve - nir Du pé - ché qui m'op-pres - se.
from Thy book, Or who can stand be - fore Thee?

2.

Bei die gilt nichts denn Gnad und Gunst,
  Die Sünden zu vergeben,
Es ist doch unser Tun umsonst
  Auch in dem besten Leben.
Vor dir niemand sich rühmen kann,
  Des muss dich fürchten jedermann
  Und deiner Gnade leben.

3.

Darum auf Gott will hoffen ich,
  Auf mein Verdienst nicht bauen;
Auf ihn mein Herz soll lassen sich
  Und seiner Güte trauen,
Die mir zusagt sein wertes Wort;
  Das ist mein Trost und treuer Hort.
  Des will ich allzeit harren.

4.

Und ob es währt bis in die Nacht
  Und wieder an den Morgen,
Doch soll mein Herz an Gottes Macht
  Verzweifeln nicht noch sorgen.
So tu Israel rechter Art,
  Der aus dem Geist erzeuget ward,
  Und seines Gott's erharre.

5.

Ob bei uns ist der Sünden viel,
  Bei Gott ist viel mehr Gnaden;
Sein Hand zu helfen hat kein Ziel,
  Wie gross auch sei der Schaden.
Er ist allein der gute Hirt;
  Der Israel erlösen wird;
  Aus seinen Sünden allen.

MARTIN LUTHER (1483-1546).

★ ★ ★

2.

On ne t'invoque pas en vain,
  Non, tu fais grâce encore.
J'espère en toi, comme au matin,
  La garde attend l'aurore.
Souverain maître d'Israël,
Toi dont l'amour est éternel,
  O mon Dieu, je t'implore.

Trad. CHARLES ECKLIN (1858-1935).

3.

Or donc, j'espère en toi, Seigneur,
  Car ma force est si frêle.
Viens, en tes mains prends donc mon
  Si faible et plein de zèle !   [cœur
Dieu Saint, Dieu des compassions,
  Toi seul ma consolation,
  Toi, mon appui fidèle.

4.

Il faut pouvoir même espérer
  Au fort de la souffrance.
L'âme, jamais ne doit douter,
  O Dieu, de ta puissance.
Ainsi fit jadis Israël
Lorsqu'il attendait l'Eternel
  Avec impatience.

5.

Si dans nos cœurs le mal est grand,
  Plus grande est ta clémence !
Si le péché règne, écrasant,
  Grande est ta délivrance.
Car, d'Israël le bon Berger,
Veut pour toujours le décharger
  Du mal, de la souffrance.

Trad. PAULINE MARTIN (1951).

★ ★ ★

2.

Thy sovereign grace and boundless love
  Make Thee, O Lord, forgiving;
My purest tho'ts and deeds but prove
  Sin in my heart is living;
None guiltless in Thy sight appear;
All who approach Thy throne must fear
  And humbly trust Thy mercy.

3.

Therefore in God my hope shall be,
  And not in mine own merit,
In Him and His wide charity
  Alone must trust my spirit.
His goodness, in His word revealed,
Is both my comfort and my shield
  For ev r and for ever.

4.

Like those who watch for midnight's hour
  To hail the dawning morrow,
I wait for Thee, I trust Thy power,
  Unmoved by doubt or sorrow.
So thus let Israel hope in Thee,
And he shall find Thy mercy free
  And Thy redemption plenteous.

Trans. BENJAMIN LATROBE
(1725-1786).

5.

Although our sins be manifold,
  He hath grace to forgive us;
His hand He will toward us hold,
  Although our fault be grievous.
The Shepherd of His sheep is He,
Who will His chosen people free
  From all their dark transgressing.

Trans. MARGARET BARCLAY
(1950).

Moderato

JOSEF HAYDN (1732-1809).

Die Sach ist dein, Herr Je-su Christ, Die Sach an der wir
Pour ta cause im - mor - tel - le, O Christ, nous lut - te-
The cause for which we strive is Thine, O Christ, our Lord and

steh'n; Und weil es dei - ne Sa-che ist, Kann sie nicht un - ter-
rons; Ses en - ne-mis, contre el - le, En vain se dres - se-
Head, And since it is a cause di-vine Can - not be van-quish-

geh'n. Al - lein das Wei-zen-korn, be-vor Es frucht-bar sprosst zum
ront. Le grain en ter - re doit pé - rir, Pour que l'é - pi puis-
èd. Yet must the grain, be - fore it spring To light and life and

Licht em-por, Muss ster-ben in der Er-de Schoss, Zu - vor vom eig - nen
se mû - rir. Com-me Christ, son mo - dè - le, Tout dis - ci - ple fi-
ri - pen-ing, Die in the dark-ness of the earth, Stripped of all hon - our

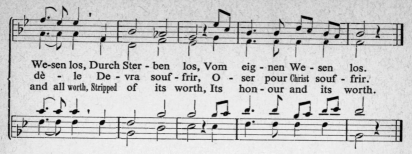

We-sen los, Durch Ster - ben los, Vom eig - nen We - sen los.
dè - le De - vra souf - frir, O - ser pour Christ souf - frir.
and all worth, Stripped of its worth, Its hon - our and its worth.

2.

Du gingst, O Jesu, unser Haupt,
  Durch Leiden himmelan,
Und führest jeden, der da glaubt,
  Mit dir die gleiche Bahn,
Wohlan, so nimm uns allzugleich
Zum Teil am Leiden und am Reich ;
Führ uns durch deines Todes Tor,
Samt deiner Sach zum Licht empor,
  Zum Licht empor,
Durch Nacht, zum Licht empor !

SAMUEL PREISWERK (1799-1871).

3.

Du starbest selbst als Weizenkorn,
  Und sankest in das Grab.
Belebe denn, O Lebensborn,
  Die Welt, die Gott dir gab.
Send Boten aus in jedes Land,
Dass bald dein Name werd' bekannt
Dein Name voller Seligkeit ;
Auch wir steh'n dir zum Dienst bereit
  In Kampf und Streit,
Zum Dienst in Kampf und Streit.

Graf F. ZAREMBA (1794-1874).

* * *

2.

Pour notre délivrance
  Le Maître a tout souffert.
Par son obéissance
  Le ciel nous est ouvert.
Nous voulons tous suivre tes pas,
Christ, ne nous abandonne pas !
Dans l'épreuve ou la joie,
Eclaire notre voie,
  Par ton amour,
Par ton fidèle amour.

3.

Réponds à la prière
  Des peuples dans la nuit,
Qui cherchent la lumière
  Et restent sans appui.
Suscite donc des moissonneurs,
Fais de nous tous tes serviteurs !
Que ton règne s'étende !
Que partout on entende
  Ton nom béni,
O Christ, ton nom béni !

Trad. J. E. SIORDET (1922).

* * *

2.

Thou tookst the path of pain and death
  That led to majesty,
And they that truly walk by faith
  Must take that path with Thee.
So be it ! bring us, one and all,
To share the glory and the gall.
The gate Thy suffering opened wide
Leads upward into morning-tide,
  To morning-tide,
Through night to morning-tide.

3.

Thyself didst die, like unto grain,
  Thou hast lain in the grave.
O source of life, give life to men,
  The men God to Thee gave.
Send heralds forth to every land,
That all the world may understand,
May magnify and worship Thee
And ready for the fight are we
  And victory,
To fight to victory.

Trans. MARGARET BARCLAY (1951).

Adapted from a melody in La Feillée.
« Méthode du plain-chant » (1808).

O quan - ta qua - li - a sunt il - la sab - ba - ta
O what their joy and their glo - ry must be,
Freu - de, o Freu - de der kei - ne sonst gleich,
Il est aux cieux u - ne joie im - mor - tel - le

Quae sem - per ce - le - brat su - per - na cu - ri - a !
Those end - less Sab - baths the bles - sed ones see !
Wenn wir einst aus - ruh'n im e - wi - gen Reich,
Qui cha - que jour ré - jou - it les fi - dè - les

Quae fes - sis re - qui - es, quae mer - ces for - ti - bus
Crown for the val - iant, to wea - ry ones rest;
Wo wir nach Stras - sen voll Schmer - zen und Streit
Car le Sei - gneur vit dans tou - tes les â - mes,

Cum e - rit om - ni - a De - us in om - ni - bus!
God shall be all and in all ev - er blest.
Got - tes Lob sin - gen ohn' Ziel und ohn' Zeit!
Les cœurs sont tous a - ni - més de sa flam - me.

2. Vere Jerusalem est illa civitas,
   Cuius pax iugis est, summa iucunditas,
   Ubi non praevenit rem desiderium,
   Nec desiderio minus est praemium.

3. Illic molestiis finitis omnibus
   Securi cantica Sion cantabimus,
   Et iuges gratias de donis gratiae
   Beata referet plebs tibi, Domine.

4. Perenni Domino perpes sit gloria,
   Ex quo sunt, per quem sunt, in quo sunt, omnia ;
   Ex quo sunt, Pater est ; per quem sunt, Filius ;
   In quo sunt, Patris et Filii Spiritus.

PETER ABELARD (1079-1142).

★ ★ ★

2. Truly Jerusalem name we that shore,
   'Vision of peace', that brings joy evermore !
   Wish and fulfilment can severed be ne'er,
   Nor the thing prayed for come short of the prayer.

3. We, where no trouble distraction can bring,
   Safely the anthems of Sion shall sing ;
   While for Thy grace, Lord, their voices of praise
   Thy blessèd people shall evermore raise.

4. Low before Him with our praises we fall,
   Of Whom, and in Whom, and through Whom are all ;
   Of Whom, the Father ; and through Whom, the Son ;
   In Whom, the Spirit, with these ever one.

Trans. J. M. NEALE (1818-1866).

★ ★ ★

2. Fern schon erschimmert die bleibende Stadt,
   Still glänzt ihr Friede auf Tage und Tat,
   Schweigendes Leuchten, das heimwärts uns weist,
   Wo Gottes Treue das Letzte verheisst.

3. Wenn dann nicht Not mehr in Sorgen uns zwingt,
   Froh sich die Stimme zum Liede erschwingt,
   Und weil's von nichts mehr als Gnade nur weiss,
   Hebt sich das Herze zum jubelnden Preis.

4. Und wir anbeten nach sehnender Fahrt
   Ihn, dessen Leben das unsere ward,
   Ihn, Gott den Vater, Gott ewigen Sohn
   Gott heil'gen Geist der Dreifaltigkeit Kron' !

Übers. ERWIN KLEINE (1950).

★ ★ ★

2. Jérusalem, c'est toi ville céleste
   Où la paix règne et non le mal funeste,
   Où toutes grâces seront accordées,
   Toutes prières seront exaucées.

3. Là, plus de deuils, plus de peines cruelles,
   Mais une joie indicible, éternelle :
   Les bienheureux chanteront des cantiques
   A l'Eternel, souverain magnifique.

4. C'est là que règne, entouré de lumière
   Le tout-puissant Créateur, notre Père,
   Dieu trois fois saint qui nous a donné l'être :
   En lui, par lui, nous voulons tous renaître.

Trad. FLOSSETTE DU PASQUIER (1951).

— 101 * —

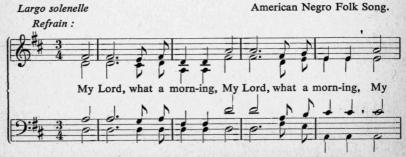

Largo solenelle
Refrain :

American Negro Folk Song.

My Lord, what a morn-ing, My Lord, what a morn-ing, My

* With the kind permission of the Hampton Institute Press, Hampton, Virginia.

Fine.

Lord, what a morn-ing, When the stars be-gin to fall.

Solo molto marc.

You'll hear de trum-pet sound, To wake de na-tions un-der-
You'll hear de sin-ner moan, To wake de na-tions un-der-

D. C. al fine

ground, Look in my God's right hand When de stars be-gin to fall.
ground, Look in my God's right hand When de stars be-gin to fall.

D. C. al fine

2.

You'll hear de Christians shout, To wake de nations underground,
Look in my God's right hand, When de stars begin to fall.
You'll hear the angels sing, To wake de nations underground,
Look in my God's right hand, When de stars begin to fall.

Refrain : My Lord, etc.

3.

You'll hear my Jesus come, To wake de nations underground,
Look in my God's right hand, When de stars begin to fall.
His chariot wheels roll round, To wake de nations underground,
Look in my God's right hand, When de stars begin to fall.

Refrain : My Lord, etc.

— 102 (61) —

« Sine Nomine » *

R. VAUGHAN WILLIAMS (1872-).

To be sung in unison

For all the Saints who from their la - bours
Pour tous les saints près de toi re - cueil-
Für al - le Heil' - gen die da ruh'n in

rest, Who Thee by faith be - fore the world con-
lis, Pour les mar - tyrs que ta Si - on comp-
dir, Die dei - nen Na - men treu be - kannt all-

fessed, Thy name, O Je - su, be for ev - er
ta, Christ nos cœurs chan - tent à ton nom bé-
hier, Sei dir, O Je - su, Eh - re, für und

* By permission of the Oxford University Press.

blest. Al - le - lu - ia !   Al - le - lu - ia !
ni : Al - lé - lu - ia !   Al - lé - lu - ia !
für ! Hal - le - lu - ja !   Hal - le - lu - ja !

2. Thou wast their Rock, their Fortress, and their Might ;
   Thou, Lord, their Captain in the well-fought fight ;
   Thou in the darkness drear, their one true Light.
              Alleluia ! (*bis*)

3. O may Thy soldiers, faithful, true, and bold,
   Fight as the Saints who nobly fought of old,
   And win, with them, the victor's crown of gold.
              Alleluia ! (*bis*)

4. O blest communion, fellowship divine !
   We feebly struggle, they in glory shine ;
   Yet all are one in Thee, for all are Thine.
              Alleluia ! (*bis*)

5. And when the strife is fierce, the warfare long,
   Steals on the ear the distant triumph-song,
   And hearts are brave again, and arms are strong.
              Alleluia ! (*bis*)

6. The golden evening brightens in the west ;
   Soon, soon to faithful warriors cometh rest :
   Sweet is the calm of Paradise the blest.
              Alleluia ! (*bis*)

7. But lo ! there breaks a yet more glorious day ;
   The Saints triumphant rise in bright array :
   The King of Glory passes on His way.
              Alleluia ! (*bis*)

8. From earth's wide bounds, from ocean's farthest coast,
   Through gates of pearl streams in the countless host,
   Singing to Father, Son, and Holy Ghost.
              Alleluia ! (*bis*)

                    Bishop W. W. How (1823-1897).

                    ★ ★ ★

2. C'est toi qui fus leur rempart ici-bas,
   Et ton Esprit toujours les éclaira
   Dans leurs souffrances et leurs durs combats.
   Alléluia ! (*bis*)

3. Nous, leurs enfants, nous irons en avant,
   Fiers de leurs noms et fidèles soldats,
   Sous la bannière du Roi triomphant.
   Alléluia ! (*bis*)

4. O temps béni, sainte fraternité !
   Eux dans la gloire, et nous suivant leurs pas,
   Ames unies pour l'éternité.
   Alléluia ! (*bis*)

5. Et si l'orage assombrit notre cœur,
   D'En-Haut, toujours, une voix descendra,
   Voix qui rassure, qui nous rend vainqueurs !
   Alléluia ! (*bis*)

   Trad. D. MEYLAN (1922).

6. Voici, le soir empourpre l'Occident,
   La nuit apporte son apaisement,
   Le bon soldat pourra se reposer.
   Alléluia ! (*bis*)

7. Un jour viendra plus glorieux encor
   Où tous les saints triomphants de la mort
   Entoureront le Seigneur tout-puissant.
   Alléluia ! (*bis*)

8. Car, en ce jour radieux entre tous,
   Les saints élus accourront de partout,
   Louant le Père et le Fils et l'Esprit.
   Alléluia ! (*bis*)

   Trad. FLOSSETTE DU PASQUIER (1951).

★ ★ ★

2. Du warst ihr Schutz und Schirm zu aller Zeit,
   Du, Herr, ihr Führer in dem heil'gen Streit,
   Ihr Trost und Licht in tiefster Dunkelheit.
   Halleluja ! (*bis*)

3. O lasst uns, die wir noch auf Erden geh'n,
   Treu wie die Heiligen im Kampfe steh'n,
   Auf uns'res Königs Blick und Wink nur seh'n !
   Halleluja ! (*bis*)

4. Dann trägt uns heiliger Gemeinschaft Band,
   Wir ringen noch, sie steh'n im Siegerland,
   Doch eins mit uns, vereint in Jesu Hand.
   Halleluja ! (*bis*)

5. Und währt es lang, und scheint der Streit zu schwer,
   Grüsst ihr Triumphgesang uns himmelher,
   Kämpft betend mit der Überwinder Heer !
   Halleluja ! (*bis*)

Übers. C. LECHLER (1923).

6. Schon grüsst der Abendsonne gold'ner Schein,
   Bald geh'n die Streiter in die Ruhe ein ;
   Süss wird sie ihnen und gesegnet sein.
   Halleluja ! (*bis*)

7. Doch schaut ! Dort bricht ein gröss'rer Tag herein !
   Triumph ! Der König naht im Glorienschein,
   Er kommt das Heer der Heiligen befrei'n !
   Halleluja ! (*bis*)

8. Von allen Küsten, aus dem fernsten Tal
   Durch Perlentore strömt es ohne Zahl,
   Singt laut dem Vater, Sohn, dem Geist zumal :
   Halleluja ! (*bis*)

Übers. JOHANN CHRISTOPH HAMPE (1951).

— 103 —

« St. Michael »
Old 134th.

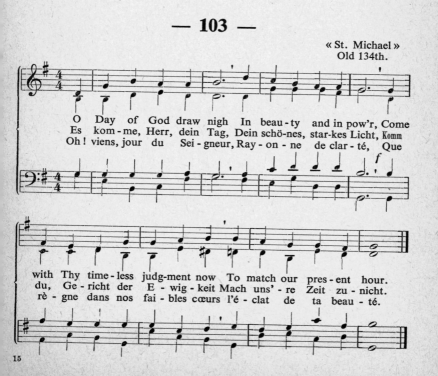

O Day of God draw nigh In beau-ty and in pow'r, Come
Es kom-me, Herr, dein Tag, Dein schö-nes, star-kes Licht, Komm
Oh ! viens, jour du Sei-gneur, Ray-on-ne de clar-té, Que

with Thy time-less judg-ment now To match our pres-ent hour.
du, Ge-richt der E-wig-keit Mach uns' re Zeit zu-nicht.
rè-gne dans nos fai-bles cœurs l'é-clat de ta beau-té.

2.

Bring to our troubled minds,
　Uncertain and afraid,
The quiet of a steadfast faith,
　Calm of a call obeyed.

3.

Bring justice to our land,
　That all may dwell secure,
And finely build for days to come
　Foundations that endure.

4.

Bring to our world of strife
　Thy sovran word of peace,
That war may haunt the earth no more
　And desolation cease.

5.

O Day of God draw nigh
　As at Creation's birth,
Let there be light again, and set
　Thy judgments on the earth.

R. B. Y. Scott (1937).*

★　★　★

2.

Dies sind wir Mann bei Mann :
　Verzagt und sehr erschreckt.
Wann kommt der Tag, o Heiland, wann,
　Der Frieden uns erweckt ?

3.

Da wir in deiner Hand
　Auf ewig sicher ruh'n,
Da nur dein Wille herrscht im Land,
　Ihn alle freudig tun.

4.

Komm, Tag, in unsern Streit,
　Du heil'ges Friedenswort,
Und treibe Hunger, Kriege, Leid
　Und Traurigkeiten fort !

5.

Es komme, Herr, dein Tag !
　Du hast das Licht gemacht,
Schaff wieder Licht, dein helles Licht
　Erleuchte uns're Nacht !

Übers. Johann Christoph Hampe (1950).

★　★　★

2.

Et donne à nos esprits
　Incertains et troublés
Le calme d'une foi qui vit,
　D'un cœur qui s'est donné.

3.

Apporte aux nations
　L'amour et l'équité
Afin que, calmes, nous vivions
　Dans la sécurité.

4.

Accorde-nous la paix,
　Que tout le genre humain
Connaisse enfin le don parfait
　De ton salut divin.

5.

Viens, jour du Dieu vivant
　Et, comme au premier jour,
Fais resplendir sur tes enfants
　Ta face, ô Dieu d'amour.

Trad. Flossette Du Pasquier (1951).

* Words used by permission of Mr. R. B. Y. Scott.

« Coleshill »
Barton's Psalms (1706)
(Later version of melody)

Andante

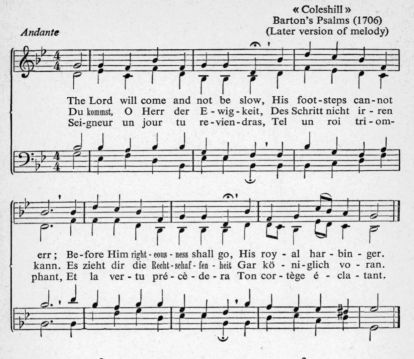

The Lord will come and not be slow, His foot-steps can-not err; Be-fore Him right-eous-ness shall go, His roy-al har-bin-ger.

Du kommst, O Herr der E-wig-keit, Des Schritt nicht ir-ren kann. Es zieht dir die Recht-schaf-fen-heit Gar kö-ni-glich vo-ran.

Sei-gneur un jour tu re-vien-dras, Tel un roi tri-om-phant, Et la ver-tu pré-cè-de-ra Ton cor-tège é-cla-tant.

2.

Truth from the earth, like to a flower,
Shall bud and blossom then ;
And justice, from her heavenly bower,
Look down on mortal men.

3.

Rise, God, judge Thou the earth in
This wicked earth redress ; [might,
For Thou art He Who shalt by right
The nations all possess.

4.

The nations all whom Thou hast made
Shall come, and all shall frame
To bow them low before Thee, Lord,
And glorify Thy name.

5.

For great Thou art and wonders great
By Thy strong hand are done :
Thou in Thy everlasting seat
Remainest God alone.

J. Milton (1608-1674).

* * *

2.

Ja, Herr, dann wird der Wahrheit Strahl
Auf Erden neu erblüh'n,
Und herrlich wird vom Himmelssaal
Gerechtigkeit erglüh'n

3.

Komm, Gott, mit Macht richt du die
Du bist der Herr allein ! [Welt,
Eh' sie dir nicht zu Füssen fällt,
Kann doch nicht Friede sein.

4.

Der Völker erdenweite Schar,
Die ward auf dein Geheiss,
Bringt niederfallend sich dir dar
Zu deines Namens Preis.

5.

Denn du bist gross, von Anfang schon
Sind alle Wunder dein.
Auf unvergänglich hehrem Thron
Bleibst du, Herr, Gott allein.

Übers. ERWIN KLEINE (1950).

* * *

2.

La vérité s'élancera
  Comme un rameau fleuri,
La justice illuminera
  Le seuil de tes parvis.

3.

Seigneur, viens juger l'univers,
  Confondre les méchants,
Et, dans ce monde si pervers,
  Viens régner, triomphant.

4.

Les peuples que tu as créés
  Soumis t'adoreront,
Devant ton trône, prosternés,
  Ils chanteront ton nom.

5.

Ton bras puissant accomplira
  Miracles étonnants,
Du haut des cieux tu veilleras,
  Seul Dieu, sur tes enfants.

Trad. FLOSSETTE DU PASQUIER (1951).

— 105 (81) —

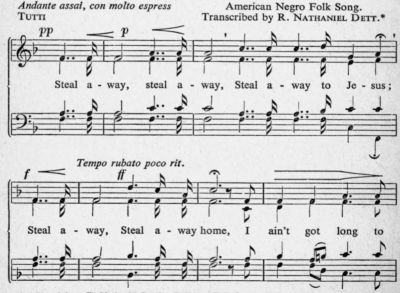

Andante assai, con molto espress
TUTTI

American Negro Folk Song.
Transcribed by R. NATHANIEL DETT.*

Steal a - way, steal a - way, Steal a - way to Je - sus;

Tempo rubato poco rit.

Steal a - way, Steal a - way home, I ain't got long to

* Adapted from R. Nathaniel Dett's "Religious Folk Songs of the Negro", published with the kind permission of the Hampton Institute Press, Virginia.

SOLO *Con molto espressione*

stay here. My Lord, calls me, He calls me by the

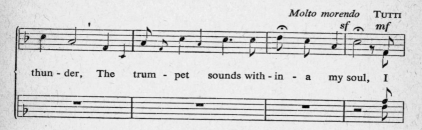

Molto morendo TUTTI

thun - der, The trum - pet sounds with - in - a my soul, I

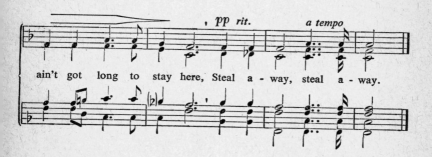

pp rit. *a tempo*

ain't got long to stay here, Steal a - way, steal a - way.

2. Steal away, steal away,
   Steal away to Jesus;
   Steal away, steal away home,
   I ain't got long to stay here.
   Green trees are bending,
   Poor sinner stands a-trembling;
   The trumpet sounds...

3. Steal away, steal away,
   Steal away to Jesus;
   Steal away, steal away home,
   I ain't got long to stay here.
   Tombstones are bursting,
   Poor sinner stands a-trembling;
   The trumpet sounds...

4. Steal away, steal away,
   Steal away to Jesus;
   Steal away, steal away home,
   I ain't got long to stay here.
   My Lord calls me
   He calls me by the lightning;
   The trumpet sounds...

106

MELCOMBE.
SAMUEL WEBBE (1740-1816).

New ev' - ry morn - ing is the love Our
O Got - tes - lie - be, wie ge - treu Weckst
A - ni - mé d'un nou - vel a - mour Je

wak' - ning and up - ris - ing prove; Thro' sleep and dark - ness
du uns al - le Mor - gen neu. Durch Schlaf und Dun - kel -
rends gloire à Dieu cha - que jour, Et res - tau - ré par

safe - ly brought, Re - stored to life and pow'r and thought.
heit be - wahrt, Be - gin - nen wir des Ta - ges Fahrt.
le som - meil, Je lui rends grâce à mon ré - veil.

2.

New mercies, each returning day,
Hover around us while we pray ;
New perils past, new sins forgiven,
New thoughts of God, new hopes of heaven.

3.

If on our daily course our mind
Be set to hallow all we find,
New treasures still, of countless price,
God will provide for sacrifice.

4.

Old friends, old scenes, will lovelier be,
As more of heaven in each we see ;
Some softening gleam of love and prayer
Shall dawn on every cross and care.

5.

The trivial round, the common task,
Will furnish all we ought to ask, —
Room to deny ourselves, a road
To bring us daily nearer God.

6.

Only, O Lord, in Thy dear love,
Fit us for perfect rest above;
And help us, this and every day,
To live more nearly as we pray.

JOHN KEBLE (1792-1866).

* * *

2.

Zu danken, faltet sich die Hand,
Wieviel Gefahr du abgewandt,
Vergabst uns neu' und alte Sünd,
Dass unser Herz den Himmel find't.

3.

Wenn dieser Erde Pracht und Glanz
Erfüllet uns're Seele ganz,
So schenkt Gott Gaben ungezählt
Zu Opfern, reich und wohlerwählt.

4.

Der Freundschaft Gabe ist mehr wert,
Wenn deinen Segen sie erfährt.
Dein milder Glanz und Himmelsschein
Verklärt selbst uns're Sorg' und Pein.

5.

Es schenkt alltäglich Werk und Pflicht
Worauf sich uns're Bitte richt'
Des Eigenwillens steter Tod
Bringt immer näher uns zu Gott.

6.

O Herre Gott, gib, dass auf Erd'
Dein' Lieb' uns ein und alles werd',
Dass dieser Tag und alle Frist
Ein Weg zu deinem Herzen ist.

Übers. ERWIN KLEINE (1950).

* * *

2.

Tous les matins quand j'ai prié
De grands bienfaits Dieu m'a comblé
Et pardonnant tous mes péchés,
Les cieux il m'a fait espérer.

3.

A mon travail de chaque jour
Si je me donne avec amour,
Mon œuvre portera des fruits
Et mes efforts seront bénis.

4.

Pour moi tout sera précieux
Si j'y trouve un reflet des cieux;
Je comprendrai mieux mes amis,
J'oublierai tous mes soucis.

5.

Reconnaissant de tes bienfaits
Pour toi, mon Dieu, j'accomplirai
Sans peine des travaux mesquins,
Seigneur, mais prends-moi par la main.

6.

Seigneur, mon Dieu, par ton amour
Fais qu'en toi je repose un jour;
Sans ton appui je ne puis rien,
O montre-moi le droit chemin.

Trad. FLOSSETTE DU PASQUIER (1951).

107

Melodie 1527 — Satz 1934.

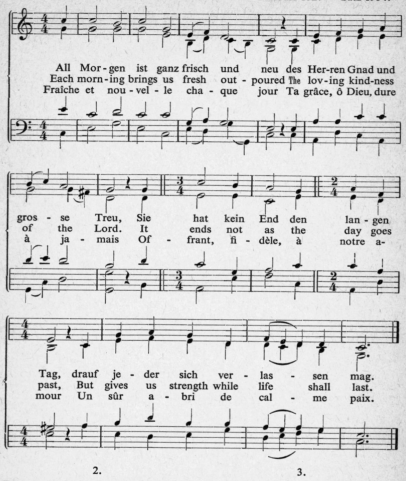

All Mor-gen ist ganz frisch und neu des Her-ren Gnad und
Each morn-ing brings us fresh out-poured The lov-ing kind-ness
Fraîche et nou-vel-le cha-que jour Ta grâce, ô Dieu, dure

gros-se Treu, Sie hat kein End den lan-gen
of the Lord. It ends not as the day goes
à ja-mais Of-frant, fi-dèle, à notre a-

Tag, drauf je-der sich ver-las-sen mag.
past, But gives us strength while life shall last.
mour Un sûr a-bri de cal-me paix.

2.

Drum steht der Himmel Lichter voll,
Dass man zum Leben sehen soll
Und es mög schön geordnet sein,
Zu ehren Gott, den Schöpfer dein.

3.

So hat der Leib der Augen Licht,
Dass er dadurch viel Guts ausricht
Und seh auf Gott zu aller Frist
Und merk, wie er so gnädig ist.

4.

O Gott, du schöner Morgenstern,
Gib uns, was wir von dir begehr'n:
Zünd deine Lichter in uns an,
Lass uns an Gnad kein Mangel han.

5.

Treib aus, o Licht, all Finsternis,
Behüt uns, Herr, vor Ärgernis,
Vor Blindheit und vor aller Schand
Und beut' uns Tag und Nacht dein' Hand.

6.

Zu wandeln als am lichten Tag,
Damit was immer sich zutrag,
Wir steh'n im Glauben bis ans End'
Und bleiben von dir ungetrennt.

JOHANNES ZWICK (1496-1542).

* * *

2.

The heavens burn with light above
That we may see to live and move,
And all our doings be designed
To honour God Who made mankind.

3.

Light fills our being through our eyes
To show us what is good and wise,
And guide us on our God to gaze,
And mark how gracious are His ways.

4.

O God, Thou star of dawning day,
Give us that light for which we pray :
Make Thou Thy flame in us to glow,
That we no lack of grace may know.

5.

The darkness in us, Lord, dispel ;
From bitterness, O shield us well,
From ill desires, from clouded sight ;
And do Thou lead us, day and night,

6.

To walk as by the light of day,
That we may ever, come what may,
In our strong faith unwavering be,
Abiding steadfast one with Thee.

Trans. MARGARET BARCLAY (1951).

* * *

2.

Le Ciel rayonne de clarté
Pour que nous puissions voir, Seigneur,
Notre péché, ta sainteté
Et chantions notre Créateur !

3.

Ainsi la clarté de nos yeux
Peut nous guider en ces bas lieux,
Mais nous tournant vers les hauts cieux
Nous connaissons ta grâce, ô Dieu.

4.

Seigneur, étoile du matin,
Exauce-nous dans ta bonté ;
Allume en nous, brûlante enfin,
La clarté de ta vérité.

5.

Dissipe en nous l'obscurité ;
Garde-nous de haine et courroux,
D'aveuglement, de dureté,
Tends nuit et jour ta main vers nous !

6.

Or pour marcher dans le plein jour
Nous restons fermes dans la foi
Puis, nous haussant vers ton amour,
Vivons sans fin tout près de toi.

Trad. PAULINE MARTIN (1951).

— 108 —

Melodie M. VULPIUS (1609).

Die hel - le Sonn leucht' jetzt her - für, fröh-lich vom
Le clair so - leil brille au ciel bleu. Dès le ma-
Forth see the sun in brill-iance blaze : Rise we from

Schlaf auf - ste - hen wir; Gott lob, der uns in die - ser
tin, bé - ni soit Dieu! Nous re - po - sions pen - dant la
sleep in joy and praise. Praise to Him Who through dark-ling

Nacht, be - hüt' hat vor des Teu - fels Macht.
nuit, Gar - dés du mal, veil - lés par lui.
hours Pro - tect - ed us from ev - il powers.

2. Herr Christ, den Tag uns auch behüt'
   Vor Sünd' und Schand' durch deine Güt',
   Lass deine lieben Engelein,
   Uns're Hüter und Wächter sein.

3. Dass unser Herz in G'horsam leb,
   Dein'm Wort und Will'n nicht widerstreb ;
   Dass wir dich stets vor Augen han
   In allem was wir heben an.

4. Lass unser Werk geraten wo hl,
Was ein jeder ausrichten soll,
Dass unsere Arbeit, Müh' und Fleiss
Gereich zu dein'm Lob, Ehr und Preis.

NIKOLAUS HERMAN (1480-1561).

* * *

2. Seigneur Jésus, en ton amour
Protège-nous au long du jour.
Viens écarter le Tentateur
Qui veut séduire notre cœur.

3. Oh ! donne-nous de te servir,
Heureux d'aimer et d'obéir !
Que nos yeux soient fixés sur toi,
Notre modèle et notre Roi.

4. Reste avec nous et daigne encor
De nos labeurs bénir l'effort.
Rends-le fécond, et fais, Seigneur,
Qu'il s'accomplisse à ton honneur.

Trad. BLANCHE D'ESTIENNE (1950).

* * *

2. Saviour and Lord, likewise we pray,
Keep us from sin and shame by day,
And in Thy love, to guard and guide,
Set Thou Thine angels at our side,

3. That, heart and mind, we may obey,
Never Thy will nor word gainsay,
And have Thee always in our thought
In everything that we have wrought.

4. Prosper our work to be begun,
The work of each and everyone,
That all our toil and labourings
May magnify the King of kings.

Trans. MARGARET BARCLAY (1950).

— 109 (34) —

Andante

Kie - dy ran - ne wsta - ja zo - rze, To - bie
With the morn in ra - diance break - ing Earth in
Quand le jour com - mence à poin - dre, Ciel et
Kommt der Tag em - por - ge - zo - gen, Ju - beln

zie - mia, To - bie mo - rze, To - bie śpie - wa ży - wił
all her glo - ry wak - ing, Sky and sea, Thine own cre-
ter - re vont se join - dre, Pour te chan - ter dans ta
dir die Mee - res - wo - gen, Busch und Halm und Ac - ker-

wszel - ki, Bądź po - chwa - lon, Bo - że wiel - ki !
a - tion Hymn Thee, Lord, in a - dor - a - tion.
gloi - re, Dieu, que bé - nit ma mé - moi - re.
kru - me Sin - gen, Herr, zu dei - nem Ruh - me.

2.

A człowiek, który bez miary
Obsypany Ţwymi dary,
Coś go stworzył i ocalił,
A czemużby Cię nie chwalił.

3.

Ledwie oczy przetrzeć zdołam,
Już do mego Pana wołam,
Do mego Pana na niebie,
I szukam Go koło siebie.

4.

Wielu snem smierci upadli,
Co się wczoraj spać pokładli,
My się jeszcze obudzili,
Byśmy Cię, Boże, chwalili.

KARPIŃSKI (1741-1825).

* * *

2.

Man whom Thou hast richly dowered,
Blessings on his head hast showered ;
All ungrateful, shamed before Thee,
Man alone does not adore Thee.

3.

Scarce from sleep my thoughts awaken
When to Thee my vows are taken ;
Thou, whose robe is gladsome nature,
Lord of every grateful creature.

4.

Death hath many captives numbered
While in peace we calmly slumbered ;
Now the new-born day arriving
Summons us to noble striving.

Trans. W. J. ROSE (1922).

* * *

2.

L'homme qui te doit la vie,
Tu l'as sauvé, tu l'appuies,
De te louer il s'empresse,
Comblé de tes dons sans cesse.

3.

Dès que j'ouvre mes paupières,
Je t'appelle, et mes prières
Vont te rendre mes hommages,
Cherchant Dieu dans ses ouvrages.

4.

Des mortels ont dû paraître,
Cette nuit, devant leur Maître.
Nous nous réveillons encore
Pour que notre cœur t'adore.

Trad. inconnu.

* * *

2.

Und der Mensch, dem du die Hände
Füllst mit Segen ohne Ende,
Dem du deinen Sohn gegeben —
Er sollt ohne Loblied leben ?

3.

Da ich öffnete die Lider,
Sah ich deine Güte wieder,
Licht aus dir, die schönen Dinge —
Und nun singe ich, ich singe.

4.

Weiss es : da mich Schlaf erquickte,
Manchen heut der Tod entrückte.
Mich hast du erweckt am Tage,
Dass ich dir mein Loblied sage.

Übers. JOHANN CHRISTOPH HAMPE (1950).

— 110 (74) —

Mélodie Loys Bourgeois (1549)
harmonisation d'après C. Goudimel (1565).

The day Thou gav-est, Lord, is end-ed, The dark-ness
Der Tag, den du uns gabst, sich nei-get, Die Nacht deckt
A l'ho - ri - zon, le jour s'é-loi-gne, L'obs - cu - ri-

falls at Thy be-hest; To Thee our morn-ing hymns as-
dei - ne Er - de zu. Wie Mor-gen-sang zum Him-mel
té des-cend sur nous. Comme au ma - tin, nos mains se

cend - ed, Thy praise shall sanc - ti - fy our rest.
stei - get, Ein Lob - lied lei - te uns zur Ruh.
joi - gnent, Et nous te lou-ons à ge - noux.

2. We thank Thee that Thy Church unsleeping,
   While earth rolls onward into light,
   Through all the world her watch is keeping,
   And rests not now by day or night.

3. As o'er each continent and island
   The dawn leads on another day,
   The voice of prayer is never silent,
   Nor dies the strain of praise away.

4. The sun that bids us rest is waking
   Our brethren 'neath the western sky,
   And hour by hour fresh lips are making
   Thy wondrous doings heard on high.

5. So be it, Lord ; Thy throne shall never,
   Like earth's proud empires, pass away ;
   Thy Kingdom stands, and grows for ever,
   Till all Thy creatures own Thy sway.

J. ELLERTON (1826-1893).

★ ★ ★

2. Die heil'ge Kirche wachsam stehet,
   Die Erde reckt empor zum Licht,
   Ihr stetes Werben nicht verwehet,
   Und Tag und Nacht sie ruhet nicht.

3. Wie über ferner Länder Weiten
   Ein Tag sich an den andern reiht,
   Der Sehnsucht Stimmen Weg bereiten,
   Gebete, Hymnen, Gott geweiht.

4. Ist uns die Sonn' zur Ruh gegangen,
   Weckt sie die Brüder übern'm Meer,
   Und stündlich neu wird angefangen
   Ein Loblied, das dich preist, O Herr !

5. So sei es, Herr ! Dein Thron nie falle
   Wie stolzes Erden-Königtum !
   Dein Reich ersteht und es erschalle
   Ein herrlich Loblied dir zum Ruhm !

Übers. GERTRUD DALGAS.

★ ★ ★

2. Seigneur, tandis que notre terre,
   Poursuit sa course dans les cieux,
   Toujours l'Eglise, à ta lumière,
   Est vigilante en quelque lieu.

3. Puisqu'à chaque heure, avec l'aurore,
   Le soleil luit sur un sommet,
   La voix qui te prie et t'adore,
   Seigneur, ne se taira jamais.

4. Quand je repose, d'autres veillent,
   A l'Occident, sous ta clarté,
   Et, chantant bien haut tes merveilles,
   Ne cessent pas de t'exalter.

5. Jamais le soleil ne se couche
   Sur ton Royaume, ô Dieu puissant !
   Il faut qu'un jour, toutes les bouches
   Disent ta gloire, en saints accents.

Trad. H. ECUYER (1930).

JOHANN GEORG EBELING (1607-1676).

Die güld' - ne Son - ne voll Freud und Won - ne
The sun a - scen - dant, in joy re - splend - ent,
Toi qui flam - boi - es, So - leil de joi - e,

bringt un - sern Gren - zen Mit ihr - rem Glän - zen ein herz - er -
Lights our re - pi - ning By its clear shi - ning With its own
Donne à notre â - me Ta sain - te flam - me Ta bien - fai-

quik - ken - des, lieb - lich - es Licht. Mein Haupt und Glied - er, die
liv - ing and quick - en - ing blaze. Long lay I dark - ling, But
sante et joy - eu - se clar - té. Dans ma dé - tres - se, Je

la - gen dar - nie - der, a - ber nun steh ich, bin mun - ter und
by its spark - ling I am a - ris - en From out of my
pleu - rais sans ces - se Mais je me dres - se, Fort de ta pro-

fröh - lich, schau - e den Him - mel mit mein - em Ge - sicht.
pris - on, And on the ra - di - ant heav - ens may gaze.
mes - se Le - vant au ciel un re - gard en - chan - té.

2.	3.
Abend und Morgen	Gott meine Krone,
Sind seine Sorgen ;	Vergib und schone,
Segnen und mehren,	Lass meine Schulden
Unglück verwehren	In Gnad und Hulden
Sind seine Werke und Taten allein.	Aus deinen Augen sein ferne gewandt.
Wenn wir uns legen,	Sonsten regiere
So ist er zugegen ;	Mich, lenke und führe,
Wenn wir aufstehen,	Wie dirs gefället ;
So lässt er aufgehen	Ich habe gestellet
Über uns seiner Barmherzigkeit Schein.	Alles in deine Beliebung und Hand.

4.

Kreuz und Elende,
Das nimmt ein Ende ;
Nach Meeresbrausen
Und Windessausen
Leuchtet der Sonne gewünschtes Gesicht.
Freude die Fülle
Und selige Stille
Darf ich erwarten
Im himmlischen Garten ;
Dahin sind meine Gedanken gericht.

PAULUS GERHARDT (1607-1676).

★ ★ ★

2.	3.
Evening and morning,	Father, O hear me !
Sunset and dawning,	Pardon and spare me !
Wealth, peace and gladness,	Calm all my terrors,
Comfort in sadness,	Blot out my errors, [scanned.
These are Thy works; all the glory be Thine;	That by Thine eyes they may no more be
Times without number,	Direct all my doings ;
Awake or in slumber,	Order my goings
Thine eye observes us,	As it may please Thee,
From danger preserves us,	Retain or release me ;
Causing Thy mercy upon us to shine.	All I commit to Thy fatherly hand.

16

4.

Griefs of God's sending,
Soon have an ending;
Clouds may be pouring,
Wind and wave roaring;
Sunshine will come when the tempest is past.
Joys still increasing,
And peace never ceasing,
Fountains that dry not,
And roses that die not,
Blooming in Eden, await us at last.

Trans. RICHARD MASSIE (1800-1887).
First verse trans. MARGARET BARCLAY (1951).

* * *

2.

Dans la lumière
Tu viens, ô Père ;
La nuit s'approche,
Et tu es proche,
Car tu te penches sur moi chaque jour.
Quand je sommeille,
Sur moi tu veilles,
Quand je m'éveille,
Tu verses, merveille
Tes dons de grâce, de paix et d'amour.

3.

Dieu, ma couronne,
Toi qui pardonnes,
Par ta clémence,
Ta bienveillance,
Daigne écarter mon péché de tes yeux.
Viens et m'éclaire,
Soutiens, ô Père,
L'âme si frêle,
La foi qui chancelle ;
J'ai tout remis en tes mains, ô mon Dieu !

4.

Car la misère
Prend fin sur terre,
Après l'orage,
Les lourds nuages,
Tu resplendis, ô soleil attendu;
Père si tendre,
Je puis donc attendre
Devant ta face
Ta paix et ta grâce !
Vers ces clartés mes espoirs sont tendus !

Trad. PAULINE MARTIN (1951).

— 112 —

« Tallis Canon L. M. »
Abridged from a melody by
THOMAS TALLIS (c. 1520-1585).

All praise to Thee, my God, this night, For
Sei - gneur, quand vient l'obs - cu - ri - té Bé-
Ich will dich lo - ben Gott zur Nacht, Der

all the bless - ings of the light ! Keep me, O keep me,
ni sois - tu pour ta clar - té, Et quand sur nous la
seg - nend du den Tag be - dacht. O blei - be nah und

King of kings, Be - neath Thy own al - might - y wings.
nuit des - cend Dans tes bras gar - de tes en - fants.
schen - ke du Im Schat - ten dei - ner All - macht Ruh.

2. Forgive me, Lord, for Thy dear Son,
The ill that I this day have done,
That with the world, myself, and Thee,
I, ere I sleep, at peace may be.

3. Teach me to live that I may dread
The grave as little as my bed ;
Teach me to die, that so I may
Rise glorious at the awful day.

4. O may my soul on Thee repose,
   And with sweet sleep mine eyelids close, —
   Sleep that may me more vigorous make
   To serve my God when I awake.

5. When in the night I sleepless lie,
   My soul with heavenly thoughts supply;
   Let no ill dreams disturb my rest,
   No powers of darkness me molest.

6. Praise God from whom all blessings flow;
   Praise Him, all creatures here below;
   Praise Him, above, ye heavenly host;
   Praise Father, Son and Holy Ghost.

Bishop T. KEN (1637-1711).

* * *

2. Pardonne-moi mon vil péché
   Au nom de ton Fils bien-aimé,
   Afin que je m'endorme en paix
   Sous ton regard, ô Dieu parfait.

3. Fais que je vive saintement
   Afin qu'à mes derniers moments
   La mort me soit un gain béni,
   Et prends-moi dans ton paradis.

4. Fais qu'en toi je repose, ô Dieu,
   Et quand je fermerai les yeux
   Restaure-moi par le sommeil
   Pour mieux te servir au réveil.

5. Si parfois le sommeil me fuit
   En toi je cherche mon appui.
   Seigneur, protège mon repos
   Et garde-moi de tous les maux.

6. Chantez à Dieu, vous ses enfants
   Et vous, ses anges triomphants :
   Gloire à celui qui nous bénit,
   Au Père, au Fils, au Saint-Esprit.

Trad. FLOSSETTE DU PASQUIER (1950).

* * *

2. Weil Christ für uns gelitten hat,
   Vergib, was ich heut missetat,
   Was ich, eh' mich der Schlaf nimmt hin,
   Mit dir und all'n in Frieden bin.

3. Lehr mich so leben, dass ich dann
   Das Grab als freundlich Bett schau an.
   Lehr mich so sterben, dass dein Tag
   In ew'gen Licht mich finden mag.

4. O lass die Seele in dir ruh'n,
   Lass Schlaf die Augen schliessen nun,
   Damit ich morgen kräftiger
   Dir dienen kann, mein Gott und Herr.

5. Und läg' ich schlaflos, lass den Sinn
   Getrost sich wenden himmelhin.
   Bewahr das Herz vor dunklem Traum,
   Verwehr dem Bösen Recht und Raum.

6. Lobt unsern Gott, was Leben hat,
   Und stets hier lebt von seiner Gnad'
   Es lobe ihn, was himmlisch heisst,
   Gelobt der Vater, Sohn und Geist.

Übers. ERWIN KLEINE (1950).

— 113 —

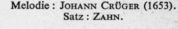

Melodie : JOHANN CRÜGER (1653).
Satz : ZAHN.

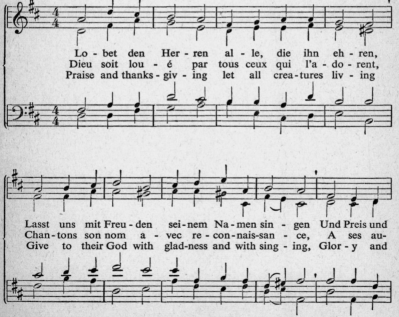

Lo - bet den Her - ren al - le, die ihn eh - ren,
Dieu soit lou - é par tous ceux qui l'a - do - rent,
Praise and thanks - giv - ing let all crea - tures liv - ing

Lasst uns mit Freu - den sei - nem Na - men sin - gen Und Preis und
Chan - tons son nom a - vec re - con - nais - san - ce, A ses au -
Give to their God with glad - ness and with sing - ing, Glor - y and

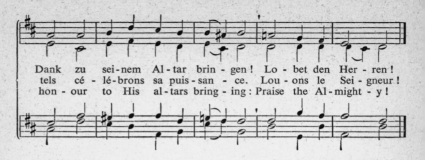

Dank zu sei-nem Al-tar brin-gen! Lo-bet den Her-ren!
tels cé-lé-brons sa puis-san-ce. Lou-ons le Sei-gneur!
hon-our to His al-tars bring-ing: Praise the Al-might-y!

2. Der unser Leben, das er uns gegeben,
   In dieser Nacht so väterlich bedecket
   Und aus dem Schlaf uns fröhlich auferwecket:
        Lobet den Herren!

3. O treuer Hüter, Brunnen aller Güter,
   Ach lass doch ferner über unser Leben
   Bei Tag und Nacht dein Hut und Güte schweben:
        Lobet den Herren!

4. Gib, dass wir heute, Herr, durch dein Geleite
   Auf unsern Wegen unverhindert gehen
   Und überall in deiner Gnade stehen:
        Lobet den Herren!

5. Treib unsern Willen, dein Wort zu erfüllen;
   Lehr uns verrichten heilige Geschäfte,
   Und wo wir schwach sind, da gib du uns Kräfte:
        Lobet den Herren!

6. Richt uns're Herzen, das wir ja nicht scherzen
   Mit deinen Strafen, sondern fromm zu werden
   Vor deiner Zukunft uns bemüh'n auf Erden:
        Lobet den Herren!

7. Herr, du wirst kommen und all deine Frommen,
   Die sich bekehren, gnädig dahin bringen
   Da alle Engel ewig, ewig singen:
        Lobet den Herren!

PAULUS GERHARDT (1607-1676).

* * *

2. C'est l'Eternel qui nous a mis au monde,
   Et qui la nuit sur nous tendrement veille
   Puis au matin, pleins d'espoir, nous éveille:
        Louons le Seigneur!

3. Que ta bonté dans tes sentiers nous garde,
   O bon Berger, source de toute grâce,
   Que nuit et jour sur nous veille ta face:
        Louons le Seigneur!

4. Permets, Seigneur, que tous à ton service
   Nous parcourions notre route sans peine,
   Et que partout ta grâce nous soutienne :
       Louons le Seigneur !

5. Veuille changer notre faiblesse en force
   Soumets nos cœurs à ta volonté sainte
   Pour que toujours nous vivions en ta crainte :
       Louons le Seigneur !

6. Par ton amour, daigne éclairer nos âmes,
   Emplis nos cœurs d'un zèle salutaire
   Pour amener ton règne sur la terre :
       Louons le Seigneur !

7. Puis tu viendras avec tous tes disciples
   Ils uniront leurs chants à ceux des anges,
   Le monde entier chantera tes louanges :
       Louons le Seigneur !

Trad. VIOLETTE DU PASQUIER (1950).

★ ★ ★

2. Lives of His making brings He to their waking :
   Night-long He had us in His gracious keeping,
   And into light now calls us from our sleeping :
       Praise the Almighty !

3. Steadfast Defender, Giver great and tender,
   Shield us from ill both day and night for ever,
   And shed Thou down on us Thy bounteous favour :
       Praise the Almighty !

4. Grant by Thy leading, no ill thing impeding,
   We go our ways this day with Thee to guide us,
   And Thy sustaining grace to be beside us :
       Praise the Almighty !

5. Frame our desiring to do Thy requiring :
   That to Thy glory may be all our dealing :
   And, where we fail, grant Thou us strength and healing :
       Praise the Almighty !

6. Cause us, we pray Thee, freely to obey Thee,
   Ever our own will to Thy great Will bending,
   Till Thou shalt come, and time shall have an ending:
       Praise the Almighty !

7. And in that hour when Thou com'st in power,
   Thou shalt raise up those whom Thou lov'st before Thee,
   Where all the host of heaven doth adore Thee :
       Praise the Almighty !

Trans. MARGARET BARCLAY (1951).

— 114 (40) —

Moderato

Orthodox Church Liturgy.*

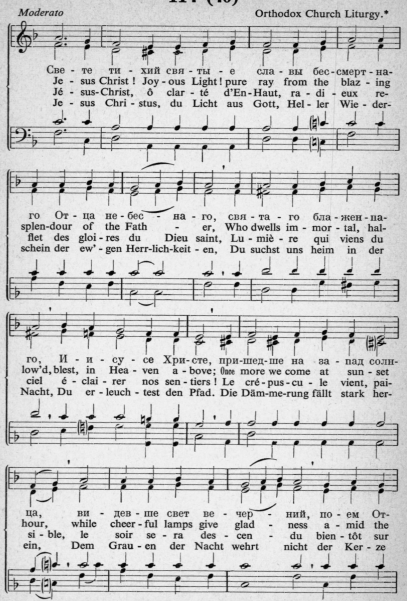

Све - те ти - хий свя - ты - е сла - вы бес - смерт - на -
Je - sus Christ! Joy - ous Light! pure ray from the blaz - ing
Jé - sus-Christ, ô clar - té d'En-Haut, ra - di - eux re -
Je - sus Chri - stus, du Licht aus Gott, Hel - ler Wie - der -

го От - ца не - бес - на - го, свя - та - го бла - жен - на -
splen-dour of the Fath - er, Who dwells im - mor - tal, hal -
flet des gloi - res du Dieu saint, Lu - miè - re qui viens du
schein der ew' - gen Herr - lich - keit - en, Du suchst uns heim in der

го, И - и - су - се Хри - сте, при - шед - ше на за - пад солн -
low'd, blest, in Hea - ven a - bove; Once more we come at sun - set
ciel é - clai - rer nos sen - tiers! Le cré - pus - cu - le vient, pai -
Nacht, Du er - leuch - test den Pfad. Die Däm - me - rung fällt stark her -

ца, ви - дев - ше свет ве - чер - ний, по - ем От -
hour, while cheer - ful lamps give glad - ness a - mid the
si - ble, le soir se - ra des - cen - du bien - tôt sur
ein, Dem Grau - en der Nacht wehrt nicht der Ker - ze

* Voir la note précédant la table des matières. — See note preceding the general index.
Vergleiche die Vorbemerkung vor dem Inhaltsverzeichniss.

ца, Сы-на, и свя-та-го Ду-ха Бо- га. До-
gloom, One God we praise, Father, Son and Ho-ly Ghost. To
nous. Lu-mière é - ter-nel-le, nous t'a-do- rons ! A
Schein. Komm Du, Gott Va-ter, Gott Sohn, Gott hei - li-ger Geist, Dich

сто - ин е - си во вся вре - ме - на пет бы - ти
Thee, Ev - er - last - ing Son of the Fa - ther, sac - red
toi, Pè - re saint, ô Dieu de clar - té, à Jé-
wol - len wir rüh - men in E - wig - keit. Herr Christ,

гла - сы - пре - по - доб - ны - ми, Сы - не Бо - жий, жи-
an - thems ev - er we should sing; Thou art worth - y of
sus ton Fils, au Saint - Es - prit, Nos can - ti - ques re-
schlies - se auf un - sern Mund, Dass wir dich lo - ben

вот да - яй: тем - же мир тя сла - вит.
all wor-ship, life e - ter - nal Thou didst bring.
con - nais-sants. Sois bé - ni pour ja - mais.
auf rech - te Art. Ge - prie - sen seist du e - wig - lich.

— 115 (58) —

HENRY ISAAC (1440 ?-1517).

Nun ru - hen al - le Wäl - der, Vieh, Men-schen,
Now all the woods are sleep - ing, And night and
Les bois, les champs s'a - pai - sent Et tous les

Städt und Fel - der, Es schläft die gan - ze Welt; Ihr
still - ness creep - ing O'er ci - ty, man and beast; But
bruits se tai - sent, Le monde en - tier s'en-dort; Pri-

a - ber, mei - ne Sin - nen, Auf, auf, ihr sollt be-
thou, my heart, a - wake thee, To prayer a - while be-
ons Dieu no - tre maî - tre Qui nous a don - né

gin - nen, Was eu - rem Schöp - fer wohl - ge - fällt.
take thee, And praise thy Ma - ker e'er thou rest.
l'ê - tre Car seul, il a vain - cu la mort.

2.

Wo bist du, Sonne, blieben ?
Die Nacht hat dich vertrieben,
Die Nacht, des Tages Feind.
Fahr' hin, ein' and're Sonne,
Mein Jesus, meine Wonne,
Gar hell in meinem Herzen scheint.

3.

Der Tag ist nun vergangen,
Die güldnen Sternlein prangen
Am blauen Himmelssaal ;
Also werd' ich auch stehen,
Wenn mich wird heissen gehen
Mein Gott aus diesem Jammertal.

4.

Der Leib eilt nun zur Ruhe,
Legt ab das Kleid und Schuhe,
Das Bild der Sterblichkeit :
Die zieh ich aus, dagegen
Wird Christus mir anlegen
Den Rock der Ehr und Herrlichkeit.

5.

Breit aus die Flügel beide,
O Jesu, meine Freude.
Und nimm dein Küchlein ein ;
Will Satan mich verschlingen,
So lass die Engel singen :
Dies Kind soll unverletzet sein.

PAULUS GERHARDT (1607-1676).

★ ★ ★

2.

O Sun, where art thou vanished ?
The Night thy reign hath banished,
Thine ancient foe, the Night.
Farewell, a brighter glory
My Jesus sheddeth o'er me,
All clear within me shines His light.

3.

The last faint beam is going,
The golden stars are glowing
In yonder dark-blue deep :
And such the glory given
When, called of God to heaven,
On earth no more we pine and weep.

4.

The body hastes to slumber,
These garments now but cumber,
And as I lay them by
I ponder how the spirit
Puts off the flesh to inherit
A shining robe with Christ on high.

5.

My Jesus, stay Thou by me,
And let no foe come nigh me,
Safe sheltered by Thy wing ;
But would the foe alarm me.
O never let him harm me,
But let Thine angels round me sing.

Trans. CATHERINE WINKWORTH (1829-1878).

★ ★ ★

2.

Soleil, où est ta face ?
La nuit du ciel te chasse
Quand vient la fin du jour ;
Mais Christ par sa lumière
Met fin à ma misère,
Il brille en moi par son amour.

3.

Et quand le jour s'achève,
Au ciel déjà se lèvent
Les astres dans la nuit.
Et moi, dans ma souffrance,
J'attends ma délivrance
De Dieu qui, seul, est mon appui.

4.

Mais la faiblesse humaine
Au sommeil nous entraîne
Quand nos corps sont trop las ;
De cette chair mortelle
Dans la vie éternelle,
O Dieu, tu nous délivreras.

5.

En toi je me confie,
Jésus, tu es ma vie,
Ne m'abandonne pas ;
Et quand le mal m'assiège
De grâce me protège
Dès maintenant jusqu'au trépas.

Trad. EVA DUBSKA-KUSHNER
et FLOSSETTE DU PASQUIER (1950).

— 116 —

Melodie 1599.
Satz: Jak. Praetorius (1604.)

Wa - chet auf, ruft uns die Stim - me, Der Wäch- ter
Wake, O wake! with tid-ings thrill - ing The watch-men
Des veil - leurs, la voix so - no - re du haut des

sehr hoch auf der Zin - ne, Wach auf, du Stadt Je - ru - sa-
all the air are fill - ing, A - rise, Je - ru - sa - lem, a-
tours, a - vant l'au - ro - re Sou - dain, vi - brante, a re - ten-

lem! Mit - ter - nacht heisst die - se Stun - de,
rise! Mid - night strikes! no more de - lay - ing,
ti: Que Si - on en - fin s'é - veil - le!

Sie ru - fen uns mit hel - lem Mun - de: Wo seid ihr
'The hour has come!' we hear them say - ing. Where are ye
Jé - ru - sa - lem, prê - te l'o - reil - le! Pour toi le

klu - gen Jung-frau - en? Wohl - auf, der Bräut'-gam kömmt, Steht auf,
all, ye vir - gins wise? The Bride-groom comes in sight, Raise high
temps est ac - com - pli. O vier-ges, le - vez - vous! De - bout,

die Lam - pen nehmt! Hal - le - lu - ja! Macht euch be - reit zu
your tor - ches bright! Al - le - lu - ia! The wed-ding song Swells
voi - ci l'é-poux. Al - lé - lu - ia! Pré - pa - rez - vous à

der Hoch - zeit; Ihr müs - set ihm ent - ge - gen geh'n!
loud and strong: Go forth and join the fest - al throng.
l'ac - cueil - lir, Vers lui cou - rez pour le ser - vir.

2.

Zion hört die Wächter singen,
Das Herz tut ihr vor Freude springen,
  Sie wachet und steht eilend auf.
Ihr Freund kommt vom Himmel prächtig,
Von Gnaden stark, von Wahrheit mächtig;
  Ihr Licht wird hell, ihr Stern geht auf.
    Nun komm, du werte Kron,
    Herr Jesu, Gottes Sohn!
      Hosianna!
Wir folgen all, zum Freudensaal
Und halten mit das Abendmahl.

3.

Gloria sei dir gesungen
Mit Menschen und mit Engelzungen,
  Mit Harfen und mit Zimbeln schön.
Von zwölf Perlen sind die Tore
An deiner Stadt, wir steh'n im Chore
  Der Engel hoch um deinen Thron.
    Kein Aug hat je gespürt,
    Kein Ohr hat mehr gehört
      Solche Freude.
Des jauchzen wir und singen dir
Das Halleluja für und für.

PHILIPPUS NICOLAI (1556-1608).

* * *

2.

Sion hears the watchmen shouting,
Her heart leaps up with joy undoubting,
  She stands and waits with eager eyes ;
See her Friend from heaven descending,
Adorned with truth and grace unending !
  Her light burns clear, her star doth rise.
  Now come, Thou precious Crown,
  Lord Jesu, God's own Son !
    Hosanna !
    Let us prepare
    To follow there,
Where in Thy supper we may share.

3.

Every soul in Thee rejoices ;
From men and from angelic voices
  Be glory given to Thee alone !
Now the gates of pearl receive us,
Thy presence never more shall leave us,
  We stand with Angels round Thy
  Earth cannot give below   [throne.
  The bliss Thou dost bestow.
    Alleluia !
    Grant us to raise
    To length of days,
The triumph-chorus of Thy praise.

Trans. FRANCIS CRAWFORD BURKITT.*

★ ★ ★

2.

Des veilleurs, le chant appelle
Ecoute, ô Sion, la nouvelle !
  Ton cœur tressaille de bonheur.
Du ciel vient dans sa puissance
Avec grâce et magnificence
  L'Epoux divin, ton Rédempteur.
  Trésor si précieux,
  Viens, Jésus, Fils de Dieu,
    Alléluia !
Nous te suivons à ton destin
Pour goûter un bonheur sans fin.

3.

Gloire à Dieu, honneur, louange
Chantez, les hommes et les anges,
  Vous, instruments, jouez sans fin.
Dans la ville aux murs de perles
Vos hosannas, joyeux déferlent
  Autour du trône du Dieu saint.
  Notre œil, jamais n'a vu
  Nos cœurs, jamais connu
    Tant de joie !
Nous adorons et t'exaltons,
Unis, Seigneur, et triomphants.

Trad. *Eglise et Liturgie*, L'Office divin (1947).

* From the English Hymnal, by permission of the Oxford University Press.

117

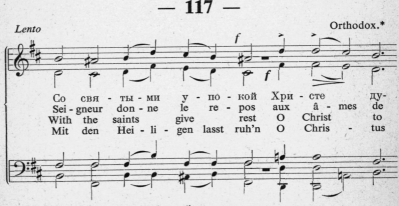

* Voir la note précédant la table des matières.
  See note preceding the general index.
  Vergleiche die Vorbemerkung vor dem Inhaltsverzeichniss.

— 118 —

M. Teschner (1724).
(Swedish adaptation.)

Animato

Pris va - re Gud, som lå - ter Oss gla - da vak - na
Preis sei dir, Gott, der frö - lich Uns wie - der weck - te
From peace - ful slum - ber wak - ing We sing, O Lord, Thy
Lou - ons tous no - tre Pè - re Qui, dans son grand a-

opp Och ö - ver jor - den å - ter En nå - de - dag gå
auf Und ü - ber uns führt gnä - dig Den neu - en Tag her -
praise, When o'er the world is break - ing An - o - ther day of
mour Fait naî - tre sur la ter - re En - core un nou - veau

opp, En dag, som skall förs - vin - na Lik den i går för -
auf. Auch die - ser wird ver - ge - hen, Wie's Lauf der Zei - ten
grace, A day that soon shall per - ish, As yes - ter - days are
jour. Au jour quand je m'é - veil - le, Le cœur rem - pli d'ar-

gick; O må vi då be - sin - na Dess dy - ra ö - gon - blick.
ist. So lass uns recht ver - ste - hen Die kur - ze Gna - den - frist.
past. O, teach us, then, to cher - ish Each mo - ment as our last.
deur, Sou - vent je m'é - mer - veil - le De ta bon - té, Sei - gneur.

2.

O må vi noga märka
  Vad Gud av oss begär
Och med all trohet verka,
  Så länge dagen är,
Att icke syndens minne
  Vårt hjärta klagar an,
När aftonen är inne,
  Då ingen verka kan.

3.

Att åt sin arma nästa
  Råd, hjälp och hugnad ge,
Ej blott på eget bästa,
  Men ock på andras se,
Ej blott Guds vilja veta,
  Men vandra i hans bud,
Det är att kristen heta,
  Det är att tjäna Gud.

4.

Och salig är och bliver,
  När Herren komma skall,
Den tjänaren, som giver
  Så akt uppå sitt kall,
Han dela skall den fröjden,
  Som intet öga sett,
Men Herren uti höjden
  Åt sina barn berett.

JOHAN OLOF WALLIN (1812).

★ ★ ★

2.

O lass genau uns fassen,
  Was Gott von uns begehrt,
Dass wir die Treu' nicht lassen,
  Solang der Tag noch währt.
Dass nicht die Last der Sünden
  Dann unser Herz klagt an,
Wenn sich der Abend findet,
  Da niemand wirken kann.

3.

Wer seinem armen Nächsten
  Rat, Trost und Hilfe gibt,
Nicht nur das eigne Beste,
  Nein, auch den Andern liebt,
Nach Gottes Willen handelt,
  Ihn nicht nur weiss und nennt,
Der dient Gott recht und wandelt
  So, dass ihn Christus kennt.

4.

Und selig ist und bleibet,
  Wenn Christus kommen wird,
Der Knecht, der sich verschreibet
  Dem Herrn und sich nicht irrt.
Er wird die Freuden teilen,
  Die nie ein Aug' geseh'n,
Mit Gottes Kindern weilen
  In seinen Himmelshöh'n.

Übers. GISELA VAN SPANKEREN (1951).

★ ★ ★

2.

Father of light and beauty,
 The light divine us send
To see and do our duty,
 Lest when this day shall end
Our conscience doth accuse us
 Of sin and trespass done,
And shame our face suffuses
 At blush of setting sun.

3.

Give God thy heart, thy labor,
 Walk in thy Saviour's grace,
And be unto thy neighbor
 A present help always :
The name of Christ we hallow
 Not by our faith alone ;
If we His path would follow,
 His will through us be done.

4.

Blest be each faithful servant,
 When'er the Lord shall come ;
The dutiful and fervent
 He taketh to His home,
To share with Him in glory
 What eye hath not beheld,
Nor tongue hath told in story
 Nor mortal heart hath held.

Evangelical Lutheran Augustana Synod Hymnbook
(1925).

* * *

2.

Puissé-je enfin entendre
 L'appel du Dieu vivant
Et chaque jour apprendre
 A vivre saintement.
Et si le mal m'accable
 Quand vient sur moi la nuit
Si je me sens coupable
 Dieu calme mon esprit.

3.

O Père, tu m'ordonnes
 D'assister mon prochain :
Qu'avec amour je donne
 Mon cœur, mon temps, mes biens;
J'entends l'appel du Maître
 Et lui donnant mon cœur
Je peux enfin connaître
 Le vrai, le seul bonheur.

4.

Jésus, tu nous appelles
 Et quand tu reviendras
Tes serviteurs fidèles
 Verront enfin leur roi,
Et, sauvés par la grâce,
 Un jour, dans ses parvis,
Ils verront face à face
 Leur Dieu, avec le Christ.

Trad. FLOSSETTE DU PASQUIER (1951).

— 119 —

Frédéric Mathil (1920).

Que la grâ - ce de no-tre Sei-gneur Jé - sus
Gra-tia Do-mi-ni nos-tri Je - su Chris-
May the grace of our Lord, Je-sus
Die Gna-de un-sers Herrn Je-su Chri-

Christ, et l'a-mour de Dieu le Pè - re, et la com-mu-ni-
ti, et cha-ri - tas Pa - tris, et com-mu - ni - ca - ti-
Christ, and the love of God the Fa - ther and the fell - ow-
stus, und die Lie - be Got - tes und die Ge-mein-

on du Saint - Es - prit, Soient a - vec nous tous, A - men !
o Sanc-ti - Spi - ri - tus Sit cum no - bis om-ni-bus A - men !
ship of the Ho - ly Ghost be with us all. A - men !
schaft des Heil'-gen Geis - tes sei mit uns al - len, A - men !

— 120 (95) —

CHRISTIAN GREGOR (1723-1801).

Ἡ χά - ρις τοῦ κυ - ρί - ου Ἰη-σοῦ Χρι- στοῦ καὶ ἡ ἀ-

Gra-tia Do-mi-ni nos-tri Je - su Chris - ti Et

Que la grâ - ce de no-tre Sei-gneur Jé-sus-Christ, et l'a-

May the grace of our Lord Je-sus-Christ, and the

Die Gna - de un - sers Herrn Je-sus Chris - tus, und die

γά - πη τοῦ θε - οῦ καὶ ἡ κοι-νω-νί - α τοῦ ἁ - γί-ου πνεύ-μα-

cha-ri-tas Pa - tris, et com-mu-ni - ca - ti - o Sanc-ti-Spi-ri-

mour de Dieu le Pè-re, et la com-mu - ni-on du Saint-Es-

love of God the Fa-ther and the com-mu - nion of the Ho-ly

Lie - be Got - tes und die Ge-mein-schaft des Heil-gen Geis-

τος με - τὰ πάν-των ὑ - μῶν, πάν-των ὑ - μῶν. Ἀ - μήν.

tus sit cum no - bis, no - bis om - ni - bus. A - men.

prit Soient a - vec nous tous A - vec nous tous, A - men.

Ghost, be with us all, with us all. A - men.

tes sei mit uns al - len, mit uns al - len. A - men.

HYMNS IN ENGLISH

(Hymns in italics are translations from other languages.)

First line	No.	Composer or source of tune	Author or translator of hymn
All creatures of our God and King	2	Cologne (1623). Harm. by Frédéric Mathil (1950). *German.*	W. H. Draper (about 1913). From St. Francis of Assisi (1182-1226).
All people that on earth do dwell.	7	Loys Bourgeois (1551). Harm. adapted from Cl. Goudimel (1565). *French.*	Psalm 100. William Kethe. Daye's Psalter (1560). *From the French.*
All praise to God in highest heaven	32	Melchior Vulpius (1609). *German.*	Margaret Barclay (1950). *From the German.*
All praise to Thee, my God, this night	112	"Tallis' Canon" L. M. Abridged from a melody by Thomas Tallis (1520-1585). *English.*	Bishop T. Ken (1637-1711).
A safe stronghold our God is still	70	Martin Luther (1483-1546) or Johann Walther (1496-1570). *German.*	Thomas Carlyle (1795-1881). *From the German.*
As the hind distressed and panting	65	Loys Bourgeois (1551). Harm. adapted from Claude Goudimel (1565). *French.*	R. Birch Hoyle (1923). *From the French.* Psalm 42.
A voice, a heavenly voice	56	O. Allström. *Swedish.*	Evangelical Lutheran Augustana Synod Hymnbook (1925). Third verse by Margaret Barclay (1951). *From the Swedish.*
Awake my soul, stretch every nerve	78	Scottish Psalter (1615). As given in Ravenscroft Psalter (1621).	Philip Doddridge (1702-1751).
Before Thy eyes, Lord Jesus	89	Huugo Nyberg (1873-). *Finnish.*	Unknown.
Before Thy throne, O Lord	9	Moravian melody. Hymnbook of the Dutch Reformed Church. Harm. by Leonard Johannes Mens (1879-).	Margaret and Francis House (1951) based on Revel. I. 5-7. *From the Dutch.*
Be Thou my vision	76	"Slane". *Irish traditional melody.*	Ancient *Irish* translation by Mary Byrne, versified by Eleanor Hull.

First line	No.	Composer or source of tune	Author or translator of hymn
Bread of the world in mercy broken	58	Loys Bourgeois (1558). Harm. by Claude Goudimel (1565). *French*.	Bishop R. Heber (1783-1826).
Breathe on me, Breath of God	45	"Dominica". Sir Herbert Stanley Oakeley (1830-1903). *English*.	Edwin Hatch (1878).
Brightest and best of the sons of the morning	22	Later form of melody from "Himmelslust" (1679). Harm by J. S. Bach (1685-1750). *German*.	Bishop R. Heber (1783-1826).
Christian hearts in love united	60	Brüdergemeinde (1745). *German*.	J. Miller (1789) . From the *German*.
Christ is arisen	30	Gregorian melody from the XIIth or XIIIth century. Harm. by H. L. Hassler (1608).	Margaret House (1950). From the *German*.
City of God, how broad and far	53	Johann Crüger (1598-1662). *German*.	Samuel Johnson (1822-1882).
Come, dearest Lord	46	"Hamburg", Lowell Mason (1792-1872). *English*.	Isaac Watts (1674-1748).
Come down, O love divine	44	"Down Ampney". Ralph Vaughan Williams (1872-). *English*.	Bianco di Sienna (1434). Trans. R. F. Littledale. From the *Italian*.
Come Holy Ghost, our souls inspire.	41	"Enchiridion". Martin · Luther (1483-1546). From a Gregorian Chant.	J. Cosin (1594-1672). From the *Latin*.
Come ye here in adoration	18	Pre-Reformation melody. Harm. by Johanna Wagenaar. *Dutch*.	Margaret House (1950). From the *French*.
Dear Lord and Father of mankind	90	"Lobt Gott ihr Christen". Nikolaus Herman (1485-1561). Arr. and harm. by J. S. Bach (1685-1750). *German*.	John G. Whittier (1807-1892). *United States*.
Deck thyself my soul with gladness	54	Johann Crüger (1598-1662). *German*.	C. Winkworth (1829-1878). From the *German*.
Each morning brings us fresh outpoured.	107	Melody (1527). Harm. (1934). *German*.	Margaret Barclay (1951). From the *German*.
Fairest Lord Jesus	35	Silesian Folktune. Harm. by Hoffmann von Fallersleben and E. Richter (1842). *German*.	Lilian Stevenson (1924). From the *German*.

First line	No.	Composer or source of tune	Author or translator of hymn
For all the Saints who from their labours rest	102	"Sine Nomine". R. Vaughan Williams (1872-). *English.*	Bishop W. W. How (1823-1897).
Forth see the sun in brilliance blaze	108	M. Vulpius (1609). *German.*	Margaret Barclay (1950). From the *German.*
From peaceful slumber waking . .	118	M. Teschner (1724). *German.* (Swedish adaptation).	Evangelical Lutheran Augustana Synod Hymnbook (1925). From the *Swedish.*
Glory to God the Father	6	Giovanni da Palestrina (1524-1594). *Italian.*	Te Deum, from the *Latin.*
God be in my head	71	Traditional Chorale Strophe. Harrington Shortall (1895). *United States.*	Old Saxon Primer.
God reveals His presence	5	Joachim Neander (1650-1680 ?). *German.*	F. W. Foster (1760-1835), J. Miller (1756-1790) and W. Mercer (1811-1873). From the *German.*
God the love that saved	85	Old *Chinese* melody. Harm. by Roger Vuataz (1951).	Margaret Barclay (1951). From the *Chinese.*
Good news from Heav'n	21	Melody (1539). Harm. by H. L. Hassler (1608). Geistliche Lieder, Leipzig (1539). *German.*	Arthur Tozer Russell (1806-1874) and Catherine Winkworth (1829-1878). From the *German.*
Grant good Lord that we serve Thee	93	Old *Chinese* Air.	Metric version Lilian Stevenson (1930).
Grant me to give to men	74	Old *Indian* Song. Harm. by Frédéric Mathil (1950).	Narayan Vaman Tylak (1862-1919). Trans. J. C. Winslow (1920). *Indian.*
Guide me O Thou great Redeemer .	33	"Caersalem". R. Edwards (1797-1862). *English.*	W. Williams (1717-1791). Trans. from the *Welsh*, P. and W. Williams.
Hark the herald angels sing . . .	20	F. Mendelssohn-Bartholdy (1809-1847). *German.*	Chas. Wesley (1743), and others.
Here is preached the gladsome tidings	72	Tai Jun Park. *Korea.*	Yung Oon Kim and Dr. William Scott. From the *Korean.*
Hills of the North rejoice	61	"Little Cornard". Martin Shaw (1876). *English.*	C. E. Oakley (1832-1865).
Holy God, Thy name we bless . .	1	Roman Catholic Collection. Vienna. (1774).	R. Birch Hoyle (1923). From the *Te Deum.*

First line	No.	Composer or source of tune	Author or translator of hymn
How brightly beams the morning star	10	Philippus Nicolai (1556-1608). Written in 1598. *German.*	G. R. Woodward (1910). From the *German.*
I know with full assurance	75	M. Teschner (1613). Harm. by J. S. Bach (1685-1750). St. John's Passion (1724). *German.*	R. Birch Hoyle (1923). From the *German.*
In Christ there is no East or West	62	Adapted from Christopher Tye (1497-1572). Edited by G. R. Woodward in "Songs of Syon" (1910). *English.*	John Oxenham (1908).
Its only joy Saviour and Lord . .	79	Recueil de Pierre Attaignant, Paris (1530), and Recueil d'Anvers (1540). *French.*	Nansie Anderson (1949). From the *French.* Psalm 25.
Jesus Christ, joyous light	114	Liturgy of the Orthodox Church.	R. Birch Hoyle (1924). From the *Russian.*
Jesus Christ my sure defence. . .	38	Johann Crüger (1598-1662). *German.*	Catherine Winkworth (1829-1878). From the *German.*
Jesus, priceless treasure	37	Johann Crüger (1598-1662). Harm. (1936). *German.*	Catherine Winkworth (1829-1878). From the *German.*
Jesus shall reign where'er the sun	59	"Duke Street". John Hatton (?-1793). *English.*	Isaac Watts (1674-1748).
Judge eternal, thron'd in splendour	83	"Picardy". *French* traditional Carol. Harm. by Gustav Holst (1874-1934).	Henry Scott Holland (1847-1918).
Let all mortal flesh keep silence .	82	"Picardy". *French* traditional Carol. Harm. by Gustav Holst (1874-1934).	Liturgy of St. James. Trans. from the *Greek* by G. Moultrie.
Let God arise and show His face	69	Mathieu Greiter (1525 ?). *French.*	Margaret House (1949). From the *French.* Psalm 68.
Let us with a gladsome mind . .	14	Ancient *Chinese* tune.	John Milton (1608-1674). From Psalm 136.
Lo, He comes in clouds descending	16	"St. Thomas". Melody from S. Webbe's Motetts or Antiphons (1792). *English.*	John Conninck (1750). Charles Wesley (1759).
Lo, how a rose e'er blooming . .	19	Old *German* Melody. Harm. by M. Praetorius (1571-1621).	v. 1-2: Dr. Theodore Baker (1931). v. 3-4: Margaret House (1950). From the *German.*

First line	No.	Composer or source of tune	Author or translator of hymn
Lord keep us steadfast	55	Wittenberg (1541). *German.*	Catherine Winkworth (1863). From the *German.*
Lord take Thou the reins to Thee	66	Huldrych Zwingli (1484-1531). *Swiss.*	Margaret Barclay (1951). From the *German.*
Love divine, all loves excelling	34	"Hyfrydol". Rowland Hugh Prichard (1811-1887). *Welsh.*	Charles Wesley (1707-1788).
Make me a captive, Lord. . .	87	J. S. Bach (1608-1750). *German.*	George Matheson (1842-1906).
May the grace of our Lord . .	120	Christian Gregor (1723-1801). *German.*	II Corinthians, 13, 14.
May the grace of our Lord . .	119	Frédéric Mathil (1930). *Swiss.*	II Corinthians, 13, 14.
Mist and darkness	68	"Imayo". *Japanese.*	Bishop Hugh James Foss (1930). From the *Japanese.*
Most wondrous is of all on earth	84	*Danish Folk Song.*	Jean Fraser (1951). From the *Danish.*
My inmost heart now raises . .	77	Eisleben (1598). Harm. (1939). *German.*	Catherine Winkworth (1829-1878). From the *German.*
My Lord what a morning. . . .	101	Negro Folksong. Hampton Institute Press, Virginia.	Negro spiritual.
Never, O God will my lips more be silent	95	F. F. Flemming (1778-1813). Harm. by Frédéric Mathil (1950). *South-American.*	Margaret House (1950). From the *Spanish.*
New every morning.	106	"Melcombe", Samuel Webbe (1740-1816). *English.*	John Keble (1792-1866).
Now all the woods are sleeping	115	H. Isaac (1440 ?).	Catherine Winkworth (1829-1878). From the *German.*
Now thank we all our God . . .	13	Johann Crüger (1598-1662). *German.*	Catherine Winkworth (1829-1878). From the *German.*
O Come all ye faithful	17	Composer unknown, probably XVIIIth century. *Portuguese.*	F. Oakeley (1741). From the *Latin.*
O come, o come Emmanuel . .	15	Plainsong melody. Harm. by Frédéric Mathil (1950).	J. M. Neale (1818-1866). From the *Latin.*
O day of God draw nigh . . .	103	"St. Michael". (Old 134th.) *Canadian.*	R. B. Y. Scott (1937).
O Father see my desolation . .	92	Loys Bourgeois (1542). Harm. by Claude Goudimel (1542). *French.*	Psalm 6. T. E. Lawrenson (1950). From the *French.*

First line	No.	Composer or source of tune	Author or translator of hymn
O God of earth and altar . . .	81	"Kings Lynn", English traditional melody.	G. K. Chesterton (1869-1938).
O God our help in ages past . .	63	"St. Anne". Probably Dr. Croft (1678-1727). *English*.	Isaac Watts (1675-1748).
O heavenly King, the Comforter .	43	Orthodox Liturgy. Prayer to the Holy Spirit.	From the *Russian*.
O help us Lord !	88	"Bedford". Original form of melody by W. Weale († 1727). *English*.	H. H. Milman (1791-1868).
O jubilee day.	96	Walt Rudin (1833-1921). Harm. and arr. by Frédéric Mathil (1950). *Swedish*.	Charles Wharton Storck (1881-). From the *Swedish*.
O like the deep Thy judgments are	73	Mathieu Greiter ? (1525). *French*.	V. 1-2: Mrs. K. W. Simpson in Terry Calvin's First Psalter (1539). V. 3: Margaret House (1950). From the *French*. Psalm 36.
O Lord of all, our Father . . .	47	Hussite gradual (1512). *Czech*.	Francis House (1950). From the *Czech*.
One holy Church of God appears	52	"Hummel". Heinrich Christoph Zeuner (1795-1857). *German*.	Samuel Longfellow (1819-1892). *United States*.
One who is all unfit to count .	25	"Wigtown". Scottish Psalter (1635).	From the *Marathi* of Narayan Vaman Tylak (1862-1919). Trans. by Nicol MacNicol (1870).
O sacred head sore wounded .	23	Leo Hassler (1564-1612). *German*.	Robert Bridges (1844-1930). From the *German*.
Out of the depth I cry to Thee .	98	Wittenberg (1524). Johann Walther's collection. Harm. by J. S. Bach (1685-1750). *German*.	Margaret Barclay (1950). From the *German*. Psalm 130.
O what their joy and their glory .	100	Adapted from a melody in *La Feillée*, "Méthode du plain chant" (1808).	J. M. Neale (1818-1866). From the *Latin*.
O worship the King	8	"Hanover". Ascribed to Dr. William Croft (1678-1727). *English*.	Robert Grant (1779-1838).
O Zion do not grieve	3	Johann Crüger (1598-1662). *German*.	Margaret House (1950). From the *French*.
Praise and thanksgiving .	113	Johann Crüger (1598-1662). *German*.	Margaret Barclay (1951). From the *German*.

First line	No.	Composer or source of tune	Author or translator of hymn
Praise to the Holiest	36	"Richmond". Adapted from T. Haweis (1734-1820), by S. Webbe (the Younger). *English.*	J. H. Newman (1801-1890). "Dream of Gerontius".
Praise to the Lord, the Almighty	11	Stralsund (1665). *German.*	Catherine Winkworth (1858). From the *German.*
Rejoice I the year upon its way .	42	"Psalterium Chorale". Constance (1510).	V. 1-3 : Richard Ellis Roberts (1878-1940). V. 4 : Percy Dearmer (1867-1936). From the *Latin.*
Remember Thy servants, Lord . .	86	Orthodox Liturgy.	M. M. Gowen (1949). (The Beatitudes, adapted).
Rise, faithful servant	4	Loys Bourgeois (1544). Harm. by Claude Goudimel (Ed. Jaqui, 1565). *French.*	Margaret House (1938). From the *French.* Psalm 33.
Sitting beside the Babylonian waters	91	Loys Bourgeois (1542). Harm. adapted from Claude Goudimel (1565). *French.*	Margaret House (1950). From the *French.* Psalm 137.
Spirit of God, descend upon my heart	40	"Battle". Henry Lawes (1596-1662). *English.*	George Croly (1780-1860).
Steal away, steal away to Jesus .	105	Adapted from R. Nathaniel Dett's "Religious Folksongs of the Negro", Hampton Institute Press, Virginia.	Negro Spiritual.
Strengthen for service, Lord . .	57	Melody in New Leipziger Gesangbuch (1682). Harm. by J. S. Bach (1685-1750). *German.*	Liturgy of Malabar. Trans. Percy Dearmer and C. W. Humphreys.
Teach me my God and King . .	67	"Mornington" Garret Wellesley (1735-1831). *English.*	George Herbert (1593-1633).
The cause for which we strive . .	99	Joseph Haydn (1732-1809). *German.*	Margaret Barclay (1951). From the *German.*
The Church of God a kingdom is	48	"University". C. Collignon (1725-1785). *English.*	L. Muirhead (1845-1925).

First line	No.	Composer or source of tune	Author or translator of hymn
The Church's one foundation	51	Bartholomeus Gesius (1555-1613). Harm. J. S. Bach (1685-1750). *German.*	S. J. Stone (1839-1900).
The day Thou gavest, Lord is ended	110	Loys Bourgeois (1549). Harm. Claude Goudimel (1565). *French.*	J. Ellerton (1826-1893).
The God of Abraham praise	12	Adapted from a *Hebrew* melody by M. Leoni (1770). Revised version of the Yigdal of Daniel Ben Judah (XIVth century).	Thomas Oliver (1725-1799).
The head that once was crowned	31	"St. Magnus" (Nottingham), probably by J. Clark (1670-1707). *English.*	T. Kelly (1769-1854).
The Lord's my Shepherd	64	"Crimond", Scottish Psalter (1650).	Psalm 23.
The Lord will come	104	"Coleshill", Barton's Psalms (1706). *English.*	John Milton (1608-1674).
The Saviour's precious blood	50	Tai Jun Park. *Korea.*	Yung Oon Kim and Dr. William Scott. From the *Korean* (1950).
The strife is o'er	29	Adaptation of a Gloria Patri by G. da Palestrina († 1594). *Italian.* The Alleluia by W. H. Monk.	Francis Pott (1832-1909). From the *Latin.*
The sun ascendant	111	"Die güldne Sonne". Johann Georg Ebeling (1666). *German.*	V. 1: Margaret Barclay (1951). V. 2-4: Richard Massie (1800-1887). From the *German.*
They whose course on earth is o'er	97	Pre-Reformation tune, Erfurt (1524). Harm. by Lukas Osiander. *German.*	J. M. Neale (1818-1866) and others.
Thine is the glory	28	George F. Haendel (1685-1759). Judas Maccabaeus. *German.*	R. Birch Hoyle (1923). From the *French.*
Thou Holy Spirit, we pray to Thee	39	Pre-Reformation. Collection Johann Walther (1524). *German.*	Miles Coverdale (XVIth century). Adapted. From the *German.*
Upon Thy great Church universal	49	Collection Jean A. Freylinghausen (1704). *French.*	Margaret House (1949). From the *French.*
Wake, O wake! with tidings thrilling	116	Philippus Nicolai (1599). Harm. by Jakob Praetorius (1604). *German.*	Francis Crawford Burkitt. From the *German.*

First line	No.	Composer or source of tune	Author or translator of hymn
We gather, dear Father	80	Dr. Adrianus Valerius (1626). *Dutch.*	R. Birch Hoyle (1929). From the *Dutch.*
Were you there when they crucified my Lord ?	26	American Negro Folksong. Hampton Institute, Hampton, Virginia.	Negro Spiritual.
What God is so great	24	*Byzantine* melody. Harm. by Wladimir Diakoff (1950).	From the *Greek.*
What joy to think	94	Nikolaus Hermann (1554). Precentor in Joachimstal, *Bohemia.* († 1561).	R. Birch Hoyle (1923). From the *Norwegian.*
When I survey the wondrous Cross	27	"Rockingham", adapted by E. Miller (1731-1807). Harm. by S. Webbe, a *Spanish* composer (1740-1824).	Isaac Watts (1674-1748).
With the morn in radiance breaking	109	"Piesn Poranna". *Polish.*	W. J. Rose (1922). From the *Polish.*
With the saints give rest	117	Orthodox Liturgy, extract from the service for the dead.	From the *Russian.*

CANTIQUES EN FRANÇAIS

(Les cantiques en italique sont des traductions.)

Cantiques	Nos	Compositeurs et origines	Auteurs et traducteurs
A l'horizon, le jour s'éloigne	110	Loys Bourgeois (1549). Harm. d'après Cl. Goudimel (1565). *Français.*	Hermann Ecuyer (1930). Trad. de l'anglais.
A mon Dieu je me confie	14	Ancien air chinois.	S. Bidgrain (1924). Adaptation du Psaume 136.
Animé d'un nouvel amour	106	« Melcombe », Samuel Webbe (1740-1816). *Anglais.*	Flossette Du Pasquier (1951). Trad. de l'anglais.
Assis au bord du fleuve	91	Loys Bourgeois (1542). Harm. d'après Cl. Goudimel (1565). *Français.*	Clément Marot (1539). Charles Dombre (1935). Psaume 137.
Astre brillant qui répands sur la terre	22	"Himmelslust" (1679). Harm. par J.-S. Bach (1685-1750). *Allemand.*	Flossette Du Pasquier (1951). Trad. de l'anglais.
A toi la gloire, ô Ressuscité	28	G.-F. Haendel (1685-1759). Juda Macchabée. *Allemand.*	Edmond Budry (1884).
A toi mon cœur, O Dieu Sauveur	79	Recueil Pierre Attaignant, Paris (1530). Recueil d'Anvers (1540). *Français.*	Léon Judae (1483-1542). Psaume 25.
Aujourd'hui peuple de frères	60	Brüdergemeinde (1745-). *Allemand.*	V. 1-3 : E. Budry (1902). V. 4 : Charles Westphal (1938). Trad. de l'allemand.
Brillante étoile du matin	10	Mélodie Philippus Nicolai (1556-1608). Version originale (1598). *Allemand.* Stralsund (1665). *Allemand.*	Pauline Martin (1950). Trad. de l'allemand.
Célébrons l'Eternel, notre Dieu	11		Ch. Pfender (1908). Trad. de l'allemand.
C'est un rempart que notre Dieu	70	Martin Luther (1529) ou Johann Walther (1496-1570). *Allemand.*	H. Lutteroth (1802-1892). Trad. de l'allemand.
Ceux qui nous ont devancés	97	Mélodie d'avant la Réformation. Harm. Lukas Osiander, Erfurt (1524). *Allemand.*	Violette Du Pasquier (1951). Trad. de l'anglais.
Chante mon cœur, réjouis-toi	29	D'après un Gloria Patri de G. da Palestrina (1524-1594). Alleluia W. H. Monk. *Italien.*	Flossette Du Pasquier (1951). Trad. du latin.

Cantiques	Nos	Compositeurs et origines	Auteurs et traducteurs
Charité de Dieu le Père	34	« Hyfrydol », Rowland Hugh Prichard (1811-1887). *Anglais.*	Eva Dubska-Kushner (1950). Trad. de *l'anglais.*
Chef couvert de blessures	23	Leo Hassler (1564-1612). *Allemand.*	Psautier morave (1757). Trad. de l'*allemand.*
Christ ressuscite hors de tout supplice	30	Mélodie grégorienne du XIIe ou XIIIe siècle. Harm. par H. L. Hassler (1608).	Théo Preiss et Pierre Chazel (1950). Trad. de *l'allemand.*
Comme un cerf altéré brame	65	Loys Bourgeois (1551-). Harm. d'après Claude Goudimel (1565). *Français.*	Théodore de Bèze (1519-1605). Conrart (1677). Psaume 42.
Debout mon âme, éveille-toi	78	Psautier écossais (1615). D'après le Psautier de Ravenscroft (1621).	Eva Dubska-Kushner (1951). Trad. de *l'anglais.*
Descends, Esprit de Dieu	44	«Down Ampney»Ralph Vaughan Williams (1872-). *Anglais.*	Henri Capieu (1950). Trad. de *l'anglais.*
Des lieux profonds je crie à toi	98	Wittenberg (1524). Recueil Johann Walther. Harm. J.-S. Bach (1685-1750). *Allemand.*	Charles Ecklin (1858-1935), et Pauline Martin (1951). Trad. de *l'allemand.* Psaume 130.
Des veilleurs la voix sonore	116	Mélodie Philippus Nicolaï (1599). Harm. Jakob Praetorius (1604). *Allemand.*	Trad. Eglise et liturgie. L'Office divin. (1947). Trad. de *l'allemand.*
Devant Jésus mon juge	89	Huugo Nyberg (1873). Pasteur à Helsinki. *Finlandais.*	L. Monastier-Schrœder (1923). Trad. du *suédois.*
Devant ton trône prosternés	9	Mélodie morave du VIIIe siècle, Psautier de l'Eglise réformée hollandaise. Harm. par Leonard Johannes Mens (1879). *Hollandais.*	Eva Dubska-Kushner (1949). Trad. du *hollandais.*
Dieu bien-aimé, descends des cieux	46	« Hamburg », Lowell Mason (1792-1872). *Anglais.*	Eva Dubska-Kushner (1950). Trad. de *l'anglais.*
Dieu, dans ton merveilleux amour	25	« Wigtown ». Psautier écossais (1635).	Violette Du Pasquier (1951). Trad. de *l'anglais.*
Dieu, garde-nous par ton Esprit	55	Wittenberg (1543). *Allemand.*	Pauline Martin (1951). Trad. de l'*allemand.*
Dieu soit en mon front	71	« Traditional Chorale Strophe », Harrington Shortall (1895). *Etats-Unis.*	Claire Jullien (1930). Trad. de *l'anglais.*

Cantiques	Nᵒˢ	Compositeurs et origines	Auteurs et traducteurs
Dieu soit loué par tous ceux qui l'adorent	113	Johann Crüger (1598-1662). Harm. par Zahn. Allemand.	Violette Du Pasquier (1951). Trad. de l'allemand.
Dieu tout-puissant, mes chants . .	95	F. F. Flemming (1810). Harm. Frédéric Mathil (1950). Sud-américain.	Flossette Du Pasquier (1951). Trad. de l'anglais.
Dieu vient dans sa gloire	5	Joachim Neander (1650-1680). Allemand.	Pauline Martin (1951). Trad. de l'allemand.
Doux et bon Maître	35	Chant populaire silésien. Harm. par Hoffmann von Fallersleben et E. Richter (1842). Allemand.	Pauline Martin (1951). Trad. de l'allemand.
D'un cœur contrit j'exhale	77	Mélodie: Eisleben (1598). Harm. 1939. Allemand.	Pauline Martin (1950). Trad. de l'allemand.
Ecoutez le chant des anges. . . .	20	F. Mendelssohn-Bartholdy (1809-1847). Allemand.	Violette Du Pasquier (1951). Trad. de l'anglais.
Emerveillons-nous ensemble. . . .	18	Mélodie hollandaise d'avant la Réforme, harmonisée par Johanna Wagenaar.	Charles Dombre (1936). Trad. du hollandais.
Enseigne-moi, Seigneur	67	« Mornington ». Garret Wellesley (1735-1831). Anglais.	Flossette Du Pasquier (1951). Trad. de l'anglais.
En toi Jésus sous tous les cieux .	62	D'après Christopher Tye (1497-1572). Anglais. Publié par G. R. Woodward dans Songs of Syon (1910).	F. de Rougemont (1930). Trad. de l'anglais.
Entonnons un chant de gloire. . .	72	La Woon Hyung. Corée.	Flossette Du Pasquier (1951). Trad. de l'anglais.
Esprit de Dieu, crée en nous . . .	39	Recueil de Johann Walther (1524). Allemand.	James Siordet (1903-1932). Trad. de l'allemand.
Eternel, aux cieux tu règnes . . .	83	« Picardy ». Air populaire français. Harm. par Gustav Holst (1874-1934).	Flossette Du Pasquier (1951). Trad. de l'anglais.
Eternel, ta fidélité	73	Mathieu Greiter ? (1525). Français.	Clément Marot (1543). Arr. Conrart. Psaume 36.
Fraîche et nouvelle chaque jour .	107	Mélodie (1527). Harm. (1934). Allemand.	Pauline Martin (1951). Trad. de l'allemand.
Gloire à Dieu notre Créateur. . .	6	G. da Palestrina (1524-1594). Italien.	Te Deum. Trad. du latin.

Cantiques	N°s	Compositeurs et origines	Auteurs et traducteurs
Gloire au Très-Haut	36	« Richmond ». Adaptation T. Haweis (1734-1820) par S. Webbe (le Jeune). *Anglais.*	Flossette Du Pasquier (1951). Trad. de l'anglais.
Grand Dieu, nous te bénissons	1	Recueil catholique romain (1772). Vienne (1774).	Te Deum. H.-L. Empaytaz (1790-1853). Pasteur à Genève. Trad. du *latin*.
Guide-moi, Berger fidèle	33	« Caersalem ». R. Edwards (1797-1862). *Anglais.*	Flossette Du Pasquier (1951). Trad. de l'anglais.
Hauts et puissants, cité des cieux	53	Johann Crüger (1598-1662). *Allemand.*	Pauline Martin (1950). Trad. de l'allemand.
Il est aux cieux une joie	100	Adapté d'une mélodie dans *La Feuillée*. Méthode du plain-chant (1808). *Français.*	Flossette Du Pasquier (1951). Trad. du *latin*.
Il vient ce grand jour	96	Walt Rudin (1833-1921). Harm. et arr. par Frédéric Mathil (1950). *Suédois.*	Flossette Du Pasquier et Mme Metzger (1951). Trad. du *suédois*.
Je m'abats devant toi	87	J.-S. Bach (1685-1750). *Allemand.*	Fernand Barth (1923). Trad. de l'anglais.
Je sais en qui j'espère	75	Melchior Teschner (1584-1635). Composé d'abord pour le cantique de Valerius Herberger : « Valet will ich dir geben ». Harm. par J.-S. Bach. Passion selon saint Jean (1724). *Allemand.*	J. Vincent (1934). Trad. de l'allemand.
Jésus-Christ, ô clarté d'En-Haut	114	Liturgie de l'Eglise orthodoxe.	H. Ecuyer (1924). Trad. du *russe*.
Je viens à vous du haut des cieux	21	Mélodie 1539. Harm. H. L. Hassler (1608). *Allemand.*	Pauline Martin (1950). Trad. de l'allemand.
La joie, ô Dieu, remplit mon cœur	94	Nikolaus Herman (1554). Chantre à Joachimstal. *Bohême.*	Flossette Du Pasquier (1951). Trad. du *norvégien*.
Le clair soleil brille	108	Melchior Vulpius (1609). *Allemand.*	Blanche d'Estienne (1950). Trad. de l'allemand.
Le front d'épines couronné	31	« St. Magnus » (Nottingham). Mélodie attribuée à J. Clark (1670-1707). *Anglais.*	Flossette Du Pasquier (1951). Trad. de l'anglais.
L'Eglise à Dieu seul appartient	52	« Hummel » Heinrich Christoph Zeuner (1795-1857). *Allemand.*	Flossette Du Pasquier (1951). Trad. de l'anglais.

Cantiques	Nᵒˢ	Compositeurs et origines	Auteurs et traducteurs
L'Eglise universelle a pour roc Jésus-Christ	51	Bartholomäus Gesius (1555-1613). Harm. par J.-S. Bach (1685-1750). *Allemand.*	Fernand Barth (1923). Trad. de *l'anglais.*
Le monde entier se réjouit	42	*Psalterium Chorale* Constance (1510).	Flossette Du Pasquier (1951). Trad. du *latin.*
Les bois, les champs s'apaisent	115	Henry Isaac (1440-1517). *Allemand.*	Eva Dubska-Kushner et Flossette Du Pasquier (1950). Trad. de *l'allemand.*
L'Eternel seul est mon Berger	64	« Crimond », Psautier écossais (1650).	Pauline Martin (1951). Trad. de *l'anglais.* Psaume 23.
Louange à Dieu ! louange au Christ ! Loué soit à jamais le Dieu de nos aïeux	32	Melchior Vulpius (1609). *Allemand.*	Pauline Martin (1951). Trad. de *l'allemand.*
Louons du Seigneur le nom glorieux	12	Mélodie *hébraïque* arr. par M. Leoni (1770).	Flossette Du Pasquier (1950). Trad. de *l'anglais.*
Louons le Créateur	8	« Hanover » attribué à William Croft (1678-1727). *Anglais.*	Flossette Du Pasquier (1951). Trad. de *l'anglais.*
Louons tous notre Père	13	Johann Crüger (1598-1662). *Allemand.*	Flossette Du Pasquier (1950). Trad. de *l'allemand.*
Mon Rédempteur est vivant	118	M. Teschner (1724). *Adaptation suédoise. Allemand.*	Flossette Du Pasquier (1950). Trad. de *l'allemand.*
Monts du Septentrion	38	Johann Crüger (1598-1662). *Allemand.*	Psalmodie morave (1846). Trad. de *l'allemand.*
Ne te désole point, Sion	61	« Little Cornard » Martin Shaw (1876). *Anglais.*	H. Ecuyer (1924). Trad. de *l'anglais.*
Notre barque est en danger	3	Johann Crüger (1598-1662). *Allemand.*	Félix Neff (1797-1829).
O Dieu de ton corps blessé	66	Huldrych Zwingli (1484-1531). *Suisse*	Daniel Meylan (1930). Trad. de *l'allemand.*
O Dieu, notre aide aux temps	85	Air chinois ancien. Harm. par Roger Vuataz (1951).	Henri Capieu (1938). Trad. de *l'allemand.*
O Dieu pour te connaître	63	« St. Anne », attribué à William Croft (1678-1727). *Anglais.*	Pauline Martin (1950). Trad. de *l'anglais.*
	47	Graduel hussite (1512). *Tchèque.*	Hermann Ecuyer (1930). Trad. du *tchèque.*

Cantiques	Nos	Compositeurs et origines	Auteurs et traducteurs
Oh ! que toute chair se taise	82	« Picardy ». Air populaire *français*. Harm. Gustav Holst (1874-1934).	Suzanne Bidgrain (1937). Trad. de *l'anglais*.
Oh ! viens bientôt Emmanuel	15	Mélodie grégorienne. Harm. F. Mathil (1950).	H. Ecuyer (1924). Trad. du *latin*.
Oh ! viens jour du Seigneur	103	« St. Michael ». (Old 134th). *Anglais*.	Flossette Du Pasquier (1951). Trad. de *l'anglais*.
O Jésus ma joie	37	Johann Crüger (1598-1662). Harm. (1936). *Allemand*.	G. Pucher (1949). Trad. de *l'allemand*.
O peuple fidèle	17	Compositeur inconnu, probablement XVIIIe siècle. *Portugais*.	D'après « Louange et Prière », de l'Eglise réformée de France. Traduit du *latin*.
O Roi céleste consolateur	43	Liturgie de l'Eglise orthodoxe. Prière au Saint-Esprit.	Trad. du *russe*.
Oui, sur ta sainte Eglise	48	« University ». C. Collignon (1725-1785). *Anglais*.	Pauline Martin (1951). Trad. de *l'anglais*.
Oui, ton royaume, ô Christ	84	Chant populaire *danois*.	Flossette Du Pasquier (1951). Trad. du *danois*.
O viens Saint-Esprit créateur	41	« Enchiridion » Martin Luther (1483-1546). D'après une mélodie grégorienne.	Flossette Du Pasquier (1951). Trad. du *latin*.
Pain vivant donné pour nos âmes	58	Loys Bourgeois (1558). Harm. d'après Claude Goudimel (1565). *Français*.	Henri Capieu (1950). Trad. de *l'anglais*.
Pardonne, ô Dieu, les vains tourments	90	Nikolaus Herman (1485-1561). Harm. par J.-S. Bach (1585-1750). *Allemand*.	E. Budry (1930). Trad. de *l'anglais*.
Pare-toi, mon âme heureuse	54	Johann Crüger (1598-1662). *Allemand*.	Pauline Martin (1951). Trad. de *l'allemand*.
Par la nuit environné	68	« Imayo ». *Japonais*.	Flossette Du Pasquier (1951). Trad. de *l'anglais*.
Par son sang rédempteur	50	Cantique *coréen*. Tai Jun Park.	Flossette Du Pasquier (1950). Trad. de *l'anglais*.
Pour ta cause immortelle	99	Josef Haydn (1732-1809). *Allemand*.	J.-E. Siordet (1922). Trad. de *l'allemand*.
Pour tous les saints près de toi	102	Ralph Vaughan Williams (1872). *Anglais*.	D. Meylan (1922) et Flossette Du Pasquier (1951). Trad. de *l'anglais*.

Cantiques	Nᵒˢ	Compositeurs et origines	Auteurs et traducteurs
Quand je me tourne vers la croix	27	« Rockingham ». Adapté par E. Miller (1731-1807), harm. par S. Webbe, compositeur espagnol (1740-1824). *Anglais.*	Pauline Martin (1951). Trad. de *l'anglais.*
Quand le jour commence à poindre	109	« Piesn Poranna ». Air polonais.	Trad. inconnu.
Que Dieu se montre seulement	69	Mathieu Greiter (1525 ?). *Français.*	Théodore de Bèze (1562). Arr. par Conrart (1677). Psaume 68.
Que la grâce de notre Seigneur	120	Christian Gregor (1723-1801). *German.*	II Cor. 13 : 13.
Que la grâce de notre Seigneur	119	Frédéric Mathil (1920). *Swiss.*	II Cor. 13 : : 13.
Quelle est donc cette douce voix	56	O. Ahlström (1756-1835). *Suédois.*	Flossette Du Pasquier et Mᵐᵉ Metzger (1951). Trad. du *suédois.*
Qu'en toi, je vive	76	« Slane ». *Mélodie irlandaise.*	Flossette Du Pasquier (1951). Trad. de *l'anglais.*
Réveille-toi, peuple fidèle	4	Loys Bourgeois (1544). Harm. d'après Claude Goudimel (Ed. Jaqui 1565). *Français.*	Clément Marot (1543). Revisé par Conrart (1677). Psaume 33.
Seigneur, daigne affermir ma main	57	Mélodie *Neu Leipziger Gesangbuch* (1682). Harm. J.-S. Bach (1685-1750). *Allemand.*	Violette Du Pasquier (1951). Trad. de *l'allemand.*
Seigneur, donne le repos	117	Liturgie de l'Eglise orthodoxe.	Traduit du *russe.*
Seigneur, entends nos plaintes	81	« Kings Lynn », air anglais ancien.	Flossette Du Pasquier (1951). Trad. de *l'anglais.*
Seigneur, quand vient l'obscurité	112	« Tallis Canon », d'après une mélodie de Thomas Tallis (1520-1585). *Anglais.*	Flossette Du Pasquier (1950). Trad. de *l'anglais.*
Seigneur, que ton céleste amour	88	« Bedford ». Mélodie originale de W. Weale († 1727). *Anglais.*	Flossette Du Pasquier (1950). Trad. de *l'anglais.*
Seigneur, tes enfants aujourd'hui	80	Adrianus Valerius (1626). *Hollandais.*	Flossette Du Pasquier (1951). Trad. du *hollandais.*
Seigneur, toi qui es tout-puissant	24	Mélodie byzantine. Harm. par Wladimir Diakoff (1950).	Trad. du *grec.*
Seigneur, un jour tu reviendras	104	« Coleshill ». Psaumes de Barton (1806). *Anglais.*	Flossette Du Pasquier (1951). Trad. de *l'anglais.*

Cantiques	Nᵒˢ	Compositeurs et origines	Auteurs et traducteurs
Serviable, ainsi que ton amour l'inspire	74	Ancienne mélodie *indienne*. Harm. Frédéric Mathil (1950).	Charles Westphal (1930). Trad. de l'*anglais*.
Souffle de Dieu vivant	45	« Dominica ». Sir Herbert Stanley Oakeley (1830-1903). *Anglais*.	Suzanne Bidgrain (1937). Trad. de l'*anglais*.
Souviens-toi de nous, Seigneur	86	Liturgie de l'Eglise orthodoxe. (Béatitudes.)	Trad. du *russe*.
Sur ton Eglise universelle	49	Recueil de Jean A. Freylighausen (1704). *Français*.	J.-M. de Carbon-Ferrière (1823).
Tant que le monde durera	59	« Duke Street » John Hatton (?-1793). *Anglais*.	Flossette Du Pasquier (1950). Trad. de l'*anglais*.
Toi qui flamboies	111	« Die gûldne Sonne », Johann Georg Ebeling (1607-1676). *Allemand*.	Pauline Martin (1951). Trad. de l'*allemand*.
Toi qui nous comblas	93	Ancien air *chinois*.	K. H. Ding et Flossette Du Pasquier (1951). Trad. du *chinois*.
Une fleur vient d'éclore	19	Chant de Noël du 16e siècle. Harm. par M. Praetorius (1571-1621). *Allemand*.	Pauline Martin (1951). Trad. de l'*allemand*.
Viens Esprit-Saint habiter	40	« Battle » Henry Lawes (1596-1662). *Anglais*.	Flossette Du Pasquier (1951). Trad. de l'*anglais*.
Vois descendre sur les nues	16	« St. Thomas ». Mélodie extraite de « Mottets or Antiphons » par S. Webbe (1792). *Anglais*.	Flossette Du Pasquier (1951). Trad. de l'*anglais*.
Vois ma faiblesse humaine	92	Loys Bourgeois (1542). Harm. Claude Goudimel (1565). *Français*.	René-Louis Piachaud (1932), d'après Clément Marot (1541). Psaume 6.
Vous créatures du Seigneur	2	Cologne (1623). Harm. par Frédéric Mathil (1950). *Allemand*.	Revu par J.-J. Bovet (1950). Trad. de l'*anglais*.
Vous qui sur la terre habitez	7	Loys Bourgeois (1551). Arr. Claude Goudimel (1565). *Français*.	Théodore de Bèze (1519-1605). Arr. par Conrart (1679). Psaume 100.

LIEDER IN DEUTSCHER SPRACHE

(Die in Kursivschrift gedruckten Lieder sind Übersetzungen)

Liederanfänge	Nr.	Tonsetzer und Ursprung der Melodien	Liederdichter und Übersetzer
Ach Herr ich muss vergehen . .	92	Loys Bourgeois (1542). Harmonisiert nach Claude Goudimel (1565). *Französisch.*	Konrad Jutzler (1950). Aus dem *Französischen.* Psalm 6.
All Morgen ist ganz frisch . . .	107	Melodie (1527). Satz (1934). *Deutsch.*	Johannes Zwick (1496-1542).
An jenem Tag wird Freude . . .	94	Nikolaus Herman, Kantor in Joachimstal, *Bohemia* († 1561).	Johann Christoph Hampe (1950). Aus dem *Norwegischen.*
Aus meines Herzens Grunde . . .	77	Eisleben (1598). Satz (1939). *Deutsch.*	Georg Niege (1525-1588).
Aus tiefer Not schrei ich . . .	98	Wittenberg (1524). Johann Walther Gesangbuch. Harmonisiert von J. S. Bach (1685-1750). *Deutsch.*	Martin Luther (1483-1546). Psalm 130.
Brot für die Welt	58	Loys Bourgeois (1558). Satz nach Claude Goudimel (1565). *Französisch.*	Helga Rusche (1950). Aus dem *Englischen.*
Brüder macht die Herzen weit . .	14	Altchinesisches Lied	Johann Christoph Hampe (1950). Aus dem *Englischen.*
Christ ist erstanden	30	Gregorianische Melodie vom XII. oder XIII. Jahrhundert. Harmonisiert von H. L. Hassler (1608). *Deutsch.*	Wittenberg (1533).
Dank sei dir	85	Altchinesisches Lied. Harmonisiert von Roger Vuataz (1951).	Constantin Schwann (1938). Aus dem *Französischen.*
Das Haupt dem Dornen eingedrückt	31	«St. Magnus» (Nottingham). Wahrscheinlich von J. Clark (1670-1707). *Englisch.*	Wilhelm Horkel (1950). Aus dem *Englischen.*
Der du allreich, all herrlich bist.	46	«Hamburg». Lowell Mason (1792-1872). *Englisch.*	Johann Christoph Hampe (1950). Aus dem *Englischen.*
Der keine Würde bei sich fand.	25	«Wigtown» Schottisches Gesangbuch (1635).	Johann Christoph Hampe (1950). Aus dem *Englischen.*
Der Kirche Grund hienieden . . .	51	Bartholomäus Gesius (1555-1613). Harmonisiert von J. S. Bach (1685-1750). *Deutsch.*	C. Lechler (1923). Aus dem *Englischen.*

Liederanfänge	Nr.	Tonsetzer und Ursprung der Melodien	Liederdichter und Übersetzer
Der Tag, den du uns gabst . . .	110	Melodie Loys Bourgeois (1549). Harmonisiert nach C. Goudimel (1565). *Französisch.*	Gertrud Dalgas. Aus dem *Englischen.*
Die befreit vom ird'schen Joch . .	97	Vorreformatorisch. Erfurt, Satz (1524). Lukas Osiander. *Deutsch.*	Wilhelm Horkel (1950). Aus dem *Englischen.*
Die Gnade unseres Herrn	119	Frédéric Mathil (1930). *Schweizerisch.*	II Cor. 13 : 13.
Die Gnade unseres Herrn	120	Christian Gregor (1723-1801). *Deutsch.*	II Cor. 13 : 13.
Die güldne Sonne	111	Johann Georg Ebeling (1666). *Deutsch.*	Paulus Gerhardt (1607-1676).
Die heil'ge Kirche Gottes. . . .	52	Heinrich Christoph Zeuner (1795-1857). *Deutsch.*	Erwin Kleine (1950). Aus dem *Englischen.*
Die helle Sonn' leucht' jetzt . . .	108	Melodie M. Vulpius (1609). *Deutsch.*	Nikolaus Herman (1480-1561).
Die Kirche ist des Herren Reich . .	48	« University », C. Collignon (1725-1785). *Englisch.*	Hanns Lilje (1936). Aus dem *Englischen.*
Die Sach' ist dein	99	Josef Haydn (1732-1809). *Deutsch.*	Samuel Preiswerk (1709-1871) vers. 1-2 und Graf F. Zaremba (1794-1874) vers. 3.
Die schönste Zier	84	*Dänisches Volkslied.*	Anne-Marie Schaefer (1951). Aus dem *Dänischen.*
Dir der alle Freude schenkte . . .	72	Aus dem *Koreanischen.*	Johann Christoph Hampe (1951). Aus dem *Englischen.*
Du hast vereint in allen Zonen. . .	49	Gesangbuch Jean A. Freylinghausen (1704). *Französisch.*	Johann Christoph Hampe (1951). Aus dem *Französischen.*
Du kommst, O Herr der Ewigkeit	104	« Coleshill », Barton's Psalms (1706). *Englisch.*	Erwin Kleine (1950). Aus dem *Englischen.*
Dunst und Dunkel	68	« Imayo ». *Japanisch.*	H. Laepple (1930). Aus dem *Japanischen.*
Ehr' sei dem Vater und dem Sohn	6	Giovanni da Palestrina (1524-1594). *Italienisch.*	Te Deum.
Ein feste Burg ist unser Gott . .	70	Johann Walther (1496-1570) oder Martin Luther (1529).	Martin Luther (1483-1546).
Erhalt uns Herr bei deinem Wort	55	Wittenberg (1543).	Martin Luther (1483-1546).

Liederanfänge	Nr.	Tonsetzer und Ursprung der Melodien	Liederdichter und Übersetzer
Erhebet den Herrn, sein Lob stimmet an	8	« Hanover », Wahrscheinlich von William Croft (1678-1727). *Englisch.*	Erwin Kleine (1950). Aus *dem Englischen.*
Es ging das grimme Kriegen lang .	29	Nach einem Gloria Patri von G. P. da Palestrina († 1594). *Italienisch.* Alleluia by W. H. Monk.	Johann Christoph Hampe (1950). Aus dem *Lateinischen.*
Es ist ein Ros' entsprungen . .	19	*Deutsches* Weihnachtslied aus dem XV. Jahrhundert. Harmonisiert von M. Praetorius (1571-1621).	Vorreformatorisch, Köln (1599).
Es komme, Herr dein Tag	103	« St. Michael. Old 134th ». *Englisch.*	Johann Christoph Hampe (1950). Aus dem *Englischen.*
Freude, O Freude	100	" Méthode de Plain chant " (1808).	Erwin Kleine (1950). Aus dem *Englischen.*
Freut euch ihr Hügel	61	« Little Cornard » Martin Shaw (1876). *Englisch.*	C. Lechler (1924). Aus dem *Englischen.*
Für alle Heil'gen die da ruh'n in dir	102	R. Vaughan Williams (1872-). *Englisch.*	C. Lechler (1923) und J. C. Hampe (1951). Aus dem *Englischen.*
Gedenk an uns, O Herr	86	Orthodoxe Kirchenmusik.	H. Laepple (1930). Seligpreisungen. Metrisch gesetzt.
Gelobt sei Gott	32	Melchior Vulpius (1609). *Deutsch.*	Michael Weisse († 1534).
Gib dass der Menschen Sehnsucht	74	*Altindisches* Lied. Harmonisiert von F. Mathil (1950).	Franz Spemann (1930). Aus dem *Englischen.*
Gott Abrahams	12	Aus einer *Hebräischen* Melodie bei M. Leoni (1770). *Deutsch.*	Wilhelm Horkel (1950). Aus dem *Englischen.*
Gottes Geschöpfe, kommt zu Hauf	2	Köln (1623). Satz Frédéric Mathil (1950). *Deutsch.*	Karl Budde (1929). Aus dem *Englischen.*
Gott, Herr der Erden Reich schau her	81	« Kings Lynn », *Altenglisches* Lied.	Hanns Lilje (1938). Aus dem *Englischen.*
Gott ist gegenwärtig	5	Joachim Neander (1650-1680 ?). *Deutsch.*	Gerhard Tersteegen (1697-1769).
Gott ist mein Hort	64	« Crimond » Schottisches Gesangbuch (1650). Psalm 23.	Erwin Kleine (1950). Aus dem *Englischen.*

Liederanfänge	Nr.	Tonsetzer und Ursprung der Melodien	Liederdichter und Übersetzer
Gott, regiere du allein	71	«Traditional Chorale Strophe» Harrington Shortall (1895-). *Vereinigte Staaten.*	C. Lechler (1930). Aus dem *Englischen.*
Grosser Gott, wir loben dich.	1	Katholisches Gesangbuch, Wien (1774).	Nach Ambrosius († 397). Aus dem *Lateinischen.* Te Deum.
Held, der dem Grabe	28	G. F. Haendel (1685-1759). Judas Makkabäus. *Deutsch.*	Johanna Meyer († 1921). Aus dem *Französischen.*
Herbei, O ihr Gläub'gen.	17	Komponist unbekannt. Wahrscheinlich XVIII. Jahrhundert. *Portugiesisch.*	Aus dem *Lateinischen.*
Herr meines Herzens	76	«Slane». *Altirisch.*	Helga Rusche (1950). Aus dem *Englischen.*
Herr, nun selbst den Wagen halt	66	Huldrych Zwingli (1484-1531). *Schweizerisch.*	Huldrych Zwingli (1529).
Herr um den die Engel singen.	83	«Picardy» *Französisches* Volkslied. Harmonisiert von Gustav Holst (1894-1934).	Johann Christoph Hampe (1951). Aus dem *Englischen.*
Herr unser Gott du warst	63	«St. Anne», wahrscheinlich von Dr. Croft (1678-1727). *Englisch.*	C. Lechler (1923). Aus dem *Englischen.*
Herz und Herz vereint zusammen	60	Brüdergemeinde (1745). *Deutsch.*	N. L. von Zinzendorf (1700-1760).
Hilf, Herr, der Not die uns betrat	88	«Bedford», Original Melodie von W. Weale († 1727). *Englisch.*	Wilhelm Horkel (1950). Aus dem *Englischen.*
Himmlischer Morgenstern	22	«Himmelslust» (1679). Satz : J. S. Bach (1685-1750). *Deutsch.*	Helga Rusche (1950). Aus dem *Englischen.*
Hört die Engelchöre singen	20	F. Mendelssohn-Bartholdy (1809-1847). *Deutsch.*	Johann Christoph Hampe (1951). Aus dem *Englischen.*
Ich weiss an wen ich glaube.	75	M. Teschner (1613). Harmonisiert von J. S. Bach (1685-1750). *Deutsch.*	Ernst Moritz Arndt (1769-1860).
Ich will dich loben, Gott zur Nacht.	112	Verkürzung einer Melodie von Thomas Tallis (1520-1585). *Englisch.*	Erwin Kleine (1950). Aus dem *Englischen.*
In Christus ist nicht Ost noch West	62	Nach Christopher Tye (1497-1572). Herausgegeben von G. R. Woodward in «Songs of Syon» (1910). *Englisch.*	M. Liesegang (1924). Aus dem *Englischen.*
In deinem Blut, Herr Christ.	50	Aus dem Koreanischen, Tai Jun Park.	Johann Christoph Hampe (1951). Aus dem *Englischen.*

Liederanfänge	Nr.	Tonsetzer und Ursprung der Melodien	Liederdichter und Übersetzer
Jauchzt alle / Gott sei hoch	4	Loys Bourgeois (1544). Harmonisiert nach C. Goudimel (1565). *Französisch.*	Matthias Jorissen (1739-1823). Aus dem *Französischen.* Psalm 33.
Jesu meine Freude	37	Johann Crüger. (1598-1662) Satz (1936). *Deutsch.*	Johann Franck (1618-1677).
Jesu meine Zuversicht.	38	Johann Crüger (1598-1662). *Deutsch.*	Berlin (1653).
Jesus Christus, du Licht aus Gott	114	Orthodoxe Kirchenmusik	Johann Christoph Hampe (1950). Aus dem *Russischen.*
Jesus hat seine Herrschaft bestellt	59	« Duke Street ». John Hatton (?-1793). *Englisch.*	Johann Christoph Hampe (1950). Aus dem *Englischen.*
Komm Gottes Geist	40	« Battle » Henry Lawes (1596-1662). *Englisch.*	Johann Christoph Hampe (1950). Aus dem *Englischen.*
Komm Schöpfer Geist	41	« Enchiridion » Martin Luther (1524). Nach einer gregorianischen Melodie.	Nach einem Lateinischen Hymnus.
Kommt der Tag emporgezogen . .	109	« Piésn Poranna ». *Polnisch.*	Johann Christoph Hampe (1950). Aus dem *Polnischen.*
Kommt und staunet	18	Vorreformatorisch. Harmonisiert von Johana Wagenaar. *Niederländisch.*	Wilhelm Horkel (1950). Aus dem *Altniederländischen.*
Lehr mich mein Gott und Herr. . .	67	« Mornington », Garret-Wellesley (1735-1831). *Englisch.*	Wilhelm Horkel (1950). Aus dem *Englischen.*
Liebe, komm herab zur Erde. . .	34	« Hyfrydol », Rowland Hugh Prichard (1811-1887). *Welsch.*	Johann Christoph Hampe (1950). Aus dem *Englischen.*
Lobe den Herren den Mächtigen König.	11	Stralsund (1665). *Deutsch.*	Joachim Neander (1650-1687).
Lobet den Herrn alle die ihn ehren	113	Johann Crüger (1598-1662). Satz : Zahn. *Deutsch.*	Paulus Gerhardt (1607-1676).
Lob sei dem Herrn	36	« Richmond ». Bearbeitet von T. Haweis (1734-1870), by S. Webbe (the Younger). *Englisch.*	C. Lechler (1923). Aus dem *Englischen.*
Mach uns, Gott der Huld	93	Altchinesisches Lied. Harmonisiert von F. Mathil (1950).	C. Lechler (1930). Aus dem *Englischen.*

Liederanfänge	Nr.	Tonsetzer und Ursprung der Melodien	Liederdichter und Übersetzer
Menschlich Wesen müsse schweigen	82	«Picardy». *Französisches* Volkslied. Harmonisiert von Gustav Holst (1874-1934).	Hanns Lilje (1937). Aus dem *Englischen*.
Mit den Heiligen lasst ruh'n. . .	117	Orthodoxe Liturgie. Auszug aus einem Totengedächtnis Gottesdienst.	Aus dem *Russischen*.
Niemals, O Heiland sollen ruh'n die Lippen . . .	95	F. F. Flemming (1778-1813). Harmonisiert von F. Mathil (1950). *Südamerikanisch*.	Johann Christoph Hampe (1950). Aus dem *Spanischen*.
Nimm mich gefangen, Herr . . .	87	J. S. Bach (1685-1750). *Deutsch*.	Johanna Meyer († 1921). Aus dem *Englischen*.
Nun bitten wir den Heiligen Geist	39	Vorreformatorisch, Johann Walther Gesangbuch (1524). *Deutsch*.	Martin Luther (1483-1546). Vers. 1 aus dem XIII. Jahrhundert.
Nun danket alle Gott.	13	Johann Crüger (1598-1662). *Deutsch*.	Martin Rinckart (1586-1649).
Nun jauchzt dem Herrn	7	Loys Bourgeois (1551). *Französisch*.	Psalm 100. Nach Cornelius Becker (1561-1604), und David Denicke (1603-1680). Aus dem *Französischen*.
Nun ruhen alle Wälder	115	Henry Isaac (1440 ?-1517). *Deutsch*.	Paulus Gerhardt (1607-1676).
Nur dein soll sein das Herze mein	79	Gesangbuch Pierre Attaignant, Paris (1530) und «Recueil d'Anvers» (1540). *Französisch*.	Kurt Wiegering (1950) und Wolfgang Schweizer (1950). Aus dem *Französischen*. Psalm 25.
O du ewiges Erbarmen	33	«Caersalem », R. Edwards (1797-1862). *Englisch*.	Johann Christoph Hampe (1950). Aus dem *Englischen*.
O Gotteslieb', erschein.	44	Ralph Vaughan Williams (1872-). *Englisch*.	Erwin Kleine (1950). Aus dem *Englischen*.
O Gottesliebe, wie getreu	106	«Melcombe », Samuel Webbe (1740-1816). *Englisch*.	Erwin Kleine (1950). Aus dem *Englischen*.
O Gottesstadt, wie breitest du. . .	53	Johann Crüger (1598-1662). *Deutsch*.	Erwin Kleine (1950.) Aus dem *Englischen*.
O Haupt voll Blut und Wunden .	23	Leo Hassler (1564-1612). *Deutsch*.	Paulus Gerhardt (1607-1676). Ursprünglich aus dem *Lateinischen*, Bernard de Clairvaux (1091-1153).

Liederanfänge	Nr.	Tonsetzer und Ursprung der Melodien	Liederdichter und Übersetzer
O Himmelskönig, unser Tröster .	43	Orthodoxe Liturgie. Gebet an den Heiligen Geist.	Aus dem *Russischen*.
O höre doch ! O welch' ein Ruf .	56	Ålstrom (1756-1835). *Schwedisch*.	Gisela van Spankeren (1951). Aus dem *Schwedischen*.
O komm, O komm, Emmanuel .	15	Gregorianischer Kirchengesang. Harmonisiert von F. Mathil (1950).	Aus dem *Lateinischen*.
O seliger Tag	96	Wald Rudin (1833-1921). Harmonisiert von F. Mathil (1950). *Schwedisch*.	Georg Kempf. Aus dem *Schwedischen*.
O unermessene Seligkeit . . .	42	« Psalterium Chorale » Konstanz (1510).	Johann Christoph Hampe (1950). Aus dem *Lateinischen*.
O Vater deine Güte reicht . . .	73	Mathieu Greiter ? (1525). *Französisch*.	Johann Christoph Hampe (1950). Aus dem *Französischen*. Psalm 36.
Preis sei dir, Gott	118	M. Teschner (1724). *Schwedisch*.	Gisela van Spankeren (1951). Aus dem *Schwedischen*.
Schau ich dein Kreuz	27	« Rockingham », Bearbeitet von E. Miller (1731-1807). Harmonisiert von S. Webbe, spanischgeborner Komponist (1740-1824). *Englisch*.	Wilhelm Horkel (1951). Aus dem *Englischen*.
Schaut, er will auf Wolken kommen	16	« St. Thomas ». Melodie von S. Webbe's « Motetts or Antiphons » (1792). *Englisch*.	Johann Christoph Hampe (1950). Aus dem *Englischen*.
Schmücke dich, o Liebe Seele . .	54	Johann Crüger (1598-1662). *Deutsch*.	Johann Franck (1618-1677).
Schönster Herr Jesu	35	*Schlesisches* Volkslied. Harmonisiert von Hoffmann von Fallersleben und E. Richter (1842).	Dichter unbekannt (1677).
So sassen wir verbannt	91	Loys Bourgeois (1542). Harmonisiert nach C. Goudimel (1565). *Französisch*.	Konrad Jutzler (1950). Aus dem *Französischen*. Psalm 137.
Vater, unser, lieber Herre . . .	47	Hussisches Graduale (1512). *Tschechisch*.	H. Laepple (1930). Aus dem *Tschechischen*.
Vergib, o Vater gnädiglich . . .	90	Nikolaus Herman (1485-1561). Harmonisiert von J. S. Bach (1685-1750). *Deutsch*.	C. Lechler (1924). Aus dem *Englischen*.

Liederanfänge	Nr.	Tonsetzer und Ursprung der Melodien	Liederdichter und Übersetzer
Volk Gottes, lass den Harm . . .	3	Johann Crüger (1598-1662). *Deutsch.*	Erwin Kleine (1950). Aus dem *Französischen.*
Vom Himmel hoch da komm ich her	21	Geistliche Lieder, Leipzig (1539). Satz: H. L. Hassler (1603). *Deutsch.*	Martin Luther (1483-1546).
Vor deinem Throne knien wir . .	9	Herrnhuter Melodie. Harmonisiert von Leonard Johannes Mens (1879-).	Wilhelm Horkel (1950). Aus dem *Niederländischen.*
Vor Jesu milde Augen	89	Huugo Nyberg, Pfarrer in Helsingfors (1873-). *Finnisch.*	F. Israel (1923). Aus dem *Schwedischen.*
Wach auf O Seele strecke dich. .	78	« Schottisches Gesangbuch » (1615). Wie im « Ravenscrofts Gesangbuch » (1621).	Kurt Wiegering (1950). Aus dem *Englischen.*
Wachet auf, ruft uns die Stimme	116	Ph. Nicolai (1599). Harmonisiert von Jakob Praetorius (1604). *Deutsch.*	Ph. Nicolai (1556-1608).
Weh! Atem Gottes füll uns mit Leben	45	« Dominica ». Sir Herbert Stanley Oakeley (1830-1903). *Englisch.*	Hanns Lilje (1938). Aus dem *Englischen.*
Wenn Gott erhebt sein Auge nur .	69	Mathieu Greiter? (1525). *Französisch.*	Johann Christoph Hampe (1950). Aus dem *Französischen.* Psalm 68.
Wer ist so gross wie unser Gott? .	24	Byzantinische Melodie. Harmonisiert von Wladimir Diakoff (1950).	Aus dem *Griechischen.*
Wie der Hirsch nach frischer Quelle	65	Loys Bourgeois (1551). Satz nach Claude Goudimel (1565). *Französisch.*	Ambrosius Lobwasser (1515-1585). Aus dem *Französischen.* Psalm 42.
Wie schön leuchtet der Morgenstern	10	Philippus Nicolai (1556-1608). Originalsatz (1598). *Deutsch.*	Philippus Nicolai (1556-1608).
Wir treten zum beten	80	Dr. Adrianus Valerius. Sammlung (1626). *Altniederländisch.*	Karl Budde (1896). Aus dem *Altniederländischen.*
Zu deinem Dienst, Herr	57	Melodie vom Neu-Leipziger Gesangbuch (1782). Harmonisiert J. S. Bach (1685-1750). *Deutsch.*	Wilhelm Horkel (1950). Aus dem *Englischen.*

(Hymns printed in italics are translations from other languages)

First line	No.	Composer or source of tune	Author or translator of hymn
Ack saliga dag	96	Wald Rudin (1833-1921). Harm. and arr. by Frédéric Mathil (1950). *Swedish.*	Natanael Beskow (born 1865). *Swedish.*
Adeste fideles...	17	Composer unknown. Probably XVIIIth century. *Portuguese.*	Essay on the Church Plain Chant (1872). *Latin.*
Beata nobis gaudia	42	Psalterium Chorale. Constance (1510).	*Latin.*
Chinese hymns:			
Grant good Lord.	93	Old *Chinese* tune.	St. Ignatius Loyola (1591-1556). *Chinese* trans. Y. T. Wu.
Let us with a gladsome mind	14	Old *Chinese* tune.	*Chinese.*
O Dieu de ton corps blessé	85	Old *Chinese* tune. Harm. M.-S.	Ernest Y. L. Yang (1934). *Chinese.*
Finita jam sunt praelia	29	First three lines adapted from a Gloria Patri by G. da Palestrina (1594). *Italian.*	*Latin.*
För Jesu milda ögon	89	Huugo Nyberg (born 1873). Pastor at Helsingfors. *Finnish.*	*Finnish.*
Gloria Patri et Filio	6	Giovanni da Palestrina (1524-1594). *Italian.*	Te Deum. *Latin.*
Gratia Domini nostri	119	Frédéric Mathil (1930). *Swiss.*	II Corinthians 13: 13. *Latin.*
Ἡ χάρις τοῦ Κυρίου... *(Gratia Domini nostri)*	120	Christian Gregor (1723-1801). *German.*	II Corinthians 13: 13. *Greek.*
Japanese hymn (*Mist and Darkness*)	68	"Imayo". *Japanese.*	*Japanese.*
Kiedy ranne wstaja zorze	109	"Piesn Poranna". *Polish.*	Karpinski (1741-1825). *Polish.*
Kommt verwondert u hier mensen	18	*Nederlandse* Vorreformatorische Melodie. Getaanzet door Joh. Wagenaar. Gezangenbundel der Nederlandse Hervormde Kerk.	Oud-Nederlands Lied. *Dutch.*

First line	No.	Composer or source of tune	Author or translator of hymn
Hymns from Korea:			
The Saviour's precious blood .	50	Tai Jun Park. *Korea.*	Tai Jun Park. *Korea.*
Here is preached the gladsome tidings .	72	La Woon Hyung. *Korean.*	Kim Chai Choon. *Korea.*
Nunca Dios mio .	95	F. F. Flemming (1810). Harm. by Frédéric Mathil (1950). *South American.*	Juan Bautista Cabrena (1837-1916). *Spanish.*
O Quanta Qualia .	100	Adapted from a melody in *La Feillée. Méthode du plain-chant* (1808). *French.*	Peter Abelard (1079-1142). *Latin.*
Orthodox hymns:			
Со святыми .	117	Orthodox Church Liturgy.	From the *Russian.*
Свете тихий .	114	Extract from the Service for the dead.	
Царю небесный. .	43	Orthodox Church Liturgy.	
Во царствии твоем .	86	Prayer to the Holy Spirit.	
O taenk når engang samles .	94	Orthodox Church Liturgy.	W. A. Wexels (1796-1866). *Norwegian.*
Otče náš, milý Pane .	47	Nikolaus Herman (1554). Precentor in Joachimstal, *Bohemia.* († 1561).	Kliment Bosák XVIth century. *Czech.*
Pris vare Gud .	118	Hussite Graduale (1512). *Czech.*	Johann Olof Wallin (1812). *Swedish.*
Τίς Θέος μέγας .	24	M. Teschner (1724). *German.*	*Greek.*
Vad röst vad ljuvlig .	56	Harm. by Wladimir Diakoff (1950). *Greek.*	Johan Olof Wallin (1813). *Swedish.*
Veni Creator Spiritus .	41	O. Åhlström (1756-1835). *Swedish.*	*Latin.*
		"Enchiridion" Martin Luther (1524). Gregorian Melody.	
Veni, veni Emmanuel .	15	Gregorian melody. Harm. by Frédéric Mathil (1950).	XIIIth Century hymn in Psalteriolum Catholicarum Cantionum (1710). *Latin.*
Vidunderligst af alt på jord .	84	*Danish Folk Song.*	N. F. S. Grundtvig (1783-1872). *Danish.*
Wij knielen voor uw zetel neer .	9	Herrnhut Melodie. XVIIIth Century Gesangbuch der Nederlandse Hervormde Kerk. Harm. Leonard Johannes Mens (1879- ?). *German.*	Clara Feyoena van Raesfelt-van Sytzama (1729-1807). *Dutch.*
Wilt heden nu treden .	80	Adrianus Valerius (1626). Nederlandsche Gedenck-Clanck. *Dutch.*	Danklied uit (1597). *Dutch.*

INDEX ACCORDING TO SUBJECTS
INHALTSVERZEICHNIS — TABLE ANALYTIQUE

A. *Praise and Adoration* — *Lob und Anbetung* — *Louange et Adoration*

E. Christmas — Weihnachten — Noël

F. Epiphany — Epiphanias — Epiphanie

G. Lent — Fastenzeit — Carême

H. Easter — Ostern — Pâques

U. Dedication — Heiligung und christlicher Dienst — Consécration

V. Christian Hope — Christliche Hoffnung — Espérance chrétienne

W. Life eternal — Das ewige Leben — La vie éternelle

X. Morning — Morgen — Matin

Note explicative au sujet du chant des cantiques orthodoxes
Vorbemerkung zu den Orthodoxen Kirchengesängen
Explanation concerning the singing of Orthodox hymns

Le rythme, dans les chants orthodoxes russes, est tout à fait libre et tributaire des paroles. En règle générale, les notes répétées se chantent sans accentuation et un peu plus vite que le reste de la mélodie, comme dans certains psaumes anglicans. Il est donc vain de chercher à faire coïncider les accents prosodiques de textes en langues différentes. La tonalité elle-même n'est pas fixe ; elle dépend des possibilités des chanteurs.

* * *

In orthodoxen Gesängen ist der Rhythmus frei und ganz von den Worten abhängig. Im allgemeinen werden Noten von gleicher Höhe, wenn sie einander folgen, wie etwa in gewissen anglikanischen Psalmen, ohne Betonung gesungen und ein wenig schneller als die übrige Melodie. Darum mühe man sich nicht um die Übereinstimmung der Versbetonungen in verschiedenen Sprachen. Auch die Tonhöhe ist nicht starr festgelegt ; sie hängt von den Fähigkeiten der Sänger ab.

* * *

The rhythm of Russian Orthodox hymns is quite free and dictated only by the words. Usually the repeated notes, as for example in certain Anglican chants, are sung without accentuation, and rather more quickly than the rest. It is therefore useless to try to make the stressed accents of the words in the different languages coincide with each other. The key itself is not static — it depends on the possible range at the disposal of the singers.

* * *

The numbers in brackets are those of the same hymns in the former edition of Cantate Domino.

Les numéros placés entre parenthèses, pour un certain nombre de cantiques seulement, indiquent les hymnes qui figuraient dans l'édition précédente du Cantate Domino.

Die in Klammern angegebenen Nummern beziehen sich auf dieser den Lieder in der früheren Ausgabe von Cantate Domino.

INDEX OF FIRST LINES
TABLE ALPHABÉTIQUE — ALPHABETICAL VERZEICHNIS

Imprimerie La Concorde, Lausanne (Suisse). 443/9.54.